# ONE DAY IN JUNE

COLIN  BEAZLEY

*For Harry, Gracie, Isabel and
Joshua, in the hope that they,
their generation, and all those
that follow will never
experience such events.*

Four Boys Books

**First published in Great Britain in 2012**

**Copyright © Colin Beazley 2011**

The moral right of Colin Beazley to be identified as the author of this work has been asserted in accordance with the Copyright, Design and Patents Act, 1988

**British Library Cataloguing-in-Publication Data**
A CIP record for this title is available from the British Library

ISBN 978-0-9571396-0-2

Published by
Four Boys Books
Heywood House
Chulmleigh
Devon
EX18 7QS

# Acknowledgements

I should like to gratefully acknowledge the help of the following who have given freely of their time during the preparation of this book.

Bomber Command Aircrew:
Stanley David, Alfred Flexman, Stan Hathaway, Stan Instone, Philip Jenkinson, Ken Killeen, Deryck McCusker, Eric Parker, Harry Purver, Tom Wingham.
Woking Aircrew Association members and particularly Bill Bawden

Horsa Glider Pilot : Barry Jackson

Devon Fliers :
Pip Burrow, Jeff Houlgrave, Martin Pengelly, Nigel Skinne
Richard Webber.

Christine Allbrook, Sue Bristow, Dr. Roger Duggan, Bri
Smith, Leslie Howard, Philip Kemp, Jean Lefranc, Fiona I
Masini, Nigel Schofield, Doris Trendell, Dr. Davi

Eva Hamilton (Wisienka), for allowing me to adapt
book, Wisienka's Story – by Eva Karczmarz, a
appreciate something of her exper

Scalloway Museum
The Imperial War Mus
The Yorkshire Air M
The Shetland Museum

My sincere thanks go to Charmaine T
invaluable proof reading and advice
and dedication on

Elevated numbers within the
help furnish a historical ba
notes, along with contem
and locations featured, are

# Chapter 1

Had it not been for the pig with the exploding head, or should I say the head that exploded just the once, I never would have arrived at the village in this way. The unfortunate incident not only claimed a French Landrace pig as victim, but also, more importantly, changed my life forever.

My cycling adventure took me along the lanes of glorious France. Spring was beginning to give way to early summer and all that it had to offer. As a cyclist one can so easily take in the landscape, rarely glancing to the road on which one travels, squeezing every last bit of pleasure from the moment.

The sweeping countryside holds the sweet aroma of wild flowers and the occasional pungent smell of garlic hangs heavy in the air. A water course stretches alongside the lane, its acquaintance comes and goes like an old friend. As the river bends the foaming water gleams in the bright sunlight, eddying in and out of pools before it flows smoothly on again – under the arches of bridges, passed lonely farms. The crystal clear water reveals the brown and grey gravel bed; above, groups of silver streaked fish dart about just under the surface this way and that, in the swirling shallows, searching for food. Slender young birds flit from stone to stone at the water's edge, singing, drinking and wetting their feet in the ever warming waters. Swallows fly low tracing the river course, dipping their breasts before they rise steeply into the canopy. Avenues of trees stand guard on crumbling banks whilst pigeons coo in their branches. A heron which had been patiently standing, frozen, awaiting a passing fish, flew away with its bill empty. A buzzard circles high on the thermals. Stark and dappled sunlight take it in turns to play on the lane as the breeze brings life to the high overhead branches of translucent green leaves.

A boldness heralds this new season; a season full of life, hope and promise.

1

The unexpected explosion was deafening, leaving a resounding ringing in my ears. Trees seemed to shake to the thunder of the eruption, sending a flock of roosting pigeons flapping into the distance. Horses which had been grazing contentedly in a nearby field, startled by the bang, galloped away in search of safety. Regaining consciousness, it was several minutes before I established exactly what had happened. At the time of the explosion the pig's head was firmly part of and attached to its body; this blast proved as significant a shock to the man on the cart carrying it as it did to me, following closely behind on my touring bicycle; a touring bicycle that had proved unworthy to this challenge! Amazingly I was not hurt, no breakages although my head had taken a fair clout on the road.

It would be reasonable at this point to explain that the pig, the true focus of our attention, was already deceased. Death had come to this beast at sun-up that same day, and subsequently I learnt that the pig was being transported to the nearby village of 'Cousion-sur-Cherane' to take its place on a hog spit in honour of its Annual Summer Fete. The execution of the poor creature however, had not proved anything like so spectacular as the seemingly explosive end I had witnessed. A congealed cocktail of fat and flesh coated me entirely; with the exception of my aching posterior which had been firmly planted on my leather saddle at the time of impact.

The day had got off to an altogether strange start. The hand cart, for it was no grander than that, was balanced on a pair of large wooden spoked wheels, each with the hub painted red and a wide outer tyre made of a steel band, now showing signs of extensive wear. The cart itself was of substantial construction, thick solid timbers with a board as a bench across the front, slatted side panels and a tail gate that hung and swung on a pair of rusting iron hinges. The small but muscular brown pony harnessed between the cart's shafts impatiently chomped on its bit, whinnied, shook its head and stamped restlessly.

'Olie the cartman,' for that was how he introduced himself, simply exclaimed,
"Je suis le Chariot-homme, monsieur, et je suis responsible de ce chariot . . . je m'appelle Olie."
Whilst rescuing me from the calamity, he gasped at the picture I presented. The stink of raw flesh spread over my body, heated by the noon day sun, proved too much for festering flies to resist, and my nostrils confirmed my bizarre condition: not one I would wish upon any soul . . . let alone an Englishman in his mid forties! It was quite obvious my bicycle had come to a premature end.

Olie was a man of mature years, probably in his seventies, with white bushy hair sprouting from under his black beret. His tweed jacket and thick trousers belied the warmth of the day, but I had a sense that this was what he always wore. He had a friendly smile as he passed me a cloth from the seat of the cart so I could remove the remains of the pig. It was then I realised we were not alone. Perched as large as life, was a young girl who couldn't have been more than five years of age, holding the pony's reins, looking to all intents and purposes, fully in command. So I was introduced much to my surprise to 'the mistress of the cart'. She sat on top of the bench on a tired looking old cushion, now flattened to nothing, alert and concentrating on the pony's every move. Her golden hair shone in the midday sun, framing her sweet tanned face; she looked all the lady proudly adorned in a green cotton dress. Having ensured all was securely tied on, pig as well as bike, Olie sat to one side of her and invited me to take rest the other side. The pony had now renewed its interest in the grass and was munching contentedly. The lass, with striking authority, flicked the reins to a demanding "Oya", and with a soft whinny, swish of its tail and a jolt, we were off.

I was astonished at the commanding control demonstrated over this substantial beast by such a young thing as we journeyed along this straight tree lined avenue, deeper into the countryside. The sun was now high in the sky bearing down on my head, with a soft breeze accompanying this glorious and unusual day. Having tried earlier to express my thanks, without complete success, again I ventured to enquire of Olie with regard the incident and its exact cause. After a few moments exercising my poor French, the aged white haired cartman turned and, arresting my gaze, proceeded to explain in English. The story seemed so unlikely that it must be true.

The large white, muscular and bulging boar had been slaughtered that morning in preparation for the hog roast at the fair, leaving it to the last moment to avoid the risk of rank meat.
"As is tradition . . . " Olie went on, "its head was left firmly joined to its body" A truly impressive sight on the spit I was assured, but now I had no way of appreciating that.
"The young farm hands who had killed it also prepared the beast, gutting, cleaning and stuffing its mouth with meats and spices." This latter action would prove the fatal blow to this beast's dignity, for "Amongst the sausages and liver rolls they squeezed a variety of old fireworks – just for fun!" undoubtedly to add a bit more colour and excitement on the spit. Well that's what Olie assumed having found shreds of burnt cardboard firework wrappers around the scene of the incident. The heat of the sun had proved too much, and although it is unknown precisely what caused them to ignite, ignite they did. The explosion constrained within the cavity of the hog's jaws and surrounded by vast quantities of fat only added to this amazing spectacle.

We were now travelling at a trot towards the village; the village that I had come to find. The picturesque scenery unfolded before us as we journeyed on. The idea of being able to make such progress on my travels without any effort on my part was indeed increasingly enjoyable and appealed to the lazy side of my nature. The rhythmic repetition of the pony's hooves on the road, combined with the passing shafts of sunlight breaking between the poplars which lined the road side, and the warmth of the day, hypnotically moved me to a state of sleep.  A throbbing, a

4

peculiarly penetrating throbbing started pulsating in my head. I could feel my eyelids getting heavier and my consciousness slipping away; there seemed little reason to fight it. A glance to Olie was greeted by a smile and a nod of understanding, but it proved just too much effort for me to respond. He and the lass now appeared as just vague silhouettes in the bright sunlight. The sun's warmth lifted the scent of wild garlic as the rocking of the cart lulled me still further towards sleep, my hearing became less sensitive, noises faded to the distance and a comfortable numbness became all invasive as I strived to keep awake, . . . and that's the last I can recall of my journey. I was lost to another world, a world that has no rules or limits; one with no end, and a beginning that can rarely be recalled or returned to.

Little by little my story, or should I say maybe my dream, for at times I am confused where one ends and another begins, will be told.

# Chapter 2

I awoke, the light afternoon breeze was lifting the net drapes that adorned the balcony windows at the bottom of the bed. At first glance the room appeared ordinary but it had a charming comfortable feel about it. I lay between crisp white sheets upon which a richly coloured patchwork boutis covered the bedlinen whilst a bolster offered support for my weary head. Although not fully aware of how I had got there, I felt completely at ease, assuming my new found travelling companion had had some involvement!

The room enjoyed a stream of sunlight giving it a mellow hue. A pretty cloth of a delicate floral pattern clothed the chest and matched the mat on the bedside table on which sat a dainty china clock, beside it was a table lamp crowned with a rather tired and oversized shade. All the walls and ceiling had been covered in a cream matt wash, with only pictures breaking the plainness. There were many pictures in a variety of sizes and frames: landscapes, probably of the neighbouring countryside – tranquil scenes of remote and unspoilt green wooded hills shouldering deep gorges with fast flowing rivers; a church in a pretty village and an old country railway station alive with travellers. Amongst them a more contemporary painting of Paris, a night scene with the Eifel Tower in the distance framed by buildings lining a busy avenue that bustled with Parisians in the rain going about their daily life. Buses and cars hurtled along splashing as they went; small groups of figures huddled beneath gaily coloured awnings over cafés and shops, sheltering from the downpour.

One picture was distinctive, standing out from all the others. It was a black and white photograph of children. It appeared to be a school picture . . . tiers of children were outside what looked like a grey school building. By now I had got out of bed so I could view the photograph more closely. Four rows of children were carefully arranged with the first two rows of young girls seated in

6

the foreground, whilst the other two rows of girls were standing. For some reason I was drawn to count them – thirty-eight in all, ranging from maybe five through to nine years of age, although two girls in the middle of the back row looked older than the others and were certainly taller. Some were wearing plain dresses, others, dresses of different patterns trimmed with a small butterfly collar: I guessed the period was about the 1930s. Their faces expressed every emotion from serious concern to joyful smiles. Something else I hadn't noticed immediately: there were no teachers or adults evident. No inscription appeared on either the photo or on what looked to be an expensive frame, so it was hard to work out much more about it. The photograph had a simple charm leading me to believe that there was some sort of connection between this household and someone in the picture, although something regarding it made me uneasy.

As I moved about the room I was aware of the floor creaking. Grey hessian matting covered part of the wide planked floor which had been painted black. In the corner of the room was the only other piece of furniture, a small quaint wooden framed chair with plain back, turned legs and a cane seat. Freshly laundered, lying neatly on the chair, was my jumper; my shoes were placed under the seat of the chair and my jacket hung on a peg on the back of the only door.

On approaching the lattice framed balcony windows an amazing scene unfolded before me. I looked down onto a square - 'The Village Square' that I had journeyed so far to see again. A wave of excitement coursed through the square as everyone was busying themselves building stalls, carting produce, erecting side-shows or just shouting one to another. Old bent rustic ladders were propped precariously against lamp poles with men perched high, overstretched to secure brightly coloured red, white and blue bunting. Strings of lanterns adorned the café fronts, their light soon to reach out to tables, empty but for a small gathering of mumbling old men sipping wine. Flapping gently on the breeze a long canvas banner across the square announced in vivid green letters – 'COUSION-SUR-CHERANE FÊTE DE JUIN'. A grand building, faced in buff stone work and ornate carved decoration stood impressively across the square from my window, before it a tall white pole furnished a limp and flapping French Tri-colour. The title 'MARIE' was proudly signed over the double wooden doors. At its top floor window a warm orange glow highlighted three or four people standing out on a wrought iron balcony, regarding the sight in the square below, just as I was. The air was crisp and sharp and every so often the rich aroma of coffee, mixed with the smells of cooking, drifted upward.

A team of muscular young men was at the final stages of assembling the structure of a merry-go-round, with all its horses and strings of fairy lights. Yapping about their feet a small black dog, darting this way and that, was obviously proving an irritation to the men's endeavours as every so often it would be greeted by a kick from a workman's boot; either it was too swift or maybe used to such a reception and always seemed to move out of range just in time.

To one side in the square was erected a massive white marquee – it stood quite austerely and alone. Over the entrance hung a large banner announcing 'LE CINÉMA'; my curiosity overcame me, I had to venture down into the square and explore the excitement. I left the room having put on my jumper, jacket and shoes and there facing me was a concrete stairway which led to a small ground floor hallway. Fixed on one wall was a 'Chambre' board; eight rooms, each of them numbered, but nothing else. There were no keys, no indication as to whether or not they were occupied, just the numbers and at the head of the board the name 'Hôtel-de Cherane'. One door in the hallway was ajar and peering in I discovered a totally empty bar. I called out:
"Hallo, bon-jour" but there was no reply, everywhere appeared completely deserted. The other door led me out on to a narrow alleyway that was shaded from the sun. It felt cool and its end

opened onto the square where the afternoon sun warmed me as I stood still taking in the amazing sight.

The bustle was even more striking now I was surrounded by all the activities. The day had come alive as people started to arrive to enjoy this summer celebration. Wooden wheelbarrows piled with produce were being exercised purposefully towards various stalls; a motorbike with sidecar stacked high with caged chickens roped down to its frame, careered precariously, weaving from side to side between folk and stalls alike. Gangs of young children, lads in shorts and girls in pinafore dresses chased around followed by the yapping dog; their unwelcome presence being greeted with annoyance by the workmen. An old woman in a drab dress with a shawl over her head struggled, dragging something on a rope from behind her stall. The more she tugged, the harder it was. Her grunts of command seemed to have no effect, until with a squeal, a small piglet, rope about its belly, trotted out proudly, squeaked, then scampered off in a totally different direction with the hag shuffling after it. The distant echo of the last few hammers falling suggested all was nearly ready, as stall holders, aided by the light of their newly lit lanterns arranged their produce and side show proprietors stacked their prizes attempting to make their stalls irresistible.

Suddenly I was distracted by a stout round-faced farmer from behind his meat stall crying,
"Viande fraiche locale; côtelettes de porc, des lapins, des gros poulets et des cannards. Choisi comme vous voulez; des prix speciales ..."
This ruddy gent, aproned in blue and white stripes, was waving his arms, beckoning me to savour his freshly slaughtered produce. Arranged neatly in shallow white plastic trays was meat of all shapes and sizes: thick and fatty, thin and lean, chestnut brown, bland white and all shades of grey as well as richly coloured bloody brown meat. With a shake of my head I couldn't think of anything else to say but -

"Non" and smiled at him, hoping I hadn't offended him in any way.

The next stall displayed all manner of delights. Tiered from front to back in patterns which tempted the eye to look more closely were gingerbreads and sweetmeats alongside freshly baked apple bread which smelt gorgeous, candies of all colours glistening with sugar, and pretty ribbon bowed boxes full of surprises. Pralines, plump and ready to eat sat like regiments of soldiers daring you to advance; and so it went mouth wateringly on and on.

An ample breasted woman stood at the rear of another stall selling fruit, balancing on a selection of boxes so as to reach across and oversee would be purchasers agonising over their decisions. She waited for the first to arrive.

Wandering on, I noticed the stack of crated hens of assorted colours, plain and speckled, in their cages beside an awning that shaded fresh vegetables. Baskets of mushrooms and truffles nestled alongside the trays of produce. The pungent smell of the hens irritated my nostrils bringing back memories of days when I was younger, in my twenties, a young man then taking refuge on a farm. A combination of strange odours hung in the evening air: cloves, sweet honey, apples, fresh, newly baked bread and pastries, and that unmistakable smell of farms.

Suddenly the atmosphere was disturbed by a resounding chord from a fairground organ. The musical contraption was standing in the middle of the roundabout, and beside it a beefy man was wildly cranking a handle. Slowly, ever so slowly, the roundabout started to turn, fairy lights of every colour strung around the roof awning flickered, began to glow, then shone brightly. The horses looking all the better for their bridle finery, gracefully began to rise then fall on their candy twist poles, their sluggish trot now quickened as they galloped to the music. The roundabout had come to life. Prominent, at centre stage stood the conductor, carved from wood but never the less looking every part the musical maestro. He was dressed in a sparkling red waist-coat edged with gold, under which was a cream crisply starched shirt trimmed with frills; azure blue trousers looking like velvet and black knee high leather boots completed this immaculate picture along with a small green saucepan like peeked hat. His right arm was raised and in his hand he held a baton. Both his head and arm articulated broadly in time to the music in jerky movements. Hammers hit a row of chime bars arranged vertically along the bottom of the organ and aside the conductor were two sets of organ pipes, frantically puffing and panting. To the right a big bass drum and a smaller kettle drum pounded out the beat, whilst a cymbal and triangle seemed to have a mind of their own.

The shadows of the day were lengthening and, in turn, the street lamps about the square shone, highlighting the bunting as it danced in the light evening breeze.

Giggles and laughter rang out from a group of young women who were gathered around a brazier, its flames illuminating their faces; chattering they watched a young man roasting nuts. The mellow ring of a bell in some lofty church tower faintly echoed from the surrounding buildings as it reminded all of the passing of time. Across the square side shows were beginning to attract excited crowds. A skinny whiskered old man, aided by a young ginger haired girl called out to passers by encouraging them to try their skill at hitting pyramids of cans with cork firing air rifles. Others were being tempted to throw darts into playing cards on a large revolving wheel. Children pestered parents as they discovered gaudy coloured soft toys, the reward for anyone who could throw a wooden ball into a bucket – as long as it didn't bounce out. This, however, wasn't fully appreciated until the ball didn't stay in the bucket and the soft toy stayed on its shelf! A plump middle aged woman in a big frilly hat and baggy dress suggested she could tell your future if you accompanied her into the caravan of, "Madame Giselle, La Fortune Teller". Folk looked on and

11

laughed, until a smartly dressed man in his forties, looking every bit the local lawyer surprisingly sneaked in . . . Madame followed closely behind to make or break his dreams and earn a few more welcome francs.

The melodious tones of a harp drifted lightly through the night, evoking a sense of peace and wellbeing. A figure sat in an archway dimly lit by a hanging oil lamp; across his knees was what looked like a strung shallow box which he played with a pair of hammers. His dress appeared to be medieval costume: a black, flat cloth hat flopped over his long locks, white blouse with black ribbon tie under a black coat, black breeches down to his white knee socks and his shoes, also black, were of shiny patent leather.

Just beyond where he sat and played a food van was attracting a small crowd, queuing in an orderly fashion in front of the side serving hatch. In the glare of the van's strip-light I could just make out the back of a woman inside madly attending smokey grills and spitting chip pans. In front, facing the crowd stood a burly man in a sage coloured apron busily slicing and buttering finger rolls ready for the hot dogs as he chatted continually with the customers, enquiring what they wanted. A small family with two children was first to be served and the van man greeted the father of the family.

By now the smell of the cooking was tempting more to join the queue and the van man, having tilled the money, was already greeting his next customers.
"Hallo," a shrill voice rang out. "Hallo," . . . I turned and saw Olie busy building a fire in a massive metal trough above which was skewered my pig, well the one I had encountered earlier that day.
"How is it going?" I cried to him.
"It is 'bon', Anglais . . . We soon have pig now!"
Small woven baskets sat one inside the other, ready I assumed to serve the succulent meat in; another large basket offered chunks of

French loaf, cut into generous portions, still warm, still offering that heavenly newly baked sweet aroma.

"Olie," I pointed to the hotel and smiling muttered,

"Merci beaucoup, merci," thanking him, but he was intent on the job in hand, carrying on with the final arrangements to his fire. As I strolled away I suddenly heard from behind me . . .

"Hewla, Yar . . . " and turning saw the excited figure of Olie, illuminated by a bright yellow glow from his now roaring blaze, waving his arms exuberantly and exclaiming for the whole world to hear,

"TRES JOLIE – SUPERBE!"

I couldn't help but smile to myself, appreciating the magic of the moment.

A little boy in brown serge shorts and bib 'n' braces ran up to me, flung his arms around my leg and gave me a hug. He looked up . . and with surprise on his face, realising his mistake, exclaimed,

"Pardon Monsieur," and as quickly as he had arrived darted off to a group of villagers by the marquee.

By now quite a gathering had formed by the makeshift booth in the entrance to what was the vast tent. A strangely scrawny looking woman, with tightly bunched black hair, black waisted dress and incongruous looking orange rubber boots shuffled in behind the booth, propped up a card sign which resplendently displayed the words: 'THE JAZZ SINGER avec AL JOLSON'. She immediately began to beckon folk to buy their tickets. They hurried towards her, fumbling in their pockets and searching their bags before finding sufficient loose change. Children tugged at Mothers' skirts or swung on their arms, dragging distracted parents towards the tent.

As the first few started into the marquee, a pigeon flapped out from within its temporary canvas home then soared across the square, perching loftily on my hotel roof.

"Billet . . billet, oui?" I turned and to my astonishment the unnerving ticket lady was fixing me with a glare, her eyes penetratingly black.

"Billet? Deux francs monsieur . . . "

Before I gave it a thought I replied,

"Oh, I've already seen it!"

The woman beamed and her smile revealed a mouth with fewer teeth than was intended; the creases on her face left deep furrows from her eyes and mouth making her appear almost friendly. She exclaimed,

"Non comprendre" then, seeing she had exhausted our conversation, turned her attentions to a young family beside me. I had no chance to explain to her that I had been taken by my parents in the late twenties to see it at London's Piccadilly Theatre – 'The European Vitaphone Premier'. It was the first feature length talkie, the first living picture and incredibly, although over thirty years ago, I've never forgotten it. Al Jolson's vitality was infectious, but what really struck me more than anything else was his black face, for although he was Jewish, he blackened his face to perform in public. Father said the film was about Jolson's real life; I remember I couldn't stop wondering why he didn't want to be seen as a Jew.

All about me was an atmosphere of expectation. A general boisterousness prevailed as people eagerly paid in the hope of securing the best seats in 'The House'.

# Chapter 3

There is nothing more magical than the moment when you see someone for the first time whose presence totally captivates you. You believe you must have met them before, but know that you couldn't possibly! And so it was with her; she stood there - radiant. The young woman shone, all about her just faded to nothing; I stood and watched . . . and watched . . . and dared to believe I knew her. She became the total and complete focus of my attention to the exclusion of all else. She glanced towards me, a dazzling smile lit her face as I felt myself smiling too. No words were needed; we looked at each other, our eyes meeting. In that brief moment I sensed the touching of our souls. My encounter with the young fair haired woman, was as a moment of magic. All about folk busied themselves with their lives, and there she stood as if waiting for me, quite still, quietly awaiting our first encounter. Her face was most perfectly formed: as she smiled her deep eyes of blue, shaded by long dark lashes and arched by pencil thin brows, sparkled like pools of life. Long blonde hair cascaded in ringlets, kissing her bare shoulders and fell freely down her back, her skin, cool and smooth as silk.

A warm, brown tan betrayed days spent enjoying the early summer sun. A long champagne coloured dress flowed from her tiny waist in rivulets of glimmering satin, twirling and turning about her. A white cotton ruff trimmed with lace caressed her body revealing her shoulders, her neck and just a hint of cleavage above her firm young breasts, modestly hidden by the bodice of her dress.

She was fascinatingly beautiful.

"You smile now too!" she said to me as we stared at one another. For me the moment was then, all else was nothing. No rehearsal, no audience, just the two of us knowing each other from the first moment we met.

A piercing white light flooded the tent entrance, distracting me. I turned about and again a bright white flash punctured the gloom. Across the square a young man dressed in a scarlet cloak was re-arranging his tripod before the roundabout. Bending forward to adjust his camera, another flash washed the scene. Young girls, giggling carelessly, sitting astride their funfair stallions, were chased round by lads tugging at their skirt ends, trying to keep up as the maestro, cranking the handle even faster, drove the horses on.

My attention was drawn back, this time by the wailing strings of the 'Overture'; the movie had started.
"Monsieur," and in an agitated manner, "billet?"
The ticket lady had clearly lost all patience with me and was making a last attempt, wishing to obtain a sale once and for all. As the Overture strained to a crescendo I realised the young blonde woman had vanished: she was nowhere to be seen. Without farewells or warning the moment had ended. Would there be a meeting such as this ever again? Just as quickly as it had occurred, it had gone: lost in time and maybe forever!
"Pardon . . . Monsieur" the attendant repeated.
"Who was that woman?" I interrupted, not even attempting French . . . "The woman, the blonde woman who was standing there," pointing to the spot where she had stood. From behind the ticket booth the lady stared quizzically, then a wry smile crept over her face as she shared the woman's name,
"Nicole. C'est Nicole, elle travaille dans le café . . . c'est Nicole, Monsieur!"

As the soulful sound track played from inside, I could see the story begin to unfold with scenes of a village market and fair. Children riding on a merry-go-round, laughing and clearly loving every minute; the scene changing to a young lad, accompanied by a pianist, entertaining those dining in a restaurant. A hush spread through the tent as he started to sing.

I began to stroll back to my hotel, carefully picking my steps across the cobbles in the darkness. A handful of people were leaving one of the café bars, arm in arm, singing as they disappeared down a darkened alley. The night air was crisp, chilling my lungs with every breath, my face tingled. I pulled my jacket more tightly round me now to help keep out the cool night. A pencil thin crescent moon shone high, its shape sharp against the inky black sky. On occasions its form was marred by a wisp of fluffy cloud as it drifted passed on its journey to 'who knows where?' The heavens were alive with hundreds of twinkling stars, a church bell rang out heralding the hour and a lone dog's bark echoed in the distance.

The warming glow of a tungsten lamp from the hotel greeted me. On entering I nodded at the concierge who had looked up momentarily, then returned to reading his paper. Weariness overcame me as I climbed the bare stairs and entered the room; I hadn't appreciated how much the day's events had taken out of me. Turning on the light I discovered the shutters had been partially closed; bread and cheese as well as a small bottle of wine were on the bedside table, but I had no appetite for these nor any inclination to wash, and slumped onto the mattress. I just couldn't get her out of my mind, her smile captivated my every thought, proving it impossible to think of anyone or anything else. As consciousness evaded me a feeling of well-being swept through my weary self; the desire to stay awake lost to the all consuming need to sleep. I could just hear from the cinema below the singing of Al Jolson, ever so faintly, yet enough to make out the words: words I have heard before, several times, but this time as I fought to concentrate on them I sensed that their meaning was important, and yet I didn't know why?
He almost seemed to have a tear in his voice . . .


'Never saw the sun shin' so bright
Never saw things goin' so right

Noticing the days hurrying by
When you're in love, my how they fly.
Blue days, all of them gone
Nothin' but blue skies from now on.'

I slipped away into a deep sleep.

# Chapter 4

So this is where my story truly begins: all that I have told you will make sense, but much later, for now I ask you to journey with me to an earlier time: twenty- three years earlier!

Life was much the same in many ways. Bloom and blossom still followed bud, nests bustled with young chicks, as the river fish below, weaving in the warming shallows, spawned new life. The smells of early summer erupted as the bouquet from wild flowering meadows drifted on the breeze, dancing ever so lightly. But the peace of the French countryside would soon be no more.

On June 14$^{th}$ 1940 after days of intense skirmishes, the sound of German jackboots would resound on the streets of Paris as the German army marched through the city in triumphant occupation. Hitler's War Machine would seize the very heart of France, and life for the French would never be the same. The wind of war was ever quickening soon to sweep across Europe as one of the fiercest conflicts man had ever known was about to begin. Massive military forces on land, sea and in the air would be hurriedly assembled and made ready for what was going to be for many, the most terrifying experience of their lives.

As a young man of just twenty-one I was aware of the breaking news on the radio and in the newspapers, but the implications and consequences of these events was lost on me. All of my life had been spent living on a small housing estate with my parents on the outskirts of North London. Our rented maisonette was on the ground floor and had a side alleyway to our door and rear yard, much the same as next door except they had an ornate silver scroll screwed to their doorpost. The upstairs' maisonettes had proper front doors and wooden balconies at the rear, with staircases that gave access to their back doors on the first floor. Our washing line was shared with upstairs and ran on a pulley from their balcony – I think to enjoy a better breeze for drying. Life was moderately comfortable in the safety of suburbia but all of that was about to change.

I was fortunate, at fourteen, with my 'School Leaving Certificate', I got myself a job as an Apprentice Tracer in the drawing office of a light engineering firm. In exchange for six shillings I worked a 47½ hour week, the pay of which was excused as a fair wage for learning a trade. The only bonus was that I finally left behind trays of congealed meat pie, soggy toad-in-the-hole and thick gluey tapioca pudding at school, and exchanged it for a staff canteen!

One of the great things about London for me was that it attracted all sorts of people with grand ideas. I remember the beginning of the Odeon Cinemas – *'Oscar Deutsch Entertains Our Nation'* and the impact film had on me. As a family we would go to the Odeon every weekend if we could; it was our special treat on Friday nights or Saturdays. But the real treat was a journey to London's Piccadilly Theatre to see, and for the first time, hear Al Jolson. As we went through from the foyer and our tickets were clipped, only then was the stunning grandeur of the Art Deco Auditorium displayed before us. Pinks of every shade coloured the walls and ceiling from which hung elaborate, twinkling chandeliers. The expectant chatter of the thousand strong audience became deafening; then as the movie started a hush fell and the new power and presence of cinema was magically revealed.

Two evenings a week my parents would play cards, playing Gin on their own or Bridge with friends, making the whole thing far more complicated than it deserved as far as I could see, as they exercised tactics and formulated strategies. As a youngster I would occasionally stay awake late snuggled up in bed tuned to Radio Luxemburg, or listen to a murder-mystery play on my crystal set; if I fell asleep with the headphones on my ears would feel very peculiar the whole of the next day.

Once a year for just two weeks we would all go to the seaside, usually Clacton or Southend, spending most of the time taking refuge in a tram or bus shelter along the promenade to get out of the rain, or squeezed into one of the small seafront shops trying to avoid spending any money! Butlins opened a camp at Clacton and, although we always planned to go and enjoy a holiday there, we never quite made it before our lives were turned upside down.

As a family we would often spend winter evenings gathered around the small open grate in the lounge listening to our bakolite valve radio set. The airways would sing with endless music from Jack Payne and his Band with the Beechams Reunion and Jack Hylton's – Rinso Radio Revue. Father enjoyed the variety spots, smiling and laughing at I knew not what sometimes, while mother loved the piano playing of Charlie Kunz, often humming along. On Sunday afternoons when I was a lad I would get out our wind-up HMV record player with its stack of 78s and play requests. Mum and Dad knew our collection off by heart so I never had a request I couldn't play. On occasions when the record was louder than I remembered, like Sousa's Stars and Stripes or The Flying Dutchman Overture, or if I was a bit slow with the duster in the sound box, the music would be accompanied by the foot of Mrs Harris upstairs pounding a complaint on her floor and our ceiling. She liked to have a doze on Sunday after lunch! Our family followed much the same pattern week after week, but it was fun and felt secure. On Sunday evenings before bed I would take from the top drawer of our grand oak sideboard a buff packet which contained two small black bound books, along with a shallow cardboard box. The books, a Service Prayer Book and The Soldier's Bible were both inscribed with Father's name, after his rank of sergeant and the word "GUNNER". Opening the cardboard box revealed three medals and their ribbons proudly arranged on fading red velvet. These I would carefully clean with Silvo polish and meticulously rearrange in the box before putting them back 'til the following Sunday, thinking that if I ever went to war I wouldn't want to come home without a medal or two.

I loved our little home: a bulky upholstered settee and a pair of armchairs waited invitingly in the lounge in which I would sit hugging over stuffed cushions hoping to keep warm. All our furniture, what little there was, was dark oak, chunky and with a highly polished finish. A glass bowl light hung from the centre of the ceiling, its imposing size belying the low wattage bulb Dad had fitted. He would sit in his chair by a roaring coal fire smoking, or more often just sucking, his briar pipe of Holborn tobacco and reading the evening paper by the light of an oak standard lamp. Heavy floral drapes hung from pleated pelmets which helped to exclude the drafts and reduce the condensation on the Crittal metal framed windows: windows which Dad had to regularly scrape and paint to stop them getting too rusty.

Mum and Dad had a real pride in the place even though we didn't own it. A large patterned rug covered the floorboards, a funny fan shaped art deco mirror hung over the tiled fireplace on which a wooden faced clock with brass roman numerals stood. Mum sat in a chair beside the fire, opposite Dad, with her needlework and knitting basket beside her. I don't remember many books at home, indeed I think the only books were in my tiny bedroom, which apart from the bed, had one white open shelf cupboard in it on which sat my table lamp, crystal set and 'Little Maestro – Pilot' radio. Rather surprisingly the radio's power lead would get hot: it was meant to and I would often curl it under my pillow on a winter's night. A padded easy chair was at the bottom of the bed and was nearly always piled high with clothes. The winters were bitter in our maisonette and I would often get dressed in bed, having slept with my clothes for the next day under my eiderdown. In the mornings, on the way to clean my teeth and splash my face, I would scrape the ice on the inside of the window panes to see what the day had in store. Our bathroom was always cold. Because of the chill I would sometimes just run the hot water in our cast iron bath tub so it steamed up the room, damp down a towel, 'rinse' the soap then . . . without getting in, pull the plug and empty it. The Burlington high level cistern for the loo would drip with condensation, as did the mirror over the sink. All in all it was not a great room, nor one I spent much time in, although I always liked the smell of Wright's Coal Tar Soap.

Mum and Dad's bedroom always looked far too tidy and boring.

Our kitchen was pretty small, but contained all that was essential. A white butler sink with a well scrubbed wooden draining board and a muddle of pots and pans hidden behind a curtain. Our gas cooker finished in a classic mottled-grey enamel was chipped in all the well used places. Opposite, a drop down larder with glass door cupboards top and bottom housed our provisions. If our larder was open, our folding formica table and three wooden chairs out, you could hardly move in the kitchen, let alone invite guests. When the cooker was lit it was the warmest room in the house. Our cooler was a white enamel bucket, its lid edged with blue, which Dad had buried in the ground next to our shed: in it mother stored butter, margarine, cheese and milk. The asbestos shed was home to Dad's tools and, amongst other things, my tortoise, who ever so slowly crawled round in the yard during the summer, then slept in straw all through the winter – what a great life!

In the ground floor maisonette next door to us lived a middle aged couple, Mr. and Mrs Bürnstein, whom I always regarded as foreigners: I think the unfamiliar cooking smells which emanated from their kitchen led me to that opinion. They would keep themselves to themselves but always seemed really friendly and would regularly give Mother material remnants from their workshop in the East End.

By the late thirties the Nazis had wrecked hundreds of German synagogues and arrested thousands upon thousand of the Bürnstein's fellow Jews.

# Chapter 5

Ruth and Harry Bürnstein next door had a Baird black and white television set and invited us in to witness the pictures of Chamberlain at the window of No.10 waving two agreements: The Munich Four Accord – Power Pact and An Anglo-German Declaration, signed by both Neville Chamberlain and Adolf Hitler, indicating 'the desire that our two peoples never go to war with one another again.'[1] The scene was amazing, women were in tears and folk were crying out to him, 'Thank you, thank you!' Police were unable to hold back the growing crowds.

For several years before, warning signs of Germany's unrest and Hitler's ever increasing power went unheeded; meanwhile the threat grew even greater.[2] It seemed to me that we were still getting over the enormous loss of life in World War One. For many, war was still very much alive in their memories and they were weary of it, but events had now overtaken the situation which appeared to be running out of control.[3]

On the fine summer's morning of 3rd September 1939 the prime minister, Neville Chamberlain, broadcast to the nation the steps which had finally led the country to war. From the Cabinet Room at 10 Downing Street he said, 'Now may God bless you all. May He defend the right. It is the evil things that we shall be fighting against – brute force, bad faith, injustice, oppression and persecution – and against them I am certain that right will prevail.' His words about each of us playing our part in coolness and courage, maybe by joining The Fighting Services, made a big impression on me as a young man at that time, as did the subsequent news from Europe.

Whilst my mates were reading 'Esquire', the new 'Lifestyle and Fashion for Men' magazine, I was buying 'Popular Flying Magazine', reading about the exploits of the most daring of all pilots who fought over the battlefields of Europe – 'Biggles'. The hero from the First World War and now the Second, along with his chums Algy and Ginger, had inspired me page after page as they undertook the latest death defying antics in their Spitfires and Hurricanes. The idea of flying had always excited me long before war looked inevitable. Brightly coloured model planes had often filled my Christmas stocking as a young child, providing endless hours of pleasure. When on leave, Dad's brother Art, who was in the RAF, would come over on his Enfield motor bike and play with me in the yard. When he felt really fit he'd swing me in circles around him, holding on to my arm and leg, or running about with me on his shoulders, our arms outstretched like wings pretending to be an aircraft. We would add 'aaeers . . .' mixed with machine gun noises, 'ak . . . ak . . . ak' and bomb blasts; playing until I was so tired he'd have to put me to bed.

Although I was in a 'reserve' occupation, which would exempt me from going to war – engineering being vital to our country's defence and future, I was not at all happy that that should be the extent of 'my bit'. Just sitting endlessly behind a drawing board, tracing black ink pens over large sheets of blue waxed linen seemed pointless. And anyway I wanted to fly, somehow; I didn't care what I did, pilot would be great, I just wanted to be in the air. At the beginning of '39 The Military Training Act was passed stating that all men twenty and over were liable for call up, and in September the Military Service Register published a list of us all. By the outbreak of war many of my mates had already been conscripted, most ending up in the army; this is where they were told the greatest need was! If I wanted the RAF the answer for me was to volunteer, but first of all I had to get my firm to agree to release me from work. Not really a problem as the office was mainly staffed by women and older men who were keen to stay put, and my few years of experience didn't count for a lot in the present situation. I was already visualising myself in my smartly pressed RAF uniform, collar, tie and of course, 'wings'. The idea that I was joining up maybe sooner than I needed to was of no concern; I just wanted to be in the RAF and fly. And so eagerly I went along to the local Combined Services Recruiting Centre in North London, found the RAF recruitment officer and shared my expectation with him of taking to the air. My idea that they would be desperate for me to join was confirmed by a large poster on the wall of what looked like a Wellington bomber silhouetted against a cloud covered sky and the words: 'JOIN AN AIRCREW IN THE RAF, Apply at your nearest Combined Recruiting Centre.' However, my hopes were soon dashed as he explained unemotionally that this was a service for the more intelligent and fitter recruits, the elite, not for those who didn't like water or fancy the rough and tumble of the army.

The reception couldn't have been more discouraging. The recruitment officer did explain that I shouldn't rule out altogether the idea of getting into the RAF, but in his view entry was far from certain. He concluded by reluctantly noting my name and address. The next stage was referring me for a medical inspection and eye test, a synch I thought! After all the leaflets given to me said the Royal Air Force was a new service, one with a tradition, albeit brief, of 'ebullience and even unconventionality – in short a tradition of the Spirit of Youth and all that Youth implies'. I wasn't sure what ebullience meant but was certain I fitted the rest of the bill. I was also certain however, that that was not the most difficult part of my signing up: Mum and Dad still didn't know! One thing was for sure, they soon would and I was not at all confident it would go down well.

The stores in the High Street were beginning to close for the day, rolling down their shop front shutters; as the lights went out the last members of staff filed out onto the pavement, then merged with the travellers heading home, one looking just as tired as the other. Striding out I knew the sooner I got back the better. The path from the end of the shops across the allotments towards home stretched out before me. The air was dank and water droplets hung on the wire fence that ran beside the pathway. Scurrying workers, their coats wrapped tightly round, braved the night chill hoping to reach home before they got too cold. Orderly terraced houses lined the road as I left the path, their lights aglow as folks busied themselves getting tea. Dusk was drawing in quickly now as I approached our tiny home, a dim light in the lounge was highlighting Mother at the window. I waved but I guess she didn't see me.

"I'm home," I cried whilst closing the front door behind me to be greeted by,

"Come on then," chorused by both Mum and Dad from separate rooms, with Mum adding, "tea's ready dear." A mixture of excitement and anxiousness ran through me as I hid my copy of the snappily entitled 'Joining-Up - A Handy Guide for Every Recruit. All you want to know', washed my hands and joined them by the lounge fire. I had great difficulty keeping my news to myself, but this was short lived because as Mum poured the tea Dad took me to task,

"Have you forgotten anything?" My mind was in a bit of a jumble after all that had happened but never-the-less I didn't have any idea what he meant.

"Have you forgotten what today is?" Well I suppose I had, and he must have realised that too as I stared at him blankly; we weren't talking of just 'Tuesday,' I assumed.

"Today?" I asked.

"Yes, today, what's special about it?" he continued.

"Well I've been to . . . ," and before I could explain my thrilling news he interrupted,

"No. no . . . your mother!" I could muster no glimmer of recollection from his suggestion and sat silently gazing at her. She glanced at Father sternly, then at me and smiled. What was this all about? And then it became clear.

"It's her birthday," Father retorted.

"Oh you don't need to worry dear," she murmured, but only as he added,

"Today! It is her birthday today."

There clearly was no way out of this other than to apologise whilst sounding truly surprised as to how it could occur again so soon after the last one.  As far as Father was concerned it didn't work; Mum passed me a plate of sandwiches and smiled, embarrassed. He looked down, carefully manoeuvered his cheese sandwich into a mound of pickle then proceeded to eat it, breaking off only to enquire of me,

"And what have you been up to that was so important to the exclusion of all else?"

"Well," I said and then paused, sure that what I had to say would not go down well; I continued, "I've enlisted, I've signed up for the RAF."  Dad's face hardly changed, although I thought I detected a glimmer of acknowledgement, and perhaps a smile; Mum, however, looked gloomy, and on recognising this I quickly added,

"They haven't guaranteed me a place . . . in fact the officer was positively discouraging, and only with great reluctance took my name."  Mum did not seem comforted by this, and silence reigned. Father broke the quiet by remarking to Mother that I was nearly twenty-two now, and many men of that age were living or working away anyway, and almost without a pause went on to say,

"Well, the RAF eh?  You can't do better than that . . . I was in the Artillery and Gramps, the Signals, there's nothing wrong with the RAF, the gentleman's service; obviously they recognise that the boy's intelligent Mother, that's apparent!"

"But I'm not in yet!"  I interrupted, just as Dad had left his chair and was pouring two bottles of Flower's bitter.  Mother didn't say anything other than,

"Eat up dear, you'll need your strength."  The missed birthday had been long since forgotten with the shattering news I had delivered.

So now I had to be patient, and wait.

# Chapter 6

Father's cousin Oswald and his family moved from London to the Shetland Isles when I was eleven, long before the outbreak of war. Oswald's wife Cara originally came from Shetland and they met when dancing in the Finchley Palle. Our two little families were very close seeing each other most weeks. We would spend many a summer's weekend on Hampstead Heath, picnicking with them, having fun and watching fellow park-goers swim in the ponds. Dad was very worried about them after the outbreak of war, when we read in their letter that Lerwick had been bombed by six Heinkels, and an RAF flying boat in the harbour had been set ablaze by machine gun fire. As it turned out the town hadn't been hit, but nine days earlier, the first Nazi bombs had landed on British soil, at Sullom Voe, north of the islands. It later came to light after the German invasion of Norway and its occupation, that there was a possibility that Shetland might be used as a way to attack Britain. Oswald said friends had told him that the Germans needed Norway to base their U-boats and then from there they could attack and break our navy which was blockading their supply routes. Such was the concern that twenty thousand of our servicemen were stationed on the islands, gun emplacements were installed around Lerwick harbour and elsewhere, as well as the building of two air bases for Spitfires and Hurricanes and a base for flying boats.

Shetland became a restricted area; Oswald, his family and everyone else had to have an official pass to move around the islands. Many fishing boats and small craft ran across the North Sea to and from Norway, two hundred miles of some of the roughest seas, ferrying refugees to Shetland. As well as supplies, equipment and rations for the underground forces in Norway, they also shipped vital engine parts to Shetland, and Allied agents back and forth. Oswald went on to explain that the crossings were so regular it was called the 'Shetland Bus'; literally hundreds of trips were made. Many Norwegians settled near Scalloway across the mainland from Lerwick, where Oswald worked for Moore and Sons in engineering and he got to know several of them really well. A number of refugees and agents fleeing from Norway were stopped and killed by the Germans and those that did escape often found their families were punished, men killed and houses burnt.

Oswald's most recent letter brought news of a friend who had sailed over from Norway called Steffan:

Dear Ron and Lil,

Christmas 1939
We are all well up here and very busy.

Cara has been down at James Sutherlands herring station, to the gutters huts at North Ness, off Brown's Road, on the north of Lerwick. It's where the fish catches are landed, and workers, many of them migrants, gut, and pack the herring in barrels of salt. Most days she is down there helping with the emergency accommodation being set up for the refugees that have begun to flee from Norway, following the news of the Germans. You know the whole area has been taken over by the Royal Navy now. She works for Mrs. Adie, a Norwegian woman who is in charge, and Cara prepares the food and when occasionally a mum needs help with her children she gives them a hand. She thinks some will stay on the Island if they can. She said they all seem very grateful and lovely people.
I have been working with a young chap called Steffan on some of the boats. He and his father owned a 42foot fishing boat in

30

Norway, and when he discovered the Germans were likely to invade, Steffan decided he had to leave. A couple of fellow Norwegians and a Swede had to get out as well, so with full tanks, oil and a month's worth of supplies they set out for the Islands.

He had to leave his family in Norway putting them all at risk of reprisals. The Germans already had armed patrol boats off-shore but they were able to sneak out under the cover of darkness. For two days the weather was good then it got rough and the seas wild, a Nazi flying boat spotted them and fired at them for nearly half an hour. The hammering was frightening, he had never been so scared, but luckily apart from the hull being holed above water, none of them were injured. The Dornier tried to land on the sea but there was too much of a swell so headed away. Steffan had the engine on full power for nearly two days before they spotted land.

Steffan brought his boat round Sumburgh Head to the yard at Scalloway and that's where we met up. We've been camouflaging it to make it look more like a working fishing boat, and added Lewis machine guns concealed inside oil drums on the deck. He intends to do more runs, getting people out and taking supplies in.

You wouldn't believe how busy the yard is, not like the old days at Enfield Ron. The girls think it's a great adventure; I dread to think of the Germans ever landing here, from what Steffan says, it would be hell. I expect that you're all beginning to suffer down there although I suppose you can always shelter down the tube station.

Christmas Greetings and love to you all, Christine and Kath send a big kiss to The Boy!?
Keep safe,
Your loving cousins,
Oswald, Cara and the girls.

In the New Year we, well Father, wrote back to them but we did not hear anything for a very long time.

Churchill's decision to invade the Fœroe Islands after Denmark was overrun was to pre-empt any invasion by the Nazis that would have made it difficult to defend Scotland. We were ill prepared for war in many respects: more fighter planes were desperately required to engage the German bombers, but first more metal was needed. 'Saucepans for Spitfires' was the slogan used to get pots and pans, kettles and cutlery from housewives, as well as bath tubs, iron gates and any other metal objects. Barrows and carts were wheeled by children along streets to collect scrap and metal toys. I distinctly remember handing over my collection of toy metal planes which I dug out the cupboard; but I'm not totally sure that one of the boys collecting didn't have them! Andrew across the road got in trouble with his mum for gathering bits of shrapnel, amongst which, stored in his bedroom, was an unexploded German shell or bomb, about the size of a milk bottle, that he had found on the waste ground behind the allotments.

The assumptions announced by our Air Ministry concerning future Luftwaffe bomb damage grew almost weekly. Gas attacks were another major fear, and by the outbreak of war forty-four million 'respirators' had been issued, including Mickey Mouse ones for the children. Trenches were dug in public parks and anti-aircraft guns and searchlights were put in place to play on the night sky.  Evacuation plans were drawn up and started to be implemented.  Thousands of volunteers were trained as Air Raid Precaution wardens in basic first aid and how to deal with the dangers related to gas, electrical and water supplies.  Little did they know what was in store for them!

The winter of 1939-40 was the coldest for forty-five years, so the papers said.  It started with a very mild November but it became much colder in December with severe frosts and fog at night. Heavy snow fell at the start of the New Year and in January we experienced the lowest temperatures since 1895 falling to below minus 20°C in many parts.  What was truly amazing was that the Thames was frozen for eight miles near Kingston, people were skating on the Serpentine and the news was full of the sea freezing over at Bognor, Folkestone and even Southampton.  On the fields around us freezing rain fell: the tremendous weight of ice brought down trees, telegraph poles and cables, whilst birds had great difficulty in flying due to ice on their wings.  Foxes and badgers, unsettled and cautious, came in from the countryside to where we lived foraging for food,.  A crisp white blanket of snow cloaked the ground, which looked Christmassy and fun, but disguised treacherous glassy ice below.  Elongated, glistening tentacles of frozen water hung ever longer as the temperatures plummeted and more freezing rain fell.

With thousands of children being evacuated to the country the dark streets seemed eerily quiet.  Folk shuffled around with half shaded torches pointed to the ground trying to avoid accidents or getting lost.  As battery supplies ran out so too did blackout material; people resorted to painting their windows.  ARP wardens would cycle round calling,
"Put that light out!" in the hope that the German pilots would become confused.  The gloom of war was heightened by the decisions to reduce the electricity voltage, making any lights even dimmer.  For those of us who did venture out, in spite of the government's campaign to, 'Take Care of Your Gas Mask and

Your Gas Mask will Take Care of You', the majority of us didn't carry them. Signs 'To the Shelter' seemed pointless, sandbags outside buildings were rotting away and ARP wardens appeared bored and redundant. The reality of war was dawning –
there were no air raids or gas attacks: people were of the view that the war was not happening, so children were brought home and it became known as 'The Phoney War'. Casualties from road accidents in the blackout and bad weather exceeded that of any caused by the war: but this was the calm before the storm.

# Chapter 7

Whilst the British army dug trenches and sent a hundred and fifty thousand men across the English Channel and the Royal Navy went to sea; the RAF dropped leaflets - five million on the first night of war alone and Germany grumbled that the British weren't taking the war seriously.[4]

The year 1940 was one in which Germany was actively establishing itself in Europe. German troops invaded Denmark, The Netherlands, Belgium, Luxembourg, France, Norway and entered România. At the beginning of the year Hitler ordered U-boats to attack neutral shipping, and revised plans for attacking The West; Operation 'Sea-Lion' – the invasion of Britain, which was cancelled in September, then again in October, was delayed to the following Spring.[5]

Meanwhile Heinrich Himmler, Germany's Minister of the Interior, acting on a report by SS Captain Rudolf Höss ordered the building of a camp near Oświęcim, Poland to be known as 'Auschwitz'.[6] It had a network of concentration camps, forty-eight in all, with some forty-five smaller satellite camps tens of kilometers from the main camp. Höss at the age of forty became the first commandant, moving in with his wife and four children to a house near the crematorium. Himmler identified Auschwitz II as being the place of the 'final solution of the Jewish question in Europe', it was home to the unbelievable and the unthinkable; the extermination camp.[7]

At home many were now worried by the news about our boys in France; the British Expeditionary Force was facing annihilation, having withdrawn to the channel at Dunkirk, almost three hundred and forty thousand of them, under the protection of the valiant soldiers who stayed to hold back the advancing German army and Panzers that were now only twenty miles away.[8] That summer was to see the largest evacuation in history, as hundreds of 'Little

Ships' of all types and sizes, left our shores destined for the doomed beaches of Dunkirk. The soldiers returned as heroes, from what was a massive military disaster in which over sixty-eight thousand men were lost. Churchill soberly addressed The Commons, saying that whilst he welcomed the success of the operation, "Wars are not won by evacuation."[9]

Polish friends of the Bürsteins shared with Mum, Dad and me news of a girl living in Poland during the time of the Russian occupation. They had heard of the girl's torturous experiences and believed her story needed to be told in 'The West'. At the outbreak of war Wisienka and her family were in Kraków, and even before the Polish leader, Rydz-Śmigly had finished his announcement to his people that the invasion was inevitable, German planes were bombing Poland.[10] Russians invaded the eastern half of the country, Stalin's plan was to deport the Polish to make way for Russian citizens.

Wisienka was a young girl who in 1939, at the age of nine, was arrested with her mother, at their lodgings in L'viv – Ukraine, near the eastern border with Poland. They were told by the five Russian soldiers who invaded their room where they slept, that they were being taken back to their home in Kraków, southern Poland. One soldier was different to the others: he stood to one side, head bowed, not daring to look, clearly regretting all that was happening. As he whispered to Wisienka's mother to pack all her dresses so she could barter for food, they knew for certain they were being taken somewhere far into Russia. Having dressed and quickly bundled together their belongings they were escorted to a waiting lorry at the front of the house. As the lorry turned into the High Street of L'viv she was terrified to see vehicles of all types: lorries, carts and large horse drawn wagons all packed with people: children, young people, old folk and the disabled, their bags and belongings all about, many of them crying. They were taken to the rail station and unloaded before a cattle train; guards were everywhere making escape hopeless. Herded together they

36

were crammed into one of the trucks and the sliding doors bolted behind. The truck resounded to the screams of babies, the moans and pains of the elderly, the sobs of the frightened and confused; Wisienka's mother was crying uncontrollably, despairing for their future.

After hours of waiting and repeated checks by guards, the train started and the journey in their crated prison began. Other girls with her took it in turns to stand on the piles of luggage and peer through a little grille in the side of the truck, viewing the passing fields and forests, wondering if they would ever see them again. When they reached the Polish-Russian border they stopped; a peasant woman on a bridge nearby on seeing them, put her face in her hands and wept. Crossing the frontier they left Poland far behind, perhaps they thought, forever.

The train crossed the Volga river: it was so wide with ships on it that she thought it was the sea. As they journeyed on towards Siberia there were fewer villages; sometimes days would pass without seeing a hamlet, hut or even a person. From time to time the train would stop and they would be let out to stretch and take fresh air. In the summer of 1940, having travelled through the Ural mountains, she came to the end of her train journey at the river Sos'va. They were then herded into a large steam barge. A forest swept the river edge where they landed several hours later, from where they had to walk through the dense undergrowth to their desolate 'Settlement 45' - a silent and empty camp surrounded by the dark threatening Siberian forest. About one hundred identical wooden huts stretched along two parallel paths through the camp, each having two small rooms, four people to a room. Here she stayed in the cold. Wisienka was haunted by the fear that in Siberia they may disappear for ever and dreamt of being back home in Kraków.

What Wisienka didn't know was that meanwhile, back in Poland, from sun up to dusk, armed SS soldiers, and 'Blue Police' ran throughout the cities searching for Jewish men, women and children. Huge trenches had been dug at the Jewish cemeteries in which they were then murdered. Around five point three million Poles were murdered during the Occupation. Stalin's purge intensified, becoming known as 'The Terror', and over five million people were deported to Siberian camps.

Hitler's concept of complete power and domination was coming to fruition as was his obsessive hatred of Jews.[11]

Her story made me realize just how dark our world could become if Hitler and Stalin had anything to do with it!

# Chapter 8

Peter, David and Andrew were three brothers who lived in a large detached ground floor maisonnette across The Close; the houses on that side were much smarter and newer than ours, and Dad said more expensive. They were the living example of how three boys, each only a year or two apart, in the same house, going to the same school could be so different. Every weekday morning before I had left for work, I would see them file out the front door, their mum leading the way closely followed by Peter and David clutching their school satchels. Andrew, appearing to be completely pre-occupied with his coat, satchel, hat, shoes, whatever was in his pockets, in fact anything and everything, scurried about behind, trying to keep up but not making a very good job of it. He certainly never closed the front door behind him, so it would gape ajar until Mr. Taylor peered out, checked their going, then closed it.

I had little to do with them because they were so much younger than me, but Mother would often go over of an evening or weekend and put the world to rights with Mrs Taylor, once the kids were in bed. Dad had little to do with Mr. Taylor, I don't think anyone did. He was not a well man, staying in the house most of the time. Mum said she'd heard he'd got something called Crohn's disease and also had diabetes. Often when she returned from a visit, 'Good Works' Dad called it, Mum would exclaim,
"I don't know how that poor woman copes!?" The 'poor woman' had a part time clerical job somewhere, I think it was for the local doctor which suited taking and collecting the kids from primary school.
"She has to keep the house and look after her husband," Mum would add, then went on, "and those three boys, good lads that they are, are obviously a handful." One time I inquired of her,
"Well doesn't Mister help?" at which I was quickly enlightened by Father with,

"No, they say he's too sick!"

"It's a shame, I don't know how she'll get by if rationing and everything else gets worse," Mum said; after a pause Dad thoughtfully muttered,

"Well dear, I'm sure she's grateful for your little chats," then resumed reading the paper.

One occasion I can still vividly recall was in the early days of the war, I came home from work and discovered an Anderson air raid shelter had been delivered. Over tea Dad explained in great detail his plan: it was his way.

"I wanted to get it sorted whilst you were still here to help: you never know when you'll be called up;" something I was becoming increasingly conscious of. The shelter was to be shared with next door and the two upstairs, sited in the neighbours' patch because they had more space and 'this Saturday' was 'shelter day'. On the day in question the neighbours were all mobilised and Mum had got the Taylor boys over, assuring Mrs Taylor they would come to no harm.

Tall and wiry, Peter the oldest of the boys at eleven, came across as rather serious and quiet; the others looked up to him, well David did, and Mum had said he often seemed to be helping around the house. The middle brother David was shorter and stockier, spending any spare time reading when he wasn't doing school spellings or tables. Andrew, however, was a completely different kid, into everything and full of fun, clearly a challenge to the rest of the family and enjoying every minute of it.

We worked all day digging a hole for the shelter, four foot deep and six and a half foot long, in a thick, sticky clay. Mrs Harris was very concerned about her roses, but we managed to reassure her and kept on digging. The Taylor boys would dig a bit then troop about admiring and commenting on the progress; Andrew was attentively shadowed by Mum! Father was keen to get on with the job, as he explained to all,

"If it rains and we haven't got the shelter up we'll have a huge muddy puddle on our hands, and that'll be no good for any of us!" The shelter consisted of corrugated steel sheets, each looking like a giant sledge, which were bolted together at their top to create an arch; this was sunk in the hole and the soil that had been dug out, heaped on top for protection, and a low door added at one end. Well that was the idea according to the instructions Mum discovered in an envelope tied with string to one of the sheets. We struggled to carry the sheets through the narrow sideway but eventually laid out all the parts in the rear yard. Harry next door wasn't too practical so a lot of the work fell to Dad and me; Mrs Harris was on her own and just watched from the balcony, and her upstairs neighbours – well I never even saw them. Having studied the instructions Dad and I enthusiastically tackled the task. It felt as if we undid as many bolts as we did up, but we couldn't have as it finally stood by itself. Father was a cabinet maker for the Post Office and had managed to get some wood from work to construct benches each side in the shelter. When we'd finished Mum invited the Taylors over to look and survey 'their boys' handiwork, the lads were so chuffed because their father came and had a look. Dad told Mum that when the siren went he wondered if everyone would get there in time; fortunately none of the others heard his concern.

On the few occasions when we did hear the wailing siren we would gather blankets and masks, Mum would always bring a jug of hot cocoa or broth although it never stayed hot for long, Dad carried a can filled with water and a box of dry matches. Sometimes we had to use a torch to find the shelter, but more often than not the sky overhead was alight with search lights, and the skyline glowing with fires. The Bürnsteins, Mrs Harris and ourselves would congregate in the shelter, the others never bothered to make it, and there we would sit in this cold, dark and damp coffin, sometimes playing cards or ludo by candle light. If it had recently rained the floor of the shelter would be sodden, and unless you lifted your feet up on to the bench, they would soon get freezing cold and go numb. It got so damp down there that the pillows and blankets soaked up the moisture and had to be wrung out periodically.

The 'ack-ack' of guns and 'thud' of bombs became more frequent as the weeks moved on and was increasingly deafening as well as frightening as they grew ever closer. Often we would spend what seemed like ages down there; when the 'All Clear' sounded we were so pleased we'd cheer, Mrs Harris the loudest. All of us were fortunate, our homes suffered little damage, it may well have been that Hitler's concerted offensive had not truly begun, or perhaps because we were just lucky.

Unlike some parts of the country thought to be safe, London was regarded as one of the 'danger zones', its children had to be evacuated. At the start of the bombing one hundred and twenty thousand of them left the city. Early one evening whilst we were enjoying tea indoors an agitated Mrs Taylor knocked, clearly in a state.
"I was told I had to register 'the boys' under some scheme the government has, but I never realised it would come to this," she declared as Mum let her in.
"Now what are you talking about? Go on, sit down, what is it?" Mum said, trying to pacify her.
"This 'Pied Piper' thing, they . . . the school, they want to send my boys away, surely it must be better we all stay together . . . I just don't know how they'll cope!" Mum took her into the lounge whilst attempting to console her; Dad and I finished tea.

One week later we all gathered on the pavement in The Close to see the boys off on their 'adventure' as Mum liked to call it when talking to Mrs Taylor. Peter and David had a small brown suitcase in their hands and wore rather glum looks, whilst dear old Andrew was swinging a pillowcase probably full of clothes and toys and strolling out with his gas mask in a box around his neck as if he hadn't a care in the world. Needless to say Mrs Taylor was in tears but hiding it quite well as she set about walking them to the tube station. Mister we were told was having a very bad day and only managed to come to the door and wave farewell. The next day Mrs Taylor called on Mum and told her she couldn't believe how many children there were at Waterloo; hundreds and hundreds, the platforms were packed. She said that one lady who was there working for the WVS was very kind; she tied tags on each of the boys' coats having written their names and school on them, but no destination. When asked by another mother she explained no one knew then exactly where any of them would end up. Mrs Taylor told Mum that she wasn't allowed on the platform so shouted to them that they must stay together and look out for each other; she said Peter took hold of his brothers and walked away to join the other children. The WVS lady told her and the other mothers that it was for the best and they would be far away from the bombs and safe. For some this was the first time they would see the seaside, and certainly be away from loved ones, settling down to sleep in their unfamiliar new homes, listening to the reassuring words of Children's Hour's Uncle Max saying, 'Goodnight Children, Everywhere!' We never saw a lot of Mrs Taylor after that, Mum heard she'd got some letters about them, but I never saw 'the boys' again.[12]

The long and mundane pattern of life and work carried on uneventfully and weekends really didn't herald much more. I would be riveted to my radio on returning home from work, listening for any developments of war, and every morning looking out for the postman, for news. Clearly the RAF was in no rush and whilst others appeared to be on the brink of panic, it was going to come to its decision in its own good time. Mum and Dad were well aware of my anxiety and disappointment, and after the first few weeks never raised the matter. Life dragged.

In all that time the only ray of light for me was Lindsey. She walked into our drawing office one day and introduced herself as the new secretary of the company library. I didn't care much what she did, and although having used the Engineering Reference Library on rare occasions, I certainly never noticed a secretary there before. All that would change.

It was true to say I was very aware of girls but certainly didn't claim to be either as experienced or active as some fellows. Whilst they were using the verb 'conquest', I was tinkering with the word 'contact'! My early days at school had provided not only a knowledge of words and numbers, but also of Elaine. There was little that was unique in this, as every young lad in our year at primary school had appreciated the delights of Elaine, well so it seemed, usually at the back of the sheds in the playground. When I say 'experienced', for me it started as a peck on the cheek and slowly progressed to an intense 'snog'. It was hard to ascertain the progress of others, where truth ended and fantasy began! That didn't however stop the bragging.

The singular key event that had the most impact on my 'development' did not occur at school, or even with a school lass. I was the only non Jewish guest to be invited to good old Franklin's bar mitzvah. The lovely Adina Jacht stole the day as far as I was concerned. I remember nothing of the ceremony and celebrations other than my constant efforts to engineer my presence ever nearer Franklin's cousin Adina. As the celebrations grew so did my fervour. One dance led to another which logically led to what can only be described as an extensive fondle in the cupboard where the synagogue's chairs were stored. This proved to be my 'Shangri La'. Throughout our encounter, like divers coming up for air, we would slide back into the throng for a brief interlude. Each time Franklin would catch my eye and greet it with an all knowing wink. By the time the evening had come to an end, I was more than grateful to Adina, and on parting I thanked everybody, but really was most sincere when I thanked her twice, or was it three times. Franklin said little to me that night, but privately parted with,

"Gentle by nature, gentle by name – Adina," then grinned knowingly, shook my hand and said, "had a good time?" And without waiting for an answer added, "I'll see you tomorrow, yeah?"

And now Lindsey; both the fruitless years and my diminishing patience had moved me very gradually to be more forward with ladies. It is all relative however. On our first meeting across my drawing board I felt as though there was a common energy joining us, a mutual understanding, a physiological bond, so I was somewhat taken aback the next day when I asked her out and she refused. After a sudden re-vitalised interest and realisation of the importance of 'academic reference', I would visit the library several times in a working day, even in my lunch and tea breaks. I was delighted when my competence with research was recognised by Leslie and Barbara, two mature members of staff whose boards were next to mine, when they would ask me to go to the library on their behalf. After two or three weeks of this subtle approach, Lindsey confronted me,
"Why haven't you taken me out?" I was speechless. Her original refusal, so she explained, was because she didn't think I was serious as it had been so quick! So much for my bold new confidence.

Our first date was a trip to the cinema – 'The Spy in Black' was on the big screen - the story of a World War One U-boat Commander who is ordered to attack the British fleet at Scapa Flow, he then gets involved with a school teacher on the Orkney Islands. Although it was billed as one of the top ten films of '39, it clearly was not to Lindsey's taste: maybe because it was about war, or perhaps the German U-boat bit didn't inspire, or it could have been that it was just not a very good film! In hindsight 'Brief Encounter' would have been much better and more appropriate.

So it was, that that date with Lindsey; gorgeous, perfectly petite Lindsey, with superb flowing light brown locks and fringe,

45

mysteriously sparkling eyes and a cheeky smile that caused her nose to wrinkle very slightly and ever so saucily, was not only my first date but also my last. We remained good friends, chatting over lunch but never ventured out together again.

# .Chapter 9

The days passed so slowly waiting for my letter, my call-up; and then, at the beginning of June, it arrived. I was joining the RAF. This completely disrupted our family breakfast, an interruption Mum was probably expecting sometime, but dreading never-the-less. Dad asserted,
"There will be difficult times ahead, you'll need to look after yourself Son." Mum was silent for a while, she just sat quietly glancing from me to Dad and back, coughed and whispered,
"You will take care dear, won't you?"

I was so excited, hardly being able to contain myself. The truth is that when we make life changing decisions none of us know how things will turn out, although for me I knew one thing, if I had anything to do with it . . . I would fly. There was no time to lose, so much to do, get my gear together, find out where I was going . . . and when to tell my mates, those that were still around, oh, and of course tell those at work. The family would know sooner or later, Mum would see to that. When they did hear, knowing them as I do, Aunts Gladys, Marjorie and Hilda would say,
"Not to worry Lil," reassuring and comforting her. Uncles, big Jimmy, little Jim and Bert would say very little; whereas Dad's cousin Oswald would be proud, certain our country needed 'boys' like me, then lie adding,
"I know 'The Boy' will be fine."

Once I'd left home Mum and Dad would be okay, changed and different, but okay; well that was my hope. My head was totally pre-occupied with the new life ahead of me, whatever that would be. The summer's sunlight was blazing through our kitchen window and warming the room; the day brought a new promise – a promise of adventure, danger and death, if not for me, certainly for others. I had endless questions: what would it be like? How difficult would the tests be? Would I pass them? What would the future hold? I wondered if I would be lonely and what would war really be like: how wretched would it be?

For some reason I have never doubted my desire to fly, although I had never before flown or for that matter experienced air sickness or vertigo – that was yet to come. I grasped the ream of information that had been crammed into the buff envelope and with eagerness began to read.

Behind me were the entry tests: mathematics, general knowledge, aircraft recognition as well as the medical and eye examination, and the knowledge that I had five fillings which needed to be replaced later by the RAF dentist for more suitable ones! As I travelled on the train I had no idea of what the future would hold. The carriage was packed with recruits of a similar age and possessed the atmosphere of an excited school outing, with a fair smattering of apprehension around. The sound of cheerful chatter filled the air, hardly masking the repetitive beat of the train as it clattered over lines, whispered past trackside poles and belched forth steam. The comforting rhythm encouraged me to slump in the seat as I recalled my brief life passing by. This journey had all the sense of a dream, conscious of my memories one moment, then anxious for my discoveries the next.

As the train eventually arrived at our destination I knew the prospect of 'square bashing' awaited me, I didn't know such could be more accurately described as 'aircrew bashing'. We all struggled to manage our unfamiliar bulging kit bags that had been stuffed full with some of the items in the 'Male Recruits' section of our kit list.

We almost tumbled out onto the platform where we were ordered to 'GET FELL IN'. The next stage of our adventure was at the mercy of an RAF driver as the fleet of canvas backed trucks rattled down the back roads and country lanes to what was going to be our 'prison camp' - thankfully for ten weeks only. As our vehicle bumped its way through the gates and into the base, those of us standing grabbed anything which appeared secure in an attempt to prevent us from piling onto strange and unknown budding airmen; then almost immediately we ground to a halt. For a moment fellow occupants looked about wondering what next, but before we even thought to enquire a shrill command penetrated our very being,

"Get yourself out you lazy, idle lot."

A mass of buildings, various in size and construction were arrayed before us; scores of servicemen were occupied with their duties, completely oblivious to our arrival. Following a chaotic few moments when we were herded from one place to another, we were finally organized in Flights. One of the drill instructors proceeded to take command, marching us along a series of meandering gravel paths, past workshops, beside hangers, between bunkers, to what was to be our hut, which looked identical to all the others. After having dumped our kit the cookhouse was the next stop for grub; here we were issued with a knife, fork and spoon and a large white enamelled tin mug. The food on camp wasn't that bad, contrary to the often awful smell that emanated from the kitchens. Already the rigidity of service life had become apparent to me but was quite foreign and unappealing; there I was however, and having to make a go of it. On returning to the hut I was more aware of just how big it was, like a long wide corridor. Down each side about a dozen or more iron beds were spaced, heads to the wall, feet to the middle. Each bed had the added luxury of two metal lockers, one short, one tall. Down the middle of the hut stood a number of different sized tables, some chairs and, positioned strategically towards each end, a black round heating stove, flued straight up through the roof. On each stove sat a large kettle and a brown enamelled teapot. Beside the stoves, on their hearths, were buckets of coke – bright, black coke, maybe even washed coke!! The wooden floor was well polished and the interior spick and span. Nearby, serving several huts, was the 'ablutions' block: rows of basins hung on the wall and lavatories in cubicles which appeared like lines of regimented sentry boxes.

I could just picture the mayhem in the morning as scores of airmen wanted to wash and shave at the same time, not to mention using the loo!

Our amusement was violently shattered by the bellow from a distant quarter,
"Corporal present."
Confusion reigned as a ragbag of shambolic men tottered to some sort of resemblance of 'Attention'. I thought that the drill Sergeant had work on his hands with us lot. The corporal proceeded to share his wisdom for our benefit! Firstly he explained the etiquette regarding the presence of an NCO or officer, then he outlined in detail the command structure. He made it abundantly clear we were,
"Flight two of four, of 'Salmond Sqaudron', the best flight in the squadron and will remain so, and I run it," and then continued his spiel with, "you all got that?"
"Yes Sir!" was mumbled in reply.
Without any hesitation and in an authoritative tone he stated,
"There is no room for idle layabouts, you all have to work bloody hard and I'll stand for no messing about; I hope it won't be necessary but if any of you have difficulty with that, I'll help your understanding …clear?" I heard myself say,
"Yes Sir, three bags full Sir;" fortunately quietly in my head!
The hut had to be kept tidy and absolutely spotless at all times, and inspections would help us achieve this, he delighted to tell us. He went on to explain that 'Reveille' was at 06.30, dining hall for breakfast at 07.00hrs, fall-in at 08.00 dressed in 'working blues' and boots, lights–out 22.30, exactly. As far as I was concerned breakfast would turn out to be the best meal of the day: thick porridge followed by a greasy fry-up and a mugful of 'Rosie Lee'. The corporal then selected two recruits as 'senior men' for our hut, stuck them in the beds nearest the door and ordered us to pick a bed, unpack and reminded us that lights-out was at 22.30.

As I looked about the hut it was clear we were a real mixed band; Poles, a Čzechoslavakian, a Scotsman and I could even hear a Brummie! Before I could introduce myself to the chaps in the nearby beds, two smartly uniformed men burst in with wooden clubs announcing they were on 'guard duty' and told us that when we had been issued with rifles, they had to be locked in the racks in the hut. We kipped down; 22.30 on the dot the lights went off leaving just the ghostly light of the porch bulb casting its atmospheric blue glow. Struggling to sleep, disturbed by the snoring and wheezing of inconsiderate hut mates, I mused on the letter I had received a few days earlier at home: 'A message of welcome from the Secretary of State for Air', which I am sure said, 'To be selected for air crew training is a great distinction.'

I wasn't used to early mornings, but every aspect of my life had changed and there was no way I was going to be late. Hurriedly I dressed, having washed and shaved, then assembled with the others to march to breakfast. The smart clip of steps in unison was beyond us, our best was a spasmodic shuffle, kicking those in front, but we did swing our arms well to show we were making an effort. Over breakfast I sat with the chaps who had bedded down near me, and much to my relief they all turned out to be 'damned good eggs!' Nigel was a wiry youthful chap, sharp and alert with a natural flair for looking somewhat dapper. I thought he'd been in the RAF before but he said that he hadn't. He seemed a really good lad, someone who would always be on the look out for you. One of his greatest qualities I had already appreciated the night before, being in the next bed to him: he didn't snore! This is however more than can be said for Richard who slept opposite – thank goodness, and I believe had spent an earlier life as a fog horn on a lighthouse. I was to discover that he was a most learned chap when it came to engines and aircraft, having worked on machinery down on his family farm in the West Country, an altogether nice guy. I also was to discover in time that a rather peculiar smell accompanied him, it was hard to quite pinpoint what it was. The other side of me was where Jeff bunked, a man of formidable intellect, completely at ease with the life of adventure having at one time braved the ocean waves in a dinghy, or some such craft. During one of our conversations I quizzed him as to why he hadn't joined the Navy, he paused for a moment then with conviction explained,

"Wanted to be a fighter pilot, always wanted to be a fighter pilot and rather than just sit around until I die of old age, I'd rather die for something worthwhile." That was it and, whilst we talked about many things, we never ever discussed it again. Officer material I concluded! Next to Jeff was Martin, a tall solidly built man of few words. His aircraft recognition was truly impressive; many an evening we would pass hours trying to catch the old sod out. He had a habit of throwing flying quotes into our conversations that is when he did say something. When I commented to him that the hut smelt musty and damp he conclusively replied;

"The sky is our real home." His favourite, when in the coming weeks we perhaps were getting a bit ahead of ourselves, was,

"There's nothing like the runway for bringing us down to earth." After about its second or third offering, all of us got the message and began to notice a twinkle in his eye when he said it.

For me and for many of the others we agreed life was going to be tough, at least for a bit, but only a bit we hoped. I was a tall slender young man with clear and sharp features. My manners were mild and my charm natural having been nurtured through a youth spent mainly socialising with those of more mature years. Many would comment that I had acquired an understanding which belied my age; never had this been disagreeable to me, taking pride in my ability to relate to others. At times I enjoyed a bright and joyful disposition, if not tinged with a hint of mischief; other moments I found a sense of melancholy all pervading. I was seriously unsure how easy and enjoyable this RAF life was going to be.

Our second day was full and busy. After breakfast, drill: how to come to 'Attention', to 'Stand Easy', to 'Stand at Ease' and 'Salute'. We marched and marched: straight lines, straight ahead, crashing heels, high swung arms, this way and that, up and down the parade ground, somehow turning in the process, and not a word to be spoken by us. All done to the accompaniment of profound swearing and commands directing our every move whilst explaining our shortfalls in no uncertain terms for all the world to hear. That afternoon we were sworn in and became fully fledged members of the Royal Air Force. Afterwards we were kitted out and issued with two uniforms, but before we could wear them they were taken away by a short tubby man, with a slightly weird accent, he reminded me of Harry Bürnstein, who first measured each of us whilst mumbling under his breath,
"When I am finished my dear boy these will fit you like a glove."
Next were hair cuts, a regulatory 'short back and sides' without added finesse, no fuss, no attention to styling, just a haircut every one and a half minutes!

In the evening when we were all back in the hut, a bit of a tussle took place: Angus, the beefy Scots guy, had spotted a photo of one of the lad's girlfriends stuck on the inside of his locker door; mercilessly he ragged the lad about it, winding him up. The unassuming youngster had clearly had his fill, turned on him and without warning pounded a mighty punch to the Scot's stomach. He went down with a thud, caught the edge of a bed frame and then hit his head on the locker before ending on the floor. Dazed, he rose after a minute or two, stumbled up to the lad and whilst we were expecting a battle to ensue, said,
"Fair enough," outstretched his hand and they shook. Sanity returned 'til another day! As Martin put it,
"Go in quickly, punch hard, get out!"
Just as the deathly silence in the hut had run its course one of the lads shrieked,
"Officer present!" A courteous looking middle aged man stood in the doorway, dressed as an officer and wearing a dog collar.

"Okay chaps, glad to see you all settled in and getting to know each other," with that he gave a cursory glance in the direction of the two who had just entertained us. He coughed, smiled, then continued his speech,

"As any of you can see, I am your padre, you will also note I am a wing commander," he paused for affect. "The next few weeks won't be easy, some of you will find it exciting and challenging, others, stressful and hard work. The key is to approach it with a positive spirit, living each day as it comes."

We were beginning to get the picture.

"If any of you have problems coping, approach your corporal seeking permission to speak with your flight commanding officer. In the most extreme of circumstances you can contact me: we don't want any incidences that could have been avoided! Any questions?" and without hesitation said, "No, good. May God bless you, carry on chaps," and left as noiselessly as he had arrived.

The following days were spent with drill, PT and of course, inspections. Before parade at 08.00 we had to strip our beds and put our kit in a neat pile at the foot. Blankets, sheets, greatcoats, gas mask container – everything had to be square and very tidy. PT consisted of routine exercises on the field, cross country runs, games of football and occasional basketball matches. We soon realised just how unfit most of us were. A couple of times a week our flight had an excursion to the local baths where everyone had to swim a length; if you couldn't you soon learnt! On one occasion, Mike one of our chaps, skinny dipped and got a right rollicking from Flight: he didn't try that again. We were subjected to large quantities of 'square bashing', more marching and, at times, the discipline seemed irksome and laughable, yet it wasn't always easy to raise a laugh. Our corporal, the dear, would march us around the parade ground and the camp, and route march us along the country lanes. En route he would always go on ahead, then appear standing on top of a bank or an old shed and shout at us. After the first day out it became evident what we were to expect in the future,

"Eyes forward."

"Keep those lines, eyes on the man in front."

"Rifles straight," for now we had been issued our firearms.

"No, no, you useless airmen, IN TIME."

One of our fellows dropped his rifle: all hell broke loose, he'd already struggled with the swimming and being a 'short arse' had difficulty in most things. This was not the man to win awards for his drill prowess either. That evening we reflected on Percy's performance and decided that 'there's one of him in every squad, and he was our one!' A podgy and insipid character yet reminiscent of a tenacious weasel: one who I am sure would squirm their way in and only let go with total reluctance, you might spend time with him but not for long, and knowingly he'd cling beyond his welcome. We wondered what would become of him, probably a desk job, admin, he was certainly too short to be a gunner, although he wouldn't take up much space in the plane. I suppose if they extended the controls, you never know, he might turn out to be an 'Air Ace'.

Between these physical delights we were taught about the history of the RAF, service law and the 'Gas Rule', we even had to go into a hut full of tear gas to see if our masks leaked! Arms drill became a daily routine with lessons on firearm safety, how to clean our rifles, take them apart and put them back together time and time again, until we could do it with our eyes closed. We spent just one afternoon on the range learning how to shoot at a target. I quickly came to the conclusion that this particular skill was not going to save my life let alone that of others. A few days into our training on an especially cold morning we had a shock: little beknown to us we had paraded for our jabs! One jab will do for lots of things the medic told us; however, he failed to let us know that one needle would do for lots of men. The queue was formidable, but not as formidable as the cigar sized glass syringe and needle, which appeared to be the same size as Mother used to knit with.  Duly delivered, we had to re-assemble on parade; but our dear corporal - our guide, our mentor, our protector, and now our torturer - had his work cut out trying to corral the many fainting souls.  Martin, the moment before his injection, exclaimed to the medic, whom he towered over,

"Height gives one the advantage you know," then promptly fainted!

# Chapter 10

In the early summer of 1940 all the talk was of France, and particularly of Paris. Radio reports had been broadcast by different war correspondents, alarming accounts of Paris's impending fall and of the confusion that was sweeping through the city. The French people themselves were unaware of many of the events which were shaping their immediate future as government censorship hid much from them. Rumours concerning quarrels amongst politicians, and incompetence and betrayal in the army high command were rife, so when the leadership of Paris finally disbanded, chaos and panic took over. The French had put their trust in the supposedly impregnable 'Maginot Line', kilometre after kilometre of intense defences which shadowed its border with Germany between Luxemburg and Switzerland. The women of France planted roses along the line so it looked pretty for their men as they guarded France; but the three-billion -franc wall of protection failed them: on 10th May the Germans marched into France.

On Friday morning, June 14th, we were all gathered around the radio in our hut to hear the news on the 'Home Service': "PARIS HAS FALLEN; NAZI TROOPS MARCH INTO THE CITY, FRANCE IS LOST". Martin's comment wasn't crafted with his usual poetic prowess, he just uttered,
"Bugger!"
Over the ensuing days our mood was somber in spite of efforts by the NCOs and officers to shake us into shape. In their wisdom we were given passes to go into the nearby town one night, but I recall little of what we did other than stare into pints, and mull over Hitler's next move.

Just over a week after we heard the first news of Paris, our corporal posted on the hut's notice board the copy of a dispatch our wireless boys had picked up; it was a 'Communique from an American War Correspondent' who had witnessed the fall of

Paris: it made grim reading.[13] France had been ripped apart, partitioned as seen fit by the Germans. Marshall Pétain assumed absolute powers as 'Head of State', but there was little enthusiasm for either him or his government. Philippe Pétain's heroics of the last war were largely forgotten now, many seeing him as a defeatist. The Germans occupied the north of France and the Atlantic coastline, allowing Pétain to govern southern France from Vichy, to be known as the so called 'Free Zone', some two fifths of the country. Widespread devastation existed north of Paris: towns and villages destroyed, large areas of countryside deserted, crops rotting alongside corpses of men and animals. Any food which was available went first to the occupying forces, then those who worked for the Germans and collaborated, and lastly to the French people.

I heard a broadcast over the BBC by General Charles de Gaulle: a large obscure, prickly Frenchman, who fled to London to form the 'Free French Army'. He defiantly rallied the people of France to establish the resistance movement.[14] It was stirring stuff and he went on to assure the people of France they were not alone: behind them was a vast empire, the British Empire, and the immense resources of the United States. He stated that the destiny of the world was at stake. He concluded by promising to them and the world,[15]
"Whatever happens, the flame of French resistance must not, and shall not die."

Yet Paris was still Paris.

The white-domed Basilica of the Sacré Coeur overshadowed the nightclub district known as Montmartre; this was outside the city limits, free of Paris and had become a popular area of pleasure. Here theatres, cinemas, cabarets were always full, regardless of air-raids. The Germans, normally unarmed, loved the extravagant shows and would flock to Le Moulin Rouge and Les Folies Bergère in vast numbers, often escorting young French women;

for the Germans had begun to love Paris.[16]  Amid the plush décor and dim lighting they would sip French champagne, surrounded both by the amorous low life and the decadent bourgeoisie.  Here was where the exotic and erotic, the bawdy and breathtaking would play alongside one another.  With the dramatic colliding of orchestral sound and the dancers cries as they high kicked their can-can across the stage, it must have been easy to put the pain of war out of their minds, albeit only for a moment.  Some women might well learn to forget their missing men and find fresh pleasures; old men would just sit and fish in the Seine.  There was widespread resignation amongst the French people that took on the mantle of indifference; for the Nazis, Paris had become their Babylon, every Nazi's favourite playground.  The Metro was running again, albeit on German time, and if you were careful or knew a German you could avoid the 8.00pm curfew.

Letters identifying Jewish families and their possessions poured into the authorities; nearly five million informant's letters in 1940 alone.  France had been home to the largest Jewish community in western Europe – two hundred and seventy thousand - of whom three-quarters lived in Paris.  Reinhard Heydrich, chief of the Reich Main Security Office, would preside over a meeting to determine the final solution to the Jewish problem, and how Vichy could help avoid French retaliation against the Germans as they implemented such plans.

The Germans had pushed back the Allied armies to Dunkirk, but Hitler's Panzer divisions had momentarily stood-down allowing many to escape; the French army was disbanded and the forty day long 'Battle of France' was over: the 'Battle for Britain' was now to begin.

There was never a victory parade in Paris: Hitler concluded they were not at the end yet.

# Chapter 11

"Allbrook, Burrow, Chappell, Coucher . . . " declared the airman as he passed out the mail; "Cross, there you go, Dixon, Goodwin, Hadden," pausing between names for the airmen to retrieve. "Hollingsworth," the list of names seemed endless, "Kilma, Walpole . . . "

Nige came up to me thrusting an envelope in my hand and happily declared he had got my letter when he grabbed his, then strolled over to his bed to read.

"Youll, Zajac," the airman cleared his throat then said, "that's it boys," and exited.

Before I even opened the envelope I knew exactly who it was from: Mum always wanted to look after me and just because I was away was no reason to stop! She started the letter as her letters to me always started and, as was her way, came straight to the point.

*July 1st 1940*

*My dearest,*

*I had thought by now we would have heard from you but father says it's early days and you would be pretty well occupied! Hope RAF life is good dear and you've made lots of new friends. Is the training as interesting as you thought it would be and have you flown yet?*

*Father has just come in from being on the allotment after work, we are truly grateful that we have the plot as it does mean we don't feel the pain of rationing in the same way as other poor dears. How you would survive love with just 2oz of bacon and 1 egg in a week for all of us I don't know. Father said you were probably better off than us; I do hope so.*

*Let us know how you're getting on dear and when you are on leave.*

*God bless,*

*Mum and Dad xx*

*P.S. Audrey Taylor said the boys all ended up on a farm near Okehampton somewhere in Devon and seem okay, but isn't it sad news about France.*

Many nights I slept well probably through sheer exhaustion, but none more so than after our first experience of the assault course, formidable was the word, justly describing the challenge. The rumours of what we were about to face worried many of us but the reality exceeded our wildest nightmares.

We assembled on the parade ground in our PT kit early. It was a cold, sharp morning as we marched to a clearing in the adjoining woods where each group of eight men collected their pole: a three hundredweight telegraph pole which we had to carry over our heads and then run with it to the start of the course. As if that wasn't enough to contend with we had glorious words of encouragement from our drill instructor who ran alongside,
"Let's go for a little jog lads, on the double." In a matter of a few steps he was barking again;
"Yendell, keep your head up."
"Sir," came the reply.
"Straight arms men . . . do you understand me?"
"Yes Sir," we cried in unison, between ever quickening gasps.

It probably wasn't very far, but by the time we reached the course we were breathing heavily and glad to put our load down - our arms were already burning. Another squad had already arrived and two more were behind us, so fortunately we were not the first to attempt the course. We all then had the benefit of the NCO's pep-talk,
"If any of you think this is not what you signed up for, raise your hand," and with the expectation of no dissenters continued, "this ain't going to be easy for any of you, but for some it will be pure hell; everyone of you will finish the course – is that clear?"
An unconvinced, "Sir," whispered from us.

"Is that clear?" he bellowed.

"Sir, yes Sir," came our forced response.

The course was outlined briefly but no words prepared me for what was to come.

The squad that arrived ahead of us was ordered to step up to the mark, and with a command from the NCO, was off. It became evident very quickly that the ground was wet, very wet and sticky. Sliding and slipping, the men of the first squad seemed to have their work cut out just to stay on their feet. Their drill yelled at one chap,

"Get off your fat arse Scottie."

As we stood at ease in line, our seasoned instructor passed, eyeballing us one after the other, almost nose to nose; stopping at Richard he questioned him as to what the strange smell was,

"Is it grime lad or perhaps talc or cologne?"

"No Sir," came his reply.

"No Sir, indeed," repeated our instructor who proceeded to tell him exactly what he did smell of, "it's garlic isn't it airmen, and I want none of that Frenchie business here – understood?"

A meek but required answer was forthcoming, "Sir."

Without further ado it was our turn to stand by the start line ready for the off. The drill told our corporal,

"If they stop moving, kick 'em!"

"Go! Go!" rang out, and eight of us tore towards the first obstacle; one man fell.

"Shift it Turner," was ordered from somewhere.

A wide seven foot high wall was before me; on realising its magnitude I put on a spurt and launched myself towards the top, just grasping it sufficiently to haul myself over, tumbling down the other side, and grateful for the soft mud. The next complication was the horizontal trunk, over a trench, which we had to run across without sliding off. Then, faced with a gaping pit, I grabbed the sodden sisal rope and swung on to a cargo net suspended from an overhead beam which I scrambled up in the most ungainly fashion. The net had a mind of its own, swinging

to and fro, side to side, never still, forever on the move, resisting my every attempt to climb upwards. I swung my leg up and hooked it over the beam, pulling my body until I could manage to roll over the top and clambered hurriedly down as a fellow was being chastised mercilessly behind me,
"You're the only one who can't make it, you fat worthless lump – shift yourself."

My focus now was on how to manoeuvre up a rope ladder that led to a high suspended twin rope Tarzan crawl; by the time I reached the top and started to drag myself along, my arm muscles were on fire. Pain was beginning to wash through my whole body, with every grasp and pull my shoulders ached, my muscles throbbed, and the ropes burnt deeply into my legs. I had to keep cuffing my nose and forehead to stop the snot and sweat. Along the way I faltered, the ropes wobbled badly and I found it hard to control the sway. Gathering my concentration, and steadying myself, I made it across. A rope monkey slide from the tower got me to the tunnel, no problem, although I could feel my concentration failing and I hit my head badly in the crawl pipe as I wallowed in icy mud. The last barrier between me and the finish, so I thought, was the belly- crawl under a net of barbed wire. Having learnt a lesson from the tunnel, I laid low and out-stretched, digging my fingers into the earth, relentlessly clawing, dragging and kicking myself forward. Out, I sprinted for the line utterly drained and just as I crossed a voice declared,
"Good time mister, you can go round and run again!" as another screamed,
"This ain't a picnic Bragg; put your back into it Trendell."
My heart sank, and my body was exhausted.
I was not certain that I was assaulting the course: in truth, it was more that the course was assaulting me. Many of us on the following morning found it hard to stir. I rolled over to see Jeff sitting on the side of his bed facing me, lancing a blister on his ankle. I didn't know he was a medic!

Our duties consumed the endless time we had. Down on all fours polishing our hut floor 'til it shone like a mirror; cleaning windows, not all of which closed; stocking the camp huts with buckets of fuel from the huge coke heap out back, and the never ending cookhouse duty. I soon learnt how to scrub out fifty gallon stock pots, what and where a grease trap was, how it smelt and, if that wasn't enough, how you cleaned it. Another totally boring job was 'eyeing' potatoes: the machine peeled them but someone had to 'eye' them before they were boiled. Chain link posts and border stones had to be regularly washed and painted white, as did notice boards and the flag poles. Guard duty either meant patrolling armed with a wooden club and a Thunderer whistle as defence, or manning the main gate. Such duties proved most eventless, thank goodness, with the only excitement being games of darts or hands of cards. Most of the time was spent being cold, wet and tired: a miserable existence.

'The days slipped joyfully by!'

One particular day is prominent in my memory, the day when we were all able to be blood donors. Assembling in the NAAFI, we formed an orderly queue, and one by one, escorted by a nurse to a camp bed, we were subjected to the surgical procedure. In true form Martin looked doubtful about the whole affair and explained in great detail to the attending doctor that he still hadn't fully recovered from a bad cold. It didn't work, and after his dramatic stalls and stumble into the nurse's arms, his generous offering of a pint and almost total collapse on the bed, Jeff said to Martin, as he lay recovering from his pantomime performance,
"It's crucial that you never fly straight and level for more than 30 seconds in the combat area airman!" adding, "You certainly seem to have mastered that Martin."

More drill with our ancient 303 Lee Enfields ensued. You had to have the correct angle of the rifle on your shoulder as you marched about, and the butt on the ground at the side of your left

64

boot as you stood at ease, and, as if that wasn't enough, the correct sequence of travel of the rifle from shoulder to vertically in front of your nose was vital in a salute. Cleaning one's kit became routine for each day: 'bulling up' boots took ages, 'blanconing' belts, rifle sling and your haversack, and then there was Duragliting buckles and buttons. And of course the rifle had to be stripped down, cleaned out and re-assembled before it could be locked in the rack with the chain passing through its trigger-guard: all quite tedious really.

Parades played a significant part in our lives with 'Pay Parade' being the most rewarding: the pay clerks would sit at a table, coins and notes neatly arranged before them. As they uttered name and initials, the NCO repeated them so everyone could hear, whereupon you marched to the table, smartly saluted and having cried out the last three figures of your service number, collected your pay.

I clearly had been less than diligent as a son in keeping in touch with home as I had written only the day before, when another letter from mother arrived!

> ....I had hoped we would have heard from you dear by now, how are things going, but as father said, life is probably hectic for you. Lots of things have happened since you were home. We've put up black-out curtains and I've taped across the windows in case we get any bombs. We'll have to make do a bit better in the future, and I'll have to mend a few things.
>
> Father's taken on a bigger patch over the allotments, it's a way to help us with food, it's really busy over there of an evening. 'Dig for Victory' seems to have fired people into action, that or the rationing! He said one of the old boys has got a pig hidden in a shed which he feeds on swill he collects from your old school canteen. Good luck to him I say.

*When we go out we're meant to carry our gas masks, great big things that they are, it's silly, and identity cards so if we're stopped by police or soldiers we can show them who we are, and prove we're not Germans!!*

*I nearly forgot the biggest news, father's joined the LDV, he says it's now called something like, 'Home Guards'? Albert, who he had worked with, asked if he wanted to join the Royal Observer Club or Corp which he was in. They stand at the same spot for twenty four hours, a whole day or more, every day just looking for aircraft, any aircraft; then when they see one they telephone someone else. Well dad said he couldn't cope with that, he thought it sounded boring, so he joined the Home thingy, but he'll tell you all about it. He said he'll write to you sometime.*

There her second letter ended with the usual sentimental farewell, telling me to keep safe and how much she missed me. I mused on it for a bit and concluded that they were getting busier – good stuff; and fortunately they still hadn't suffered any heavy bombing.

A special treat awaited us chaps one Saturday night: the screening in the mess hall of Howard Hughes' 'Hells Angels' with Jean Harlow. Set in the First World War, Harlow starred as a real vamp, playing one guy off against another. It ended with the British invading the Germans and a hearty cheer from us lads. A real whirlwind of a yarn and one that I hoped would not predict my experience!! On the way back to our hut, Richard who had been quite quiet all evening remarked,
"They'd never have been able to get that German plane back into the air you know," and Nige commented,
"We didn't see much of Jean Harlow did we?"

Every Sunday church parade was compulsory and by attending one of the churches in the town we boosted their waning congregations. The hymns were a bit dour at times as the organist seemed to have the tempo of a snail. Our padre took turns to share the pulpit with the local minister, and both provided an interesting break from the far too loud organ. The occasion did give us a chance to get off camp and share our good looks with the young women who lined our route into town.

The time was fast approaching for our passing out. An expectant air was evident amongst us chaps. By midweek we had undergone several dress rehearsals for the parade. Midway down the side of the parade ground was constructed a platform upon which stood the officers scrutinising our every move as we marched. The weather had all in all been grim, and on the last rehearsal a fine drizzle fell, soaking us right through. This made it doubly hard work to get our uniforms clean, dry and pressed, boots and buckles polished to a shine never seen before ready for final parade. My kit was immaculate.

As the corporal entered our hut we all stood to our feet, his cry rang out:
"I've got 'em lads. Your Postings!" He held them high in the air in his hand, waving them about. Soon we were to discover where each of us was destined to go next, but more importantly what we were to do in this air force. He called out the postings one after another with sufficient delay between where necessary to allow for group derision. Jeff was off to RAF Jurby on the Isle of Man for Initial Officer Training; this news immediately resulted in shouts of,
"Lucky sod," and "have to grow a moustache Jeff". Richard was heading to the Defence College of Aeronautical Engineering at Cosford, Shropshire. Morpeth in Northumberland was to be Martin's next stop to train at the Air Gunnery School. He whispered to me,
"They fly Botha's and mostly it's Poles up there you know." I didn't, so I just nodded. Nige was travelling to RAF Kinloss in the far north of Scotland and the 19 Operation Training Unit: he

was going to be a pilot. That news brought a cheer. I muttered to him,
"Nice one Nige, you deserve it." For me I was destined to be a navigator and on my way to Canada; oh and Percy, well he had duly been identified for his latent culinary skills and was going to train as a cook, with that raucous laughter broke out.

It seemed strange to think that these short lived friendships were already over; we'd been through some tough times together but as our corporal said this was only the start. There would be many new friends, but I would never forget these guys. After much congratulating, slapping backs and shaking of hands, we set about the serious business of the moment and completed our final preparations for the following day. The parade programme was posted on our notice-board.

The great day arrived. The weather was grand and the group captain and our officers on the platform looked pretty well chuffed as we paraded precisely to the sound of the military band. A crowd of relatives stood expectant, trying to spot their man amongst the hundred or more men. Mum and Dad were there; somewhere. The Inspecting Officer's Address to the gathered assembly was articulated, loud and clear,
"These men have accomplished a great deal in order to pass out today. Their endurance and endeavour is the price for their achievement and you should feel justly proud of them. We are grateful and encouraged to see a crowd here supporting the recruits' final parade. Those on parade today have completed their basic training and move to their specialist phase. As trained airmen they will then be deployed on operations.
On behalf of the permanent staff, the squadron and the Royal Air Force I wish all you men success; you will be given the best aircraft and armaments we can produce. The honour of the Royal Air Force is in your hands. Good Luck men"

All that remained for us to do the following day was to pack our kit, return our rifles to the armoury and bedding to the store and say our farewells after our last meal together. In the warmth of the afternoon, with RAF rail passes in hand and carting our kitbags, we headed for the station. Laughter disguised the underlying sadness of our parting and uncertainty of our future as we wished each other 'Good Luck'. Martin turned to us and with a wry grin and philosophical air quoted,

"It's far better to be unsure of where you are and know it, than to be certain and wrong!"

He had the ability to bring us back to reality, and this was no exception, as we started our journeys into an unknown future in the Royal Air Force and the war.

# Chapter 12

As I sank into the tired and worn train seat, a puff of dust drifted lightly in the air and glistened in the sunlight before it settled again; I reflected on my first few weeks in the RAF. The comradeship, something I'd never before experienced, the laughter, and of course the discipline had all had such a dramatic impact on me. With a gentle jolt, a hiss of steam and the guard's piercing whistle, our train was slowly but definitely on the move. I was now heading home for a few days before the next stage of my training . . . and an exciting future. On clearing the station and deserted stock yards, we gathered speed and by the time we passed an old grey concrete water tower, were traveling at a pace. The autumn green countryside stretched as far as the eye could see. Ribbons of golden gorse, occasionally broken by upright clumps of pink foxgloves lined the track edge. The river was now forging on, rejuvenated and charged from the fresh downpour of the morn. Time passed easily with little effort; my journey sped by. Suddenly all was dark, apart from the electric carriage lamps; a double blast from the engine's whistle echoed through the tunnel, announcing our presence and passing. As quickly as we had entered, we were out, out into the blinding sunlight and warmth. Mile after mile the rhythmic beat of the track played until our train was brought to a temporary standstill at a crossing. Here cars and trucks with livestock and cargo nervously sped over the line, away into the distance and out of sight. We pushed on through the valley, coppices of slender trees with their roots wading in marshy ground reached for the sky. Vast areas of fields lay flooded, as waders and gulls flocked overhead.

A short gradient led us down under an ancient stone bridge and towards a station stop, passing sidings and sheds. We finally came to rest alongside the platform waiting for new travellers to replace those alighting. Blue and white hydrangeas burst forth from well tended flower beds with pink hollyhocks peeking between. The silence was disturbed as a Red Cross train rattled past in the opposite direction on an adjacent track and soon was gone: a reminder of what was happening in the world. The guard waited on the platform although there were no more comings and goings, studied his pocket watch until the exact time, then waved his flag as he boarded his van and we continued on our journey.

I hadn't let Mum and Dad know I was coming although they knew I was 'on the move'. The old place looked much the same, the folks were a bit surprised but sort of expected me. As we sat down for tea 'Gert and Daisy' were on the radio: I couldn't but notice a new wireless set on the shelf above the sink. Mum said they listened to it a lot now the war had taken hold.
"At 8.30 ITMA was on," Dad explained as if I was familiar with the BBC's schedule, "Do you like Tommy Handley Son?" Before I could answer Mum chipped in enthusiastically,
"Colonel Chin Strap and Mrs Mopp make me smile, which is more than those blimin' Salvage Housewives' programmes."
This was like a foreign language to me!

It was plain to see rationing was having an impact – powdered eggs on our plate, kind of scrambled.[17] As if noticing my surprise, Dad, almost with disgust, informed me,
"Would you believe it lad, even tea's rationed, I ask you."
He smiled and as if getting the joke before it had even been told said,
"One thing would suit you Son is that to save energy we can only have five inches of hot water for a bath!" We all laughed and spent the rest of the evening talking about my weeks of training, the memorable characters and events. Mum was concerned that I should always make sure my clothes were aired so I didn't pick up a cold; Dad chuckled saying,
"Oh Lil!"

Over the next few days we caught up on all the news, including Dad telling me about his Home Guard duties.

"All sorts of men are members: the minister and doctor, a farmer or two, builders, plumbers, a scrap dealer, bank clerk and a butcher. We have weekly drill nights and manoeuvres when we have to run across open ground, climb fences and go on long route marches." It all sounded so familiar I thought! "There are also lectures and instruction, which many think are boring, so they don't turn up, they just do their duties and think that's enough, annoying the rest of us! Generally they're a good crowd though and they say the exercise is good for us, but heaven preserve us if we're called up to defend our country when the invasion comes, as come it surely will."

On Friday evening Dad came home; he'd heard from someone at work that Southend had been taken over by the military and that they were moving into many of the houses. They'd requisitioned the beach huts so they could get a proper field of fire across the sands. ARPs had sandbagged the front, barbed wire was stretched along the beach where the old deckchairs once were, and wire barriers were going to be erected along the low tide line.
"Most of the shops are closed what with the petrol rationing and shortage," Father said, "as well as there being obviously no holidays. The place is completely dead, nothing like we remember it Boy, it's a shame; I doubt we'll ever get to Butlins now eh?"

At the weekend we strolled over to the allotments, past Franklin's house; there was no sign of them - Mum said she thought they may have moved away. The plots were a hive of activity: old boys, families and young kids were all busy tending crops and harvesting. A hobby for some had now become an essential part of life. I gazed around: arrayed before me were compost heaps dusted with lime, shuttered with galvanized sheets, steaming and overflowing; upturned buckets and pails, clearly serving some purpose; and collections of antique garden tools propped against sheds. Whilst surveying the plots I could almost hear the gardeners' contentious talk regarding seed varieties; lively chat

72

about weed control, pests and diseases; learned discussion concerning crop rotation, yields, etc. as well as just healthy idle gossip. Father explained that the industrious old timer who had hidden a pig in the shed on his plot, had, after a bit of a run-in with the Allotment Association, now constructed a proper pig sty with corrugated sheets nailed to posts as a pen. He'd hung a hessian sack to one end of the low hut to act as a weather-proof door, and, during the summer when the school was closed, scrounged old veg and greens from fellow plot holders for the pigs' fodder. Taking in the pastoral scene it was hard to comprehend that we were in the midst of a war. We headed over to a particular patch where Dad introduced me as, 'Our boy in the RAF'. The old man, whose constant stooping over a spade and barrow had curved his ancient back, was delighted to hear I was in the RAF, and started to tell me about what he'd seen a couple of weeks earlier. If it hadn't been for his mangled shed and the deep freshly ploughed furrow on his plot, I may well have found his story beyond belief.

"Well you young 'un," was how Massi began his yarn, "one night two weeks back now we heard a German bomber flying over the waste ground." He paused and pointed, "over there! Well it must have been hit, it was so low and getting lower all the time, just clearing the trees. Then it dived and there was an explosion, a blast, a crash, a tremendous thud and the ground shook, and a big red flash." He had been visiting his sister whose house overlooked the allotments, and on what was a bright moonlit night, saw the whole incident.

"I got over here at sun-up the next day to discover that the Dornier had come down on the waste ground at the back there and it was still burning. The officer chappy said it must have jettisoned a couple of bombs before it crashed, one of which stopped short of the allotment fence, the other must have been going faster and bounced until it hit my shed!" With almost a surreal air he described how the bomb had smashed through the back of the shed, coming to a stop amongst sacks of his best spuds, which stood firm! The shed's sides had collapsed inwards and then the front and roof on top.

"Neatly packed up!" he confirmed. "How it didn't explode I'll never know, but explode it didn't, thank God." Everyone who undoubtedly had heard the story before laughed aloud and one old boy slapped him on the back adding,

"It gets better every time you tell it Massi."

"So what happened then?" I pressed, although he really didn't need prompting being now in full flow,

"Well the ARP warden reported it, and as there were no houses near, no one had to evacuate. Later the Royal Engineers' bomb disposal squad arrived, and a gaunt, haggard looking chap made 'em safe, sorted it all out, then took 'em away, not a job I'd give you a thank you for." He must have realised we thought the story had reached its satisfactory conclusion, so quickly stopped our assumption with,

"That weren't the worst of it you know."

"No?" I queried.

"Most certainly not," he came again, "it may not have exploded, but it might as well, the bloody thing ploughed right through my asparagus bed; I'd just cut them back and mucked 'em up for next year. Bloody inconsiderate I call it!" As we made our way across the allotments into town, Dad said he'd never seen him so angry before and Mum added it was a real pity as he'd done so much work. Sprouting from one rather ill kept plot were a collection of a dozen or two road signs, all pointing in the same direction. They'd been taken away from road junctions to confuse the enemy. I'd noticed that street names had been obliterated and Dad explained that you couldn't buy maps now, they'd even stopped the weather . . . well, that's to say, the weather forecast!

We headed through town on our way to the Saturday matinee passing the tube station, a massive circular building looking somewhat like a modern art deco flying saucer. A ring of windows, banded below the dish like roof, sparkled in the sun. The bus depot circled half way round the Underground station where queues of shoppers weaved around the stops, their bags grouped on the pavement, chatting whilst waiting for the arrival of their bus as timetabled. Ironically amongst the hoardings, posters warned of the dangers of 'Careless Talk' cautioning all about the enemy within: 'Loose Talk Can Cost Lives'; 'Keep mum, she's not so dumb'.

The Odeon billed David O'Selznick's epic 'GONE WITH THE WIND', starring Clarke Gable, Vivien Leigh, Leslie Howard and Olivia de Havilland. It was a film that had opened in the early days of the Blitz in London to sensational reviews and audiences, and unlike Mum and Dad, I'd not seen it. The line of eager cinema goers stretched around the foyer, down the steps and along the road past the nearby shops; I imagine they were expecting that a matinee would not be interrupted by an all too frequent air raid, and hoping it would help them forget the anxiety of war.

We emerged from the warmth and comfort of the theatre on what was now proving to be a fine day, chatting about the movie. What none of us knew however was that this day would become known as 'Black Saturday', the start of the Luftwaffe's concerted blitz on London, with daylight attacks and raids for fifty-seven consecutive nights. The haunting wail as the air raid siren wound up transformed our crowd's casual wanderings to a purposeful stride towards the Underground, then dash as we looked up to see the clear azure blue sky become peppered with hundreds and hundreds of black dots, scattered wide from roof-top to roof-top, slowly creeping nearer and nearer. The late afternoon sky lit up with an orange glow spreading along the southern skyline. We piled down the stairs into the tube station.

Hitler's 'Blitzkrieg' of Britain, his terror bombing of the British people had begun in earnest - he had unleashed the Luftwaffe on the people of London. For the first time since the 17th century, the city was under attack; the wrath of the German war machine would fall on cities throughout the country. Germany's air superiority was vital to preparing the way for their sea-borne invasion, first gaining control of the English Channel, then securing landing sites for the invading forces. Reich Marshall Göring was confident he could shoot us RAF lads out of the air in four weeks, and unwisely had boasted to Hitler as much.

Entire families were trying to control children who didn't know whether this was an underground adventure to be excited about, or just scared. Old tired people struggled to keep up with the dash for shelter; and the lonely, lost souls were also here, searching for a place to rest and sleep on the platform deep underground. Many were looking for friendship; the comfort of feeling safe amongst others and not having to worry about what was said or thought. Some, however, would never venture underground, whether it was because of the news of shelters being flooded by explosions bursting water mains and killing hundreds, or the collapse of tube stations from blasts creating massive craters of death. Who knows? It could have been that if death was to come they would rather die in their own beds. One bomb fell through a station ticket office, bouncing down the escalator and exploded, devastatingly killing all those taking refuge. But perhaps the most tragic loss was when, on their way down to the platform, over a hundred and fifty people were crushed to death as they stumbled and tumbled over each other.

Initially the home secretary refused to allow the London Underground to be used as a shelter, but necessity meant this was soon ignored and people went down into the subways. To begin with the facilities were appalling, no cleaning or sanitation, bunks or canteens: slowly that changed and indeed, if a regular, you could even guarantee a space to sleep on a ticket system, and whilst there, be amused by the entertainment that was laid on. Soon over one hundred and seventy thousand people spent each night down one of the eighty tube stations as increasingly more people were being bombed out of their homes.

After glancing cursorily around the throng that was packed on the platform, Mum approached a woman who was sorting her two children out, and, sitting beside her, immediately started talking. I wrongly thought she knew the mother, but it quickly became evident that this was not the case.

"I'm Lilian," she introduced herself. "Friends tend to call me 'Lil' but I much prefer 'Lily.'" Almost before she had finished the sentence the woman, ignoring Mother's clarification retorted,

"And I'm Dot, Lil, pleased to meet you." By now Dad and I had managed to shuffle up alongside them; Dad looked at me, shrugged his shoulders and quietly laughed. It was clear this was a woman who didn't bother too much with pleasantries.

"So who are these Lil?" Dot questioned looking towards us.

"Well Dot this is my husband Ron . . .," and before Mum could finish,

"And your son Lil?"

No sooner had Mum confirmed, Dot was ready with more questions, but Dad couldn't resist the opportunity to stop her in her tracks,

"Dot," she looked up, "are these two yours?"

"Aye, they're my pride and joy you know Ron." She proudly turned to them and patted each of their heads in turn.

"This is my Patricia and her twin Philip, they'll be five next month." She positively glowed, "Aren't they grand?" she asked, rhetorically. They had both been looking at us inquisitively but now they turned to their mother and beamed. As we settled down for what could well be a fair while, Dot explained to us that she'd come here every time a raid was on. Now she was on her own it was the safest place and as it turned out folks were really kind and helpful. A young girl of about twelve approached, asking Dot if it was alright for the twins to come and play Snakes and Ladders, she explained her ma would keep an eye out for them. Dot agreed and we watched them go just a few yards to a small crowd by a wall bench; the lady waved and Dot waved back. The woman called out,

"Do you want to go into the hat for the 'all clear'?" Dot replied that she'd see her later and then turned to us,

"We have little bets on when the 'all clear' will sound, and Pamie runs it! She's also our Shelter Shaker you know." Obviously noting our puzzled look she explained,

"Once the trains stop for the night, we all try to get some sleep, if anyone starts snoring, Pamie goes and gives them a prod: it's the only way to stop what can become a right old din!" Then, turning to look at her twins again, Dot said,

"It's no life for them you know, I wouldn't say anything while they're here, but this war's robbed them of their childhood."

There was a pause in her conversation, so I gently asked her why she was on her own.

"Al, my man, has been away this past year, he's in the Merchant Navy on those convoys bringing in supplies and things. I do so miss him and pray he stays safe, it's not an easy job with all those U-boats about." Dad looked at Dot and we all saw a softer side to her as he tried to comfort her with the hope that the navy and RAF would see them through. Then he explained that I was in the RAF.

"That's very kind of you to say, I know he'll be okay." She held back a tear as Mum lightly placed her hand on hers.

Further down the platform an argument erupted over what appeared to be a claim for bed space; it didn't come to anything and was disrupted by a train coming in: the carriage doors opened and passengers gingerly picked their way around the bedding and those camping out.

In an attempt to move on Dot perked up, asserting,

"Well we're not getting it as bad as my sis!" This time it begged a question and I was in first,

"Why's that?" trusting that as she'd raised it, it wasn't all bad!

"Liz lives in Guernsey and she said since the beginning of the year they've wondered what was going to happen, but after the trouble in France, islanders have been really worried. The government's not done a thing to help and told them nothing, other than they're not likely to be attacked. They wouldn't send any troops to help them but just took away any military stuff that was already over there. She was amazed! One of her neighbours, an old gent, along with a few others were guarding the power station and reservoirs on their own. Well, just a couple of months back the Germans invaded Alderney, it's only 8 miles away you know. Liz said only seven people stayed, the rest, along with over half the population of all the islands, had shipped out on any sort of craft that floated; it was a right old mess. By the end of June, after lots of flying overhead for days, the Germans bombed and machine-gunned her, well the harbour, then Jersey." She caught me with a glance, "A German pilot, all on his own, landed just up the lane from her home, then took off. They flew in loads of soldiers and their navy landed; there were men on motorbikes, officers in cars, Germans everywhere, and to think she was telling me that in March they were trying to get holiday-makers to go there, saying it was a safe place for war-time holidays! Can you believe it? It turned out the pilots had seen all these lorries lined up by the harbour and thought they were for troops. You shouldn't laugh, but they were full of potatoes and tomatoes you know. In the end a German Officer flew in to demand the surrender of all the Channel Islands.

Liz says it's so different now, their peaceful life is over. Loads of steel and concrete are being landed every day, oh, and men, lots of men to do all the building work they're doing there. I think she said it's Hitler's Atlantic Wall, I don't know what that looks like. Alderney is now a concentration camp for the Jews and anti-Nazis from Europe; they've laid thousands of mines and put massive guns around the coast pointing out to sea. The Germans have their own money and street names now and she's got food rationing like us. Can you imagine Lil, she uses potatoes for flour, and cooks with sea water because there's no salt; they even grind acorns for coffee – I ask you! No islander fired a single shot you know Ron, and she's been told to co-operate with 'em but not be helpful. I think I'm more worried for her than I am for us." She paused for the first time, then after clearly an emotional reflection, said softly as an aside,

"She said it's like living on the edge."

My leave had come to an end and now I was to head north to Liverpool.

# Chapter 13

Tombé – the beginning:

Meanwhile, many miles away amid the lush Kent countryside, a small band of men watched layers of mist lift slowly from the rolling meadows as the first morning sun greeted the day. The sodden field before them glistened in the dawning light, translucent silvery blades of grass stood in evidence to the heavy dew. The air was sharp and bit into their fresh young faces as they stared upwards towards the clouds, their every breath condensing as vapour as they scanned the sky for a hint of what the day had in store. None spoke a word during this ritual which took place every morning, when they weren't in the air chasing other pilots! The warming sun which had now been up for some time hadn't completely dispelled the layering mist across the airfield. Today could yet prove to be another turning point in the fortunes of the RAF and the Luftwaffe. Shafts of sunlight refracted from soaked wings of Hurricanes and Spitfires dispersed about the field, their propellers pointing skyward signalling their intended destination. The airfield was significant in its absence of any outstanding features, apart that is from the many buildings scattered around its periphery, and the windswept vegetation which bordered the field. Dark wooden huts with rusting corrugated roofs were arranged in regimented lines housing workshops where fitters and riggers worked all hours to keep the aircraft flying.

An occasional fresh breeze stiffened the air but the chaps stood riveted, again straining to observe any movement: every quarter of the sky was scrutinised. When they were fully content that the only things flying that morning were birds, and not until then, did the business of the day start. These were the young men who stood between defeat and victory, invasion and freedom; men, who only a few years earlier, were in school and safe at home with their families. Men who had undergone the same basic training as me; these were the men of RAF Fighter Command. A couple of old dusty armchairs were positioned in a semi-circle along with a dozen or so seats and deckchairs of various origin in front of the squadron hut, facing onto the airstrip. A flimsy card table was lodged beside one of the armchairs, on its green baize top a collection of mugs waited to be rinsed after the first cuppa of the day. On the ground, shimmering in the new day light a glass ashtray had toppled to one side, disgorging its stubs on to the sodden grass.

The brilliant azure blue sky had now chased every cloud away over the horizon. All was at peace, all still on this summer's day.

A youth in his late teens, sporting RAF blues and a light blue collarless cotton shirt, broke the silence by cheerily suggesting, "Cuppa chaps?" The novelty of making a brew hadn't yet worn off for this new recruit! No response was apparent but it was clear that all approved of the idea! He strolled over to the hut with the squadron badge mounted above the door and disappeared inside. Two of the airmen settled into the armchairs, others into the deckchairs, waiting for the inevitable call to action: one produced a newspaper and began flipping through the sheets, another browsed a copy of Picture Post, many just closed their eyes and dreamt about mastery of the skies, or perhaps home and life as it once was. By now the sun was starting to warm the day; the grass steaming off the morning dew in its heat. Lighting a cigarette, Squadron Leader 'Snowy' White, a dapper Hampshire boy, strolled out across the grass and knowingly glanced about, assessing what the day would hold. His cigarette smoke swirled about his head before drifting away in the gentle breeze. Amazingly, so far the field had not experienced the concentrated attacks by the Luftwaffe that others had, as they tried to break the back of the RAF and the resolve of the British people. But even so losses had been severe, four pilots shot down, four families informed, and in total seven planes lost, three of which were riddled with fire on the ground before they could even get away. The engineers believed they might be able to get one flying again, but it was doubtful and it certainly wasn't on if they couldn't get the parts. The real problem though was proving to be the shortage of pilots: they were being killed faster than they could be trained. A blackboard headed, '11 Group Fighter Command' was screwed beside the hut's door and listed the flights of the day for 'A' flight and 'B' flight, but revealed nothing for today.

The Germans' war of attrition from mid-July to the end of October 1940 was intended to grind down the fighting strength of the British, but they hadn't reckoned on the bravado, wrecklessness and spirit of the young men that led Britain's brave air defence. For these men though it was not only the tension and tedium that was wearing but also the sheer fatigue. Day after day the fighters were scrambled into the sky to do battle, often three or four sorties in a day. Many fighter pilots never returned from their first operational flight, and these lads were only too aware of that.

Chassé – the chase:

The shrill call of the field telephone rang out from within the hut; an anxious looking airman lurched from his deckchair, sprang into the hut and grabbed the handset. Within minutes he had reappeared and began striking the bell hanging beside the hut door . . . the call to "Scramble!" All hell broke loose.

Minutes earlier, across the channel in France the portly Reich Marshall Göring swaggered arrogantly in his gold and blue uniform as he stood on a cliff top near Calais, commanding a clear view across the channel to the cliffs of Dover. Wave upon wave of bombers and fighters from occupied airfields across Europe darkened the sky overhead as the armada of enemy aircraft set its course for its target: London. It would only take them ten minutes to cross the channel and it took four minutes for the information from the Observer Corps and radar stations at Beachy Head and Dover to be relayed via HQ at Stanmore to reach '11 Group'.

This information about both the size and height of any approaching bomber formation, often proved both vague and inaccurate.

The handful of men grabbed their gear and sprinted across the grass towards their waiting planes, engines already warm from being run in readiness earlier in the day. Every thirty second delay meant a thousand feet in altitude lost. The propellers of their fighters whirled into life, clouds of oily smoke belched from exhaust tubes as the Rolls Royce Merlins roared, straining to be given their head. Clambering aboard, they grabbed their parachute packs from the wings and clipped them on, then lowered themselves into their cramped cockpits; strapped in, flying helmets on, intercom and oxygen connected, they were ready to taxi. The ground crew disconnected the trolley accumulator cart, the pilot gave the thumbs-up, the side door was shut by the mechanic and all stood clear as the pilot opened the throttle: chocks away. The fighters began to roll across the grass for take-off. The little fighters weaved down the field, bouncing faster and faster over the grass, wave upon wave, eager to get into the air without crashing into each other. Their tailplanes lifted and soon they would be airborne, within two minutes of the call to 'scramble'.

Heroes were about to be made or lost on that lovely summer's day.

The Supermarine Spitfire 1Bs were equipped with the old Browning machine guns, although some squadrons had aircraft fitted with two 20mm Hispano cannons but these proved unreliable in action, the pilots uncertain if they would fire when crucially needed. In a dogfight there was more than enough to cope with, tight turns at high speed in dives and climbs caused some pilots to black out momentarily. The Rolls Royce piston engine achieved a maximum turn of speed of 448mph with a ceiling altitude of forty-three thousand feet; as the Spit arched across the sky it produced a distinctive whistling call.

They climbed in a wide spiral at low boost until all aircraft were in place, then opened up to high throttle setting to gain altitude as fast as possible. The skies were still clear, awaiting the playing out of that day's aerial ballet. It would take a full thirteen more minutes for the fighters to achieve sufficient altitude to engage the enemy. The formation leader would hear the distant voice of the fighter controller in the operations room many miles away at Sector HQ Biggin Hill. The message on his headset was clipped and difficult to make out over the interference. A new vector was relayed through; taking the new compass heading for interception with the bandits, the fighter formation turned and continued its climb slowly into the distance.

Frappé – the strike:

Roads and fields disappeared beneath them as they climbed to twenty thousand feet and waited to intercept the attackers. For some this was just another op, but for others the thought of killing or being killed left them with a twisted and sick sensation deep in the pit of their stomachs, petrified at what they might face. You could hear the German planes someway off, their engines would drone and drone, ever louder and nearer. As the attack was soon to commence, the fighters rose above the little cloud that there was; positioning themselves with the sun behind them, poised to spring the attack. The number of enemy in the sky seemed to grow ever greater: an air armada of a hundred and fifty at least, in formation, creeping across the sky with three groups of frustrated Messerschmitts circling about them, protecting these lumbering bombers. The tension was draining, waiting for the first plane to break formation and strike the enemy.

A Hurricane briefly climbed then banked and dived, bursting fire at a lead Messerschmitt 110 'Destroyer'; the rest of the chaps followed, attacking into the thick of them. Göring's fighters swarmed like angry flies, then scattered every which way, but by now the Spitfires and Hurricanes had singled out their foe and were in pursuit. Within minutes the sky was awash with smoke and gunfire, the aerobatics being performed for real – this was a matter of life or death; it was every man for himself.

The stub-winged Messerschitt 109 was a loud and unforgiving aircraft, faster only in the dive than the Spitfire, although its turning radius was far greater than its Allied adversaries. The 109 also had problems with its machineguns on top of the engine, often suffering stoppages; its cannon rate of fire was very slow, although its range was greater than that of its machineguns. Luftwaffe pilots were always told that in a dogfight they could not hope to hit anything further than fifty meters; it was essential to close to a short distance on their enemy.

Yellow nosed Me 109s banked and rolled, climbed and dived, their cannon firing through their propeller shafts. Fabric ripped open on the in-board leading edge of the Hurricane's wings as their gun muzzles spewed their rounds; eight machine guns, three hundred rounds each, fourteen seconds of continuous fire, so each burst had to count. A Messerschmitt half rolled, burst into flames as it spun and plummeted to the ground. The fight was on, command of the sky was at stake, London's survival in the balance and victory was the prize. Tracer streaked across the sky, criss-crossing in every direction, the battle raged, pilots and engines strained to stay in the air. The Me 109 was considered quite simply the best fighter in the world, and the slower three bladed Hurricane was a poor match for this aircraft. Luftwaffe pilots were justly proud of its speed and agility and many had considerable experience at the controls. RAF pilots treated the 109 with great respect and needed to employ skill and cunning tactics to seize the advantage: never be caught in a climb, you were easy meat. Over fifty aircraft exchanged fire as the dogfight took hold; who had the upper hand was hard to judge. What was clear, however, was that below, the formation of German bombers slowly droned on towards its target, although some, especially those on the edge of the formation were beginning to take fire. A Spitfire was on Jerry's tail, blasting into the bomber, the Junkers 88 nose dived as its ammunition exploded. There was a massive blast as it hit the deck, the ground shook and burnt; the first of many bombers that day had been destroyed. The heavens were a swirling cauldron of aircraft; the noise of the engines, the scream of propellers, the rattle of machine guns and the thud of cannons was deafening; flames and black smoke poured out from behind aircraft as they fell from the sky. It seemed as if this aerial battle was going on for hours; it was vital that our pilots, gripped by the moment, stayed cool headed whilst anticipating the enemy's next move.

A few Hurricanes attacked the lead bomber of the formation, which acted as their pathfinder - the master bomber that would drop bombing markers for the others to home in on. A pilot strained, lining his sights on the enemy aircraft as it grew larger by the second. The clumsy bomber didn't deviate from its course, it didn't move; two bursts of fire from the eight guns decisively struck its air frame. As the fighter tightly banked away, a red glow emanated from the bomber, and flames started to lick about its fuselage.

The Hawker Hurricane was the main stay in the Battle of Britain, comprising two thirds of the Allied monoplanes in combat and destroying more enemy aircraft than all other of our air or ground defences. Unlike the Spitfire which was all metal, the lighter Hurricane, built as a tubular construction with fabric covering, was easier, cheaper and quicker to produce and repair and could take greater punishment than the Spitfire. It was a superior gun platform, being the world's first eight-gun fighter. Rolls Royce worked to improve the Merlin engine: the new design and increased octane of the fuel, boosted the engine's horse power by a third. This startling improvement in the performance of both the

Hurricanes and Spitfires from the summer of 1940 puzzled and greatly worried the German pilots.

Again it was the turn of the Spitfires to try and occupy the skies and take out Göring's fighters. A flight of Spitfires zoomed in, continually checking the sky about them, avoiding steep dives which could cause the engine to cut out; down, down they fell on the other bombers and fighters, guns firing; bits of fuselage and wings flew in all directions as bombers and fighters spiralled earthward in flames. The odds and balance of supremacy were changing; however they needed to as the RAF was outnumbered four to one.

Two more RAF Fighter Command flights joined the attack. The Luftwaffe's invincibility as the most powerful air force in the world was beginning to be shattered; the tide had turned, their surviving German fighters were on the run, their twenty minutes of flying time over England exhausted and systematically the bombers were being picked off. Just as suddenly as it had begun, it was all over, the daring chase, the incessant droning of engines, the pounding of guns and cannons, the physical pain as the pilots were thrown about the sky, the wheeling and jostling . . . it had finally ended. It was time to strike back to base.

Coda – the finale:

A pilot's life expectancy was counted in days; the ground crew stood frozen, squinting to spot the first tell tale speck of a returning fighter in the sky. Many of the pilots were younger than the twenty-two years of the RAF itself. They'd get into their airplanes, climb into the sky, fight the battle which was often all over in an hour, come back, have a cup of tea, then do it all again. War had aged these young men: how obscene it is that old men get young men to fight their wars for them.

The planes started to appear in ones and twos at first, then a group of four. Not all would make it back; perhaps they had to put down on another field because of engine problems or damage, maybe shortage of fuel would prevent them from reaching base. A new lad returning from his first 'op' was first back, making a rare old mess of it, weaving and bouncing down the field before finally coming to rest. One after the other the ground boys counted them in. For one of the experienced chaps, landing proved exciting with only the port wheel fully locked, the other having collapsed half way down the strip, resulting in him spinning off to one side and abruptly digging in with a bent prop and damage to the wing, but nothing that couldn't be fixed. He was safely on the ground. It wouldn't be until later that day, when all could be accounted for, that the final headcount would be known. And then whose to say that those who bailed out of their stricken fighter, having avoided enemy fire while hanging defenceless on their chute, are not out somewhere in the Kent countryside – safe! Well that's what was hoped.

It had proved to be a bloody awful day with three pilots unaccounted for and four planes lost.

Rupert, Red 2 of 'B' Flight, three years my junior and the only child of a farming family from Dorset, never returned. He was heading back to the safety of the field when his Spitfire was hit by a concentration of fire from a Messerschmitt. At twelve miles out the cockpit filled with smoke as machine gun bullets riddled his aircraft. Whilst fighting to get the Spitfire under control, fuel began to gush into the cockpit, flooding the floor. One of his legs was feeling numb, he grabbed his knee, his wound bled profusely turning the petrol a dirty brown colour. The screen was badly crazed with scratches and cracks and a number of rounds had destroyed some of the controls and instruments on his panel: the 'G' meter, airspeed indicator and altimeter. Splinters of metal had embedded in his leg and punctured the back of the thin metal fuel tank. Amazingly his Marconi radio still worked as he called up reporting his status.  He headed for home praying that the plane would hold and the fuel would last; he was completely trapped and only had one hope.  Five miles off, again smoke filled and shrouded the cockpit from under the panel; he switched off the engine . . .  the fuel must have ignited and with a massive explosion all was over for this nineteen year old who believed he had his whole life ahead of him.

As darkness fell on another day of fighting, exhausted pilots turned in; the empty beds that night told the day's story.

During the three and a half months of the Luftwaffe's incessant campaign, over three thousand Germans were believed killed. The total Allied losses from all thirteen countries that played their part was four hundred and forty-six pilots killed in action of a total of two thousand, three hundred and sixty-five who flew.  The RAF won the Battle of Britain, but at such a cost.

Riding upon the whirlwind of war, men slew and fell like archangels.  May their God bring rest to their souls.

# Chapter 14

And so it was after years behind me as a lad at home, I began my real adventure, as a man.

Eighteen RAF boys and I, following three weeks in holding barracks, left Liverpool docks setting sail for Halifax in Nova Scotia. Out into the Irish Sea, Ireland rose up in the distance, then slowly fell away as we headed into the Atlantic on my first ocean crossing, and one I will always remember. Our craft, the SS Carina II, built in Glasgow and owned by Elders & Fyffes, was a redundant banana boat, and having now been commissioned to carry troops to and from Canada, was to be my home for the next nineteen days. The Carina, at some four hundred and twenty-five feet in length and six thousand tons, ploughed through the waves, steaming in a 'fast' convoy numbering thirty ships and naval escorts. Its twin screws drove us on at about fourteen knots as its single funnel belched grey acrid clouds into the air which billowed, drifted, and sometimes in the wind, washed over the deck. I gazed day after day at the disappearing rim of land on the horizon; the waves' folds and furrows became almost hypnotic in their watching. Swirls of foam vanished just as quickly as they had appeared, magically created in that moment in time. At night the deep sky was speckled with glimmering stars whilst galaxies passed overhead: a heavenly tranquility which belied the turmoil here on earth. The sea stretched in every direction, broken only by the grey forms of other craft; nothing else interrupted this mighty mantle.

After five days out, we fought a different battle, this time against the sea; the waves, the currents, the drenching rain and the winds were our adversaries as our vessel tumbled downward then rose skyward, from trough to crest, forging on, creaking and groaning as she went. Our fragile boat balanced above miles of green seething ocean, whist the overflowing of the waters spilt about our deck as the wintry storm bit hard. There was nowhere else for us to go. The passage of winds stirred the ocean again and again throwing itself at our tiny craft; gaining headway proved ever harder. The immense strength and hostility of this unfamiliar adversary was inspiring: this was my first real experience of such a duel with the elements. Hour after hour we soldiered on as conditions deteriorated; night fell, the full moon shone brightly on us but the wild spray obliterated any view of the other ships sailing with us, each helpless to aid the other. All hands stood in readiness holding firm as the cruel sea rose now straight up then under us, our bow lifted, we yawed then crashed, cutting into the swell. Again we were tossed high, then rolled, but held firm. The treacherous seas powered passed, breaking onboard with a deafening thunder. My muscles ached, trying with all my strength to cushion the blows and resist being thrown about.

We were to learn that near to these waters, some four weeks earlier, the SS City of Benares out of Liverpool, steaming from Quebec and Montreal was torpedoed. She sank within thirty minutes of being hit; over half the crew and passengers were lost, and seventy-seven of the ninety child evacuees on board fleeing the Blitz in Britain, were killed.[18] Surely the same fate did not await us?

After two more fearful days in the early hours of the morning, the storm abated, but only after all of us chaps had emptied our stomachs over the side. The calm returned as the winds died, exhausted, and the seas grew softer, passing by our hull like rippling blue-black silk. The peaceful majesty of the sea returned. Once again it was possible to admire the night sky, with the stars twinkling in the dark abyss overhead, lone shooting stars scribed bright paths across the heavens as they travelled on their way to oblivion. We steamed on, the days passing uneventfully.

Our conditions on board were basic, sleeping on steel framed bunks with just a thin grey blanket to keep each of us warm. A single bulb dimly lit our cabin, and once our eyes got accustomed to it we could move about without continually bumping into things. I was cold nearly all the time, warming only occasionally from the heat of the stoves in the galley. It was a hard life for the crew on board: they laboured from 5am to 6pm, sweeping decks, cleaning brass, painting steelwork, cooking, carrying dixies of steaming tea, scrubbing the mess room, galley and loos, running continually up and down ladders to the engine room and hold from where they would haul up sack upon sack of potatoes. The work was endless. I guess the sea must be in their blood. Merchant seamen and women faced the same dangers of war as us regulars, but they did so without all the armaments and defences, in ships which were never designed to go to war. The Carina's only protection was a six inch gun which we learnt to load and fire, our target, a forty gallon drum floating out to sea. An eerie silence would descend to my world for two to three minutes after every firing! As the sun set on another cold day, I couldn't help but wonder what far dangerous waters Dot's Al was sailing, struggling in hazardous conditions to carry not just troops, but vital food, fuel, equipment and munitions to wherever needed, so that survival and victory could be assured.

The morrow brought a bright clear start to its day, clear enough for us to make out tiny specks on the distant horizon, looking quite still and menacing. The look-out cried 'Bedford Basin', a cheer rang out from the crew and us chaps: at last we had reached Nova Scotia. Eventually, after much manoeuvering, our vessel came alongside the dock and moored; we disembarked at Pier 21, Halifax Harbour, from where we made our way with the 'Matlows' to the Green Lantern for a much welcomed farewell drink.

The next stage of our adventure was to travel overland by train to New Brunswick where we would experience pilot training. Here in Ground School we were subjected to intensive studies in navigation, flight techniques, mechanical engineering, mathematics, telegraphy and aircraft identification. Screening was by the selection board as they decided if any of us had the aptitude for becoming a pilot, navigator or bomb-aimer, or indeed should be sent to another trade. Many found the news that they were washed-out from being pilots hard to stomach. I was destined to be trained as an observer, with my primary duties being navigation. I don't know whether this was because I showed a greater aptitude for maths or if they just couldn't see me mastering a massive four engine crate, with a load of bombs on board, whilst being gunned down! Whatever the reason, I would be responsible for ensuring we both found and dropped our load on the right target, and got back to base.

We then travelled for several days by train due west to No.9 Air Observer School St. Jean in the Province of Quebec. At the outbreak of war, Britain had approached Canada to establish an air training programme – the 'British Empire Air Training Scheme'. Part of the largest single training programme in history, it would need over three thousand five hundred aircraft, more than twelve times the pre-war strength of the Royal Canadian Air Force, and would cost more than $607 million. Its aim was to produce twenty thousand pilots and thirty thousand personnel, and to achieve this about ninety flying training schools were needed. The United Kingdom was viewed as totally unsuitable as a location for air training, due to possible enemy attack, the busyness of our airfields and our unpredictable weather. Conversely, Canada was seen as being the ideal location, with ample fuel, superb wide open skies that held no threat of the Luftwaffe, and facilities for aircraft production and repairs. The St. Jean Military Base was built to temporarily house the training school, and was clearly under great strain coping with the ever increasing number of personnel and trainees like ourselves. It sat on the east bank of the River Richelieu and was better known as Iberville, an ancient fort town which was home to Free French Canadians who were predominantly Catholic.

Our training involved both flight and ground work; the private company of Dominion Skyways managed the flight training, employing civilian flying instructors; often they were older expert bush pilots, real characters well used to the demanding terrain and conditions. A cheery English guy, Walter 'Babe' Woolett was overseeing our school and would regularly encourage us chaps with his bright spirit and endless stories. We flew in Avro Ansons, initially used for coastal reconnaissance patrols, but we were told much better suited as multi-role trainers. Its twin engines achieved a dazzling top speed of 190mph, the only other aircraft faster at that time was the fighter. What I most remember about the Anson was the physical effort needed to wind up the landing gear. It was the first RAF monoplane with a retractable undercarriage, but oh what a struggle that was. Whilst lowering was relatively easy, raising it required what seemed like a hundred or more turns of a hand crank: we often made short flights with the landing gear down, even though it reduced our speed and increased our fuel consumption. Otherwise it was a joy to fly. Night flying played a large part in our training and I can recall the challenge when trying to use a sextant in an aircraft that was forever moving; I don't think the sextant was ever really designed for this!

The ground instructors were all RCAF officers and they took us through the theory of flight, engines, meteorology, navigation, photography and signals. Much course work concentrated on mathematical principals and navigation: using charts, compasses, sextants and astronomical navigation as well as fairly primitive radio aids. This was all excitingly interspersed with exams and psychological or aptitude tests. What we were taught in ground school would then be applied in the air. With the onset of winter, temperatures dropped to minus 10°C, but it was a dry cold and felt somehow warmer than winter in London. Keeping the runways clear of snow was a full-time job for the motor transport bods and although they were well equipped, everything took longer and became harder going. We progressed on the Anson to more advanced flight training which was primarily to get the wireless operators and us navigators to work together successfully.

Life in the school was in many ways not unlike that of my initial training back in England. Our trips to bars in the town were not well received by the locals: we were viewed as 'Outsiders' so they had little to do with us which was quite contrary to our experience when, at weekends, we would travel by train into Montreal. One weekend I became so distracted, I was late back. My punishment was to be confined to camp and the duty sergeant ordered me to go down to the clothing store and report to the NCO. After spending hours of humping stuff around he pulled me to one side, stared at me, not saying a word but just looked me up and down. Then he started telling me that whilst my RAF uniform fitted, sort of, its material was like, well, a . . . 'horse blanket'; he continued, being more and more disparaging as he delivered his lecture. Clearly, as far as he was concerned, what I needed was a better quality uniform, a RCAF uniform, and without delay proceeded to fit me out, taking care to change my buttons. Eyeing me up and down, this time with a smile on his face, I was sent away an altogether smarter airman!

Regardless of the dismal reception we had previously received in town - and during our early days it had proved almost hostile - a crowd of us including RCAF staff and instructors, about fifty in all, cycled into town, venturing to bring seasonal cheer on this Christmas Eve. As we toured the streets on our bikes we sang carols. Crowds welcomed us to join them in the bars for refreshment before we pedaled on. I don't rightly know how many bars and cafés we frequented that night but it was a great time and a chance to practise my recently acquired pigeon French. By the time our excursion had brought us back to the training centre, completely shattered, it seemed as if we'd cycled uphill both ways; and our initial resounding chorus had been replaced with mumbling lullabies. Christmas Day was hazy in my mind and certainly there was no flying after that for a few days!

The big news that Christmas, was from the United States. President Roosevelt addressed his people and the world on December 29<sup>th</sup> 1940 .

"The Nazi masters of Germany have made it clear that they intend not only to dominate all life and thought in their own country, but also to enslave the whole of Europe, and then to use the resources of Europe to dominate the rest of the world."[19]

He then quoted Hitler's words of three weeks earlier –

"There are two worlds that stand opposed to each other. . . I can beat any power in the world."

Roosevelt went on to say that,

"Great Britain and the British Empire are today the spearhead of resistance to world conquest. They are putting up a fight which will live forever in the story of human gallantry."

For the first time I appreciated how reckless and insanely intent on war Hitler was, and the fear that now gripped even the United States.

My training went well, but with nearly a hundred hours of day and night flying under my belt I couldn't wait to get airborne in those 'big boys' back in Britain. After all the hard work I was thrilled when finally I was awarded my observer half wings, and promptly stitched it above the left breast pocket of my 'Canadian' uniform!

Whereas my outward sailing to Canada had been uneventful, apart from the horrendous storm and haunting seasickness which seemed to accompany much of my trip, the return voyage would prove anything but. The homebound convoy of seventy-four ships included our boat HMS Leticia, a former ocean liner of thirteen and a half thousand tons and five hundred and thirty feet in length, and one, that until recently, had been operating as part of the Escort Force. We departed from Halifax harbour, a port which had proved so significant to the Canadians being one of the world's deepest and largest natural harbours, its waters remaining ice free throughout the winter. From here, by the culmination of the war, almost half a million Canadian troops had departed for Europe: fifty thousand would never return. We cruised past George's and McNab's Islands, their gun batteries and fortification strategically poised for an enemy attack, and then out, out into the open Atlantic, the land becoming a distant memory. Protection duties for convoys was shared by the Canadian and British navies, but with both their resources spread so wide and thin, complete protection all the way across was not possible. In the fullness of time Allied air forces would search the open seas, seeking out and destroying the menacing U-boats which were the hidden threat as they stalked vulnerable convoys such as ours. We discovered that the theory behind the convoy system was that if there were enough merchant ships, although some would be sunk, others would get through with their desperately needed cargo. None of us found this concept at all comforting, even less so as we started to notice indistinguishable flotsam and jetsam floating past our bow. The power of the sea may prove as nothing compared to that of the Germans. In mid Atlantic a U-boat was sighted, our ships started to weave in a zig-zag pattern, varying course and speed. The submarine let loose two torpedoes then immediately dived as it came under fire. Our craft shook as one of our number was struck amidships, blowing a torrent of water into the air and ripping open a hole in its side. A second explosion hit it with terrific force sealing the destiny of this ailing craft. By now we were all on deck, ready to man the lifeboats should we be hit, and concentrating on the area of sea way off where our escorts were bombarding. It was hard to know what fate awaited Allied survivors in the hands of a German U-boat captain. Some would machine gun any survivors whilst others showed compassion and radioed their position, leaving food and water before fleeing in search of another vulnerable convoy. A massive and violent blast erupted on the other side of our convoy as an oil tanker rose out of the water, broke its back, then began to sink. It was impossible to see through the dense black smoke whether there were any survivors. Within moments the sea erupted under the bombardment from our destroyers and corvettes; a ferocious column of water burst skyward as the surrounding sea boiled, signalling the destruction of our aggressor. The Marconigram marine telegraph relayed a message to all ships for the convoy to break up and each to go their own way; a real fear that our presence had been detected and another rendezvous with the enemy was inevitable, was evident as we steamed homeward.

Who knows what life has got in store for us? We start life's journey with faith, trusting in the future, believing in humanity and that our dreams will become a reality. Without the risk of death we can not be heroes. Today I understand the journey I have chosen for myself. Life would never be the same again.

# Chapter 15

Aunt Elsie, a formidable woman in her thirties, was never one not to get involved; for her this war was no different and so her life was about to change dramatically. She was a lady blessed with a strong constitution, impressive will power and boundless energy; I don't believe she ever took 'no' for an answer. She was of average build and average height but that was about where average-ness ended – clearly Dad's brother Art must have been of that view because he married her. I can distinctly recall Mother cautioning me as a child not to annoy or pester her during our weekly visits,

"Aunt isn't used to children" she would advise me, "and won't put up with being irritated!" She and Art never had children, I don't exactly know why, but when you're a child you accept for a while all sorts of explanations, "Their house isn't really suited to young children!" I was told but it seemed okay to me, being a large four storey terraced Georgian property in Crouch End, North London. I well remember a podgy married couple with tenuous family connections inhabiting the second floor; an old woman, a very old woman, who remained a mystery to me, lived at the top. Aunt said they rarely saw her and often only when she paid the rent, but most of the time she was out working in the theatre I think. One thing they did love was a party; any excuse, any occasion they would organise a party and invite, well it seemed, the whole street. Neither Aunt nor Uncle played the piano, but that didn't stop them buying one and getting Dad and me over to help Art move it in. Plenty of folk in the family could play well however: Hilda, Gladys and cousin Jimmy. Father would stand, one hand on the piano lid whilst his other hand gestured in time to the music as he sang for all his worth, encouraging the party goers to join in. Both Hilda and Gladys needed no such encouragement and would often position their generous and well padded rears on the same stool as they performed duets. The little back room in Crouch End resounded to gay parties many a Saturday evening before the war years. Aunt and I turned out to be the best of

100

mates, the son she never had she would say, much to the delight of Mother, who recognised the achievement by commenting with a confident air, "I knew you'd both get on!"

So not being one to sit around, so to speak, once Art was away fighting for his country, Elsie was on the search for a job – something to keep her busy. Neither desk nor factory work would have suited; she needed something active with a fair share of adventure and a healthy quota of risk, a job with responsibility helping to protect the people of London, a city she loved, from the German onslaught. After all even the Minister for Labour, the great Ernest Bevin said women helped win the last war and would be equally effective in this one, and Elsie was determined to be one of those. The war years not only brought endless hardship and heartache but through necessity, boundless new opportunities, especially for women. If previously any had found life tiresome and boring they became increasingly crucial in keeping the country going, now that many of the men were away fighting. Our factories and shipyards manufacturing the tools of war, buzzed with the energy of young women, mastering the jobs many of their menfolk had undertaken. Others, in the Woman's Land Army, ploughed across fields on tractors in an attempt to harness the full potential of our beleaguered land. Home food production was so vital in these difficult times. In the face of possible starvation, our arable land expanded by half as much again within the five years. A few ladies, members of the Observer Corp, would peer upward, studying and reporting on the movements of the mighty winged warriors of the sky, which at night would be traced by the huge searchlights operated by the women of the Auxiliary Territorial Service, often temporarily blinding the enemy's bomb-aimers.[20] Dozens and dozens of clerical clairvoyants systematically scrutinised 'The Sky Lovers' post. Mail from women to their forces' sweethearts was opened and checked for every word written to ensure secrets would remain 'secret'. Refreshment stations and canteens sprung up everywhere with women of the Salvation Army, Church Army, YMCA and

WVS amongst others competing for the best tea and buns, helping to bring sustenance to tiring bodies. The WVS had been founded initially to recruit women in ARP work – 'the tin hats' - but by now they were helping evacuees and refugees as well as providing support at major bomb incidents.

The streets were largely free of traffic, except for the emergency services attempting to negotiate fallen debris, vast swallowing craters and fires, as they sped to the rescue. Occasionally drivers of more unusual vehicles commandeered for the task would brave the ordeal of finding their way around the city, including the voluntary women drivers for the Ambulance Service, ferrying nurses to where medical help was required but they could never keep pace with the need. Postwomen in their official trouser uniform delivered the mail to the properties that were still standing; they weaved cautiously between the wreckage, whilst other ladies manoeuvred horse drawn milk carts for Express Dairies, or wobbled on bicycles delivering 'Shoppers Food'. And of course there were the mortuary vans! Meanwhile all about the Pick and Shovel Brigade, the women demolition workers, the she-navvies, laboured to clear rubble to make safe and attempt to re-build the devastation that abounded throughout the streets. All wrestled with what had now become a universal struggle for survival. For the first time in their lives married women were working outside the home, living like men, fighting like men and many dying like men. They worked as hard as their men to keep the 'Spirit of the Nation' alive. For these women, it was the first time they had thought and acted in this way.

Mum meanwhile was busy distracting Mrs Harris from her 'frightful war' as she described it, by helping her plant onions and marigolds over the Anderson Shelter, hoping that the marigolds would discourage aerial attack by the onion root flies. I really don't know why an onion fly, whilst trying to navigate between the Luftwaffe fighters, bombs, incendiaries, flak, barrage balloons, towering infernos and whatever else Hell had in store, would bother with a few pitiful onions!

Aunt's idea of a more active and involved life was to do her bit for 'King and Country' by joining the Auxiliary Fire Service. By late 1940 the demands on the Fire Service were becoming unmanageable as attacks on London intensified. Communications were essential in co-ordinating its limited resources, but telegraph and telephone lines were down and headquarter messages had to be delivered to the crews by hand: the solution for the Fire Service was motorbike dispatch riders, and that was also the answer for dear old Aunt Elsie.

As far as she was concerned the Panther 250 motorbike was lacking in power, but still proved great fun as each morning for a couple of weeks she hurtled around New Cross Speedway Track, just off Old Kent Road, whilst being trained by the resident speedway riders of the New Cross Rangers. Known as 'The Frying Pan' the track was built inside the greyhound and athletic stadium, with exhilerating bankings all the way round. Her bike was old and rusty, whereas the women of the Royal Navy Despatch Riders, who were training at the same time, had shiny new machines and proper uniforms. Elsie kitted herself out from Pride and Clark's motorbike shop at Marble Arch, although later she did get a proper fire brigade uniform with firemen's buttons proudly punctuating the jacket, which she wore under a tracksuit when on 'missions'. Her new motorcycling career on the Panther proved exciting, offering her handling and a turn of speed which proved valuable as she negotiated her way around London. Promotion would come in the form of a more reliable BSA 350 eight months later, after a few spills that were fortunately harmless.

During Elsie's first few months on duty, based at Chelsea Fire Station, she learnt map reading, Morse code, semaphore and first aid, and was involved in checking the street fire alarms that were placed at the roadsides. Twenty riders were in each of the three teams which worked two days on and one day off covering the sub-stations. She loved the comradeship, something she'd never experienced before. Aunt quickly learnt how to maintain and service her own bike, ensuring the messages would always get through: well if she had anything to do with it!

The situation had changed earlier in 1940, when at the end of August, two German bombers that had strayed found themselves amidst a barrage of anti-aircraft fire and, countermanding Hitler's explicit orders "not to bomb London", jettisoned their bombs on the city. Churchill mounted an immediate reprisal and gave the order to bomb Berlin the following night. Bomber Command darkened the skies over that city for the next week; in the end proving more than Hitler could tolerate, as he, pressed by the Luftwaffe high command, ordered Göring to "simply erase" British cities in retaliation. Hitler was unleashing his lightning strikes, his 'Blitzkrieg' on Britain.[21] He had given up all hope of preserving London so he could stroll up the Mall in triumph after a successful invasion. As the infernal bombs rained down, hour after hour, Aunt Elsie would cycle far and wide, carefully picking her route, evading falling buildings, mangled vehicles and trams welded to their rails, ruptured gas, sewage and water mains, choking smoke and unexploded bombs, to bring vital information and quick reinforcements to the battling fire teams. Terrified people wandered about dazed and blood stained from falling masonry and flying glass, calling for help as she motored on by, unable to stop, unable to help, unable to do anything for them. For these and thousands of others, the old ways of living were gone, gone forever: the world was falling apart.

One horrific night imprinted itself vividly on her memory, when wave upon ordered wave of hundreds of Heinkel, Dornier and Messerschmitt raiders droned overhead, dropping their bomb loads on the East End of London. Searchlights and ack ack fire drifted aimlessly about the sky, overwhelmed by the massive size of this airborne armada: three hundred and twenty bombers escorted by six hundred fighters. The capital was unprepared for this scale of attack: London was almost defenceless. Devastating the Docklands, the blazing holocaust devoured row upon row of workers' houses in the nearby lanes and streets, burning and crumbling as the inferno grew. Thousands of incendiaries and over three hundred tons of high explosive bombs fell on the Victoria and Albert Docks as well as the West India and Surrey Docks that fateful night. Warehouses, refineries and arsenals were reduced to flaming ruins, their contents rose as red hot embers into the skies; buildings exploded with the combustion of paint, chemicals, alcohol, ammunition and over one and a half million tons of softwood. Flames licked high into the night. Cargo ships were ablaze, the firestorm serving as a beacon to the enemy; wave after wave of bombers targetted their payloads, crippling the entire area. As the fires took hold flames spiraled high, sucking in air, creating a horrifying inferno. Embers drifted over rooftops and trees setting new fires ablaze. The city was crying out with the screaming of sirens; shrapnel rattled and sparked and, as it hit the road the tar caught fire; the booming of guns and ack ack resounded as more planes unleashed their fury. It seemed as if the whole of London was burning. The night was as bright as a summer's day from the brilliance of hundreds of blazing fires, devouring all in their path. Across the city, five miles from the docks, Elsie was able to read her map: it was like broad daylight. The heat was unbearable; as she approached her skin became painful. Over a thousand firemen were confronted by fires the scale of which they had never experienced before, burning totally out of control. Pungent and toxic fumes climbed as gigantic black clouds billowed into the air; huge flocks of pigeons kept circling overhead, rats in their thousands screamed in retreat as hot ashes settled like thick acrid dust, covering everything and everyone. She could feel herself breathing ash; a grittiness grated in her mouth; her nose and eyes stung from the pepper hanging in the air from one of the destroyed warehouses, making her cough and sneeze. Silhouetted against the blaze, firemen struggled to connect their appliances to the few hydrants that were working, others tried in vain to quench the flames with water drawn directly from the Thames, which itself was now ablaze with floating wax and sugar. The fireboats persevered, but still they couldn't cope.

All about she was faced with the devastation of war as well as the human loss; by the morning four hundred and forty people had been killed and sixteen hundred wounded with scores of firemen having lost their lives as they fought to save the city from annihilation. By December, with the damage from the raids far exceeding anything ever seen before, the weather turned bitterly cold; icicles hung from bombed fire stations where officers and crew lay dead; fire engines stood still, immobilised by the freezing temperature, their water hoses frozen.

Elsie was gripped with fear as the air raid sirens moaned the news of yet another horrifying attack, but with no thought for herself she didn't let this show, conscious that fear was contagious. She was aware that for many the greatest battle was for their lives. For Elsie, the horrors of war and a compassion for humanity had never before confronted her in this way. This supernatural ugliness not only overshadowed London but many of our cities, and across the channel, German cities suffered alongside those in Britain. War had become all consuming.

Week after week Elsie risked her life. Each day brought new adventures, new spectacles and new horrors, but throughout it all, miracles happened. Amazingly St. Paul's remained largely unscathed whilst all the streets about were ravaged by bombs; two dozen or more incendiaries hit the cathedral, one lodging in the outer shell of the dome, melting the lead. It proved beyond the efforts of the firewatchers and the dome seemed lost, then the shell incredibly fell onto the parapet and bounced off. Pink-white smoke billowed and swirled about the gigantic dome which dominated the skyline as the surrounding wall of flames grew fiercer, illuminating the barrage balloons which floated, tethered and towering overhead. But still St. Paul's remained safe. The following morning the fires were still smouldering, and groups of people congregated on the cathedral steps; an elderly woman led the singing with, 'Praise God from whom all Blessings Flow'.

The country desperately needed a break from the raids, a breathing space. Finally it came on May 11th, 1941, Hitler ended the bombardment. By the end of the Blitz over forty-three thousand civilians had been killed, half of them in London; over two million houses destroyed or damaged. Many more people than ever envisaged found themselves homeless. Now Hitler moved his focus east, in preparation for Germany's future invasion of Russia, 'Operation Barbarossa'. The Blitz, which had penetrated across Europe, had done little to prepare the way for Germany's potential invasion of Britain – and so it was abandoned.

Elsie's endeavours over the following years of the war helped save many lives and, in the process, she had the time of her life!

# Chapter 16

Life for me had become an unrelenting round of training and travel whilst trying to avoid being killed in the process, either by my hand or that of the Jerries. Now I was back in old Blighty, it didn't look as though anything was about to change; so whilst holding-over in Harrogate, awaiting posting, I seized the chance to get down to London for a few days.

After a long wait at the station I boarded the North Eastern train, my destination, King's Cross. The carriages were heaving with folk, all sorts of people and many service personnel, crammed in tightly, baggage everywhere while some of the luggage racks played host to outstretched children. I couldn't find a seat or hardly a place to stand, but eventually propped my bag on end in a corner of the corridor, sat on top of it, and rolling my jacket up as a pillow tried to make myself comfortable. You would think that the continual clatter of the partly opened window, along with the incessant chatter would prevent the best of us sleeping, but not me! I don't know if the motion of the train did it, or the idea that I had a few days off, but whatever it was, apart from the odd moment when someone's case lurched into me, or people, including the railwayman, shoved me as they barged by, I dozed on and off all the way to London.

After a somewhat disturbed and restless journey the train slowed, whistled, and a few minutes later we drew into the huge glazed train shed, looking to all like a massive gothic cathedral. As I alighted with my fellow travellers it was clear that this place had not escaped the bombing. The platform was frantic with activity, everyone seemed to have one purpose, to get off and out as quickly as they could. As more trains arrived, disgorging weary passengers, others were building up steam to start their travels. Chaos seemed to reign as young impatient girls and elderly dignified gents battled to board their trains. Women, far too overloaded with cases, bags and babes; smartly turned-out service personnel on a mission; and many just like me, hurried down the stairs to the awaiting tube trains which scurried about in the damp and gloom under the city. It had all the makings of what could have been a badly rehearsed opera that might just be okay 'on the night' if we could all hold it together. Having journeyed north for forty minutes, I ventured out into the light to be met by Mum and Dad. As we strolled home I couldn't get over how much even this part of London had been changed by the Blitz. I had only been away for a few months but the difference and air of depression was something I wasn't expecting. Everything looked rundown and uncared for. A mood of despondency hung heavy with everyone fearing what was to come and expecting the worst. There seemed little or no hope that this would end soon.

Once back in our little maisonette, a reassuring sense of familiarity returned; the 'old place' looked no different, except that was, for the onions and marigolds blooming on the shelter! My bedroom seemed much smaller than I remembered, cosy and awfully quiet with my slippers still waiting to greet me by my bed. We sat as we had so many times in the past, around the fireplace in the lounge, although the grate was now furnished with a fire screen Dad had made and Mum had embroidered during the winter evenings. As I relaxed and sipped endless cups of tea I told them of Canada, my training and flying course, but left out the bit about the German sub. Dad asked no end of questions and Mum … well she just sat and listened, and smiled, then said,
"Well it all sounds terribly exciting dear!"

It was then my turn to catch up on the news, albeit that some of it was sad. Mother started:
"Well Mrs Harris has really thrown herself into the shelter, well you know what I mean! She more or less takes care of the inside things, as well as changing the water regularly, doesn't she Ron?"
Father seemed less enthusiastic but nodded and grunted in agreement.

"We never go short of food," she continued, "and she makes a lovely broth; all in all she's a real stalwart, isn't she?" awaiting Father's support.

"If you say so dear," he confirmed winking at me.

"Well that's what you said last week when we were stuck in there for nearly four hours."

"Did I?" and before he had hardly finished Mum added firmly, "Yes you did!"

The unrehearsed roles had nearly been played out on this occasion, and it was now time to move on I thought.

"What of the Taylor lads, any news?" I enquired. My timing was impeccable, well that's what Dad's glance seemed to imply.

"Oh yes dear, they're doing well and all together, thank God, and Mrs Taylor was able to go and see them for the day a week or so ago now. The government organised special 'cheap days' on the train so mums and dads could visit their children in the country. A lovely idea really, and she thoroughly enjoyed it, it was a nice break for her. Mister didn't go, he's no better really . . ." Dad interrupted Mum,

"He's worse, that's what they say."

"Certainly he's no better; she's an angel, the way she looks after him you know," Mum concluded.

There was a pause for a few moments, sufficient to drink my cooling cup of tea and just stretch in the chair, knowing that I could spend the night on a decent mattress and could even sleep on in the morning – bliss!

"And there's some sad news," Mum said in a quiet, uneasy voice as she wriggled in her chair. "There's new people downstairs, next door – Vera and Bert!"

Instinctively I replied,

"Oh the Bürnsteins, have they moved?"

"No dear . . ." mother paused, "they were both killed!"

"How?"

After a moment's silence Father recounted the incident of how during the terrifying bombings of the East End, Ruth and Harry were at work in their machine shop when their building took a direct hit. It seems there was no hope of them getting out, the whole place was a shambles, and the area evacuated. They knew what happened because an ARP warden nearby saw them go in a couple of hours before the blast. Nothing's been seen of them since. Mother had tears in her eyes as she explained,

"We can't even give them a burial because there's nothing left of them . . . only their names in some ARP's 'Air Raid Casualties' book!"

We sat and gazed at each other for what seemed to be an age, saying nothing. For so many the cruelty of war demands the ultimate sacrifice.

Father again eased the difficult moment,

"Vera and Bert seem a lovely couple, don't they Mother?" he didn't even give her a chance to respond, "Vera's very sweet and got a heart of gold and Bert's got a wry sense of humour. To begin with it was hard to understand their broad Glaswegian accent; they moved from up North, something to do with Bert's work; he's never really said what he does. Vera's family is down this way, somewhere between Finsbury Park and Nag's Head."

That evening we settled down to the meal of meals in our tiny kitchen – real Brown Windsor soup, not powdered, and a meat pie with gravy: thick, rich, tasty gravy. I am not sure what the meat was, Mum never said. Then blackberry pie and custard. I don't know how she did it, but she did, and Dad poured all of us a small glass of stout. What a feast! I never did really understand rationing, and still don't! We all turned in after dinner at the end of a hectic day, I asked again what the pie was made from but the cook firmly remained 'mum' on the subject! As I settled down for the night, relishing the interior sprung mattress and feather pillows, I grabbed one of my old books from beside the bed and by the dim light of the lamp began to read:

*'Biggles goes to War'*,

*"MAJOR JAMES BIGGLESWORTH, D.S.A, more often known as 'Biggles', turned down the page of the book he was reading and pulled his chair a little nearer the fire."*
I can't remember anything else.

For the next couple of days I didn't really get up to much, sitting around at home relaxing, reading, listening to the radio and catching up on the news. That May, Pathé Gazette News reported on the continuing destruction in the north of England. The pictures showed "a northern coastal town", Kingston-upon-Hull as it turned out, completely devasted by the Luftwaffe. Over a thousand people had been killed and thousands injured. It seemed that Hull often took the bombing intended for other victims as German pilots, having missed their targets, dumped their bomb loads before returning home.[22] Lord Haw-Haw had initially broadcast that the attacks would be on Sheffield again, but due to weather conditions the bombers diverted to drop their loads on Hull.[23]

The other bit of rather bizarre news was that Randolf Hess had landed in Glasgow.[24] It was reported that the Deputy Führer had come to negotiate peace - how weird is that, all on his own and to Glasgow? Dad thought he was probably a Rangers' supporter!

I had been back in the UK but a few weeks, already the peace of Canada seemed like a world away, and the craziness of war was very evident.

During my leave I did, however, get the chance to meet up with Franklin, who by now had gone into his father's business as an apprentice-cum-partner. I was never really sure what his father did, something like manufacturing precision instruments for Hawkers: prototype gauges I believe. Anyway, Franklin said it turned out okay as it kept him out of the forces.

After a little deliberation we spent my last night heading up to town, to catch a glimpse, for me the last for sometime, of what the big city had to offer, and if, in spite of everything, to see if the words of the famous BBC radio announcer, 'Carry on, London' were true?  We got off the tube at Piccadilly Circus, and as we climbed the steps out into the evening my senses were bombarded with the noise of a bustling city.  Trams and buses hurtled along the roads, crowds hung around street corners or strode out purposefully, clearly intent on getting home or to a shelter.  A newsman cried out from his stall by the tube entrance,

"Star, News, Standard," whilst an old boy beside him played a piano accordion.  I was somewhat taken aback by a timber boarded pyramid structure, on the island in the middle of the Circus, just where Eros normally was.  It looked most strange with a ladder propped up against this high tower, which must have been about thirty-five feet or more.  Franklin explained that the ladder was to help the workmen fill the structure with sandbags in an attempt to protect the statue from bombs.  To me it only lacked a slide curling itself around it to provide a helter-skelter for all to enjoy: probably not what the government had in mind though.  Strolling up Shaftesbury Avenue we then took a left into Great Windmill Street, on the edge of Soho: we were on our way to the Windmill Theatre - a first for me, I wasn't sure about Franklin.  The 'Revuderville $10^{th}$ Year' was playing, if playing is the right word!  We settled into our seats in the cosy basement auditorium, having noticed the sign fixed in the foyer,

'Recommendations to OUR PATRONS' – ARP

'You will be notified from the stage if an air raid warning has been sounded during the performance – We recommend you to remain in the precincts of the Theatre.'  None of these chaps looked as though they were about to go anywhere!

The show was a mix of non-stop variety and comedy, all of which seemed to have little impact on our audience.  What did have an impact, however, were 'The Girls': a dozen nimble starlets, scantily costumed who appeared dancing or frozen in tableaux, nude; and those not completely naked were dressed as Red Indians with Annie Oakley chasing, or as mermaids snapped at by clams! The costumes were amazing, what few there were, and as small as they were, obviously delighting and proving easy on the eye of the enthusiastic male audience! The poses and feats of the Windmill Girls were certainly inspired, but a foxy brunette who appeared in a number of the sketches, dressed partly in country tweed, I thought was the most stunning. I am not completely sure but Joan Jay or maybe Joan Joy was her name; here she was on the threshold of her career, the bottom rung so to speak and I wonder if fame would ever move her higher? For me the most comical event of the evening was the spectacle at the end of the show, when the 'customers' from the back rows made a mad dash over the top of the seats to nab the front row seats for the next performance, which started almost straightaway.

We headed out and, finding a local public house, downed a pint or two. Franklin said little after the show although when I asked him if he had enjoyed it, he curtly replied,
"Oh, very much."
It might be that in Franklin's case, the rationing of food was not his greatest rationing challenge!

Riding on the No. 33 tram and 641 trolley bus, heading home, I casually enquired after the lovely Adina: was she still as lovely? Franklin grimaced, then positively tiraded me with his opinion,
"No, is she heck, she's fat and pregnant."
"Well", I offered, "that's why she's fat!"
"Nope, she's only four months gone, she eats like a horse."
That seemed a bit harsh I thought; however, the vision of fat Adina wasn't appealing!
"What's she up to these days?"
"She married one of those Welsh Bevan Boys, and would you believe, his father is a miner, his uncles are miners and his granddad was a miner; and if that wasn't enough, she's moved to South Wales."

114

With this Franklin was clearly looking to me for some sort of sympathetic acknowledgement of her unwitting plight,

"Is she happy?" I gently enquired.

"I suppose so," he replied, "but can you imagine how boring it must be."

We laughed, and I for a brief moment recalled that educational encounter in the synagogue store cupboard - and smiled.

# Chapter 17

West Freugh in Wigtownshire was my next destination, changing trains at the great northern station of Crewe. An armament training camp, West Freugh served as a base for bombing trials and its Air Observer School was being reformed for Advance Training. We mostly flew the old familiar and reliable Ansons, but Oxfords were also used. The Pratt and Witney twin engined Airspeed AS-10 Oxford was equipped with dual controls which made it ideal as an all-round trainer, and when the second controls were removed a bomb aimer could take up a prone position and drop smoke practice bombs for us observers. The co-pilot's seat could be slid back and a chart table hinged to the fuselage was equipped for instrument training.

Large wood and cork target rafts were floated out into the loch and round the Mull of Galloway into Luce Bay for bombing practice. Gunners would get the chance of air to air firing practice from the Oxford's mid-upper turret, and drogues were towed behind yellow and black striped Fairey Battle light bombers, which served as target tugs. A vital part of our training was to accustomise ourselves to wartime conditions and that of the Black-Out; we hadn't really experienced these in Canada but were now in the thick of it.

I was introduced to a new chap who had just joined, April 1st to be exact: the fictitious Pilot Officer Percy Prune. As it turned out he became one of the most talked about pilots in the RAF and his antics appeared regularly in the Tee Emm: a sort of RAF training bulletin . . . I think. Well Prune certainly got around and had no end of 'novel' quotes - old Martin would have been proud of him, in fact he could even have been Martin! Prune's navigator, Flying Officer Fixe, would always share the gem,
'That a good landing is one you can walk away from'.

My rank had been elevated from AC2 (Aircraftman Second Class), the lowest of the low, to the heady height of LAC (Leading Aircraftman) when I left Canada, and I was now aiming to attain that of Flying Officer. The sky is truly the limit, as they say.

Our training included sitting through a lecture on the 'History of the RAF'. I wasn't at all certain that this would make us better pilots, or gunners, or whatever, or equip us for the fighting ahead, but there you go. A senior officer proceeded to inform us of this vital information,
"The RAF is the world's oldest independent air force; it was founded on the 1st April during the First World War." He coughed to clear his throat then continued,
"It was an amalgamation of the Royal Flying Corps and the Royal Naval Air Service. The RAF's Mission Statement," here we go I thought, "reads, and I'll paraphrase,"
"An agile, adaptable and capable air force that, person for person, is second to none, and that makes a decisive air power contribution in support of the UK Defence Mission."[25]

The officer then talked us through Bomber Command, explaining that many of its personnel were an extraordinary mix drawn from overseas, with many coming from occupied European countries including Poles, Czechs, French, Norwegians and Belgians; he said there were even a few chaps from Luxembourg.
"Bomber Command is a military unit which was formed in 1936, its role is that of strategic and tactical bombing." Our lecture continued and in fact some of the lads looked as if they really couldn't care less and just wanted to get to the NAAFI, and yet on he rambled.
"RAF Officers fall into three categories: Air Officers, Senior Officers and Junior Officers. The other ranks are: Warrant Officers, Senior Non-Commissioned Officers and the lowest of the low," here we go I thought, "Airmen."
For the first time in the twenty minutes he smiled, not a significantly glowing smile, but a smile nevertheless. Maybe he

was human after all; he certainly saw a joke in the prized rank of Airman.

"In conclusion," in an attempt to inspire us, "the motto of the Service is 'Per Ardua ad Astra - Through Struggle to the Stars'; make sure, men, you come down afterwards in one piece, well at least your aircraft." And would you believe it, a real beam this time filled his face.

"That's all men."

The RAF station was only five miles from Stranraer and I was billeted out to a local family in the town: the McDougan's. The wife was a woman of means and intellect, keeping an orderly home as well as caring for her husband, Roger. She instructed the local teenagers in science at the college. Roger was a projectionist in the local cinema at the weekends and worked on the boats during the week. They had two grown up children of whom I saw little. My time with them was great and they looked after me like one of the family. On alternative Friday nights the Royal Dance Hall down Dalrymple Street would host '*Evenings to Remember*'! Two bands shared the stage, each with a vocalist, playing melodious favourites by Cole Porter as well as more rousing reels, and always concluding with the Gay Gordons. In one sense I was lucky as Roger was able to get me in for free, but that's where my luck ended. Whether it was my lack of boldness, stumbling rumba and foxtrot, or even my spotty complexion that let me down; the fact is romance always escaped me even though I danced the nights away.

To the south of the RAF Station was Luce Bay leading across open sea to the Isle of Man. To the north lay Loch Ryan, stretching 8 miles inland with Stranraer at its head, and beyond that, the North Atlantic. The loch was busy with war time activity. The settlement of Cairnryan located halfway up the east side of the loch was developing into an important secondary sea port, available should the Mersey or Clyde be crippled by bombing. Marine piers were constructed and shore side work continued throughout the time I was there, supporting the port's growing importance. Sunderland flying boats were based on the loch to protect Allied ships, destined for either Liverpool or Glasgow, from the German U-boat menace in the Atlantic, fast becoming the scourge of our shipping.

For the next stage of my advance training I had to travel to Staffordshire. Wartime train journeys were never good, but this was the worst yet - we seemed to stop at every station between Stranraer and Wolverhampton. Here we go again, I remember thinking to myself: more training, more trains!

Situated in South Staffordshire, 8 miles south west of Wolverhampton, the small airfield of Bobbington was home to No. 51 Group, Flying Training Command, and No. 3 AFU Air Observer School. Wisely, it would appear, the boffins at the top had decided to establish the majority of training airfields around the Midlands, well clear of operational air space over eastern England. Laying low in a hollow it was a fog and frost trap, and in the summer the surrounding fields put up some interesting thermals: something which not only exercised the fully loaded Ansons, but also some of our stomachs!

One early summer's day as we were lounging in deck chairs beside the strip, watching a farmer with horses ploughing a nearby field, one of our crews approached for landing. It was clear from their finals, all was not well: the undercarriage was not down, the consensus was it must be a hydraulics problem. The second time around it came in fast and low; opting for the grass he belly-landed and skidded off the end of the strip through the hedge and came to rest in the field which the farmer was in the process of ploughing. Fortunately all were safe but amazingly the farmer just kept going, up and down the field with his plough and pair, towards the airfield and the beleaguered plane. As he got nearer he showed no acknowledgement of the crew who were now climbing from their wreck. Finally, in despair, the pilot stopped

119

the farmer and appealed to him not to plough the field between their plane and the airfield, explaining that it would be a damn sight easier to get the ailing craft out. The farmer looked at him with contempt exclaiming angrily,

"You mean you've requisitioned three parts of my farm for the airfield, and not satisfied with that you want more?"

Gerrard, the exhausted pilot, told us the old boy's complete disdain was self evident as he returned to his team and plough, carrying on as if nothing had happened!

At this stage in my training, I was expected to be able to do everything in the aircraft, except that is, pilot it. Our flying instruction concentrated on controls, taxiing, straight and level flight as well as climbing, gliding and stalling; we practiced turns, with and without engines, and of course, the vital landing in all conditions, circuits and bumps. I enjoyed every moment signing in as 'Second Pilot, Pupil or Passenger'. Bombing and gunnery proved great fun, learning how bombs and magnesium incendiaries were designed and made, as well as more practical aspects such as terminal velocity and bombsites. We dropped no end of practice bombs and fired hundreds of rounds. Many more flying hours were logged, with long distant flights way out over the Irish Sea and beyond. Valuably for me, and I guess for many, we learnt how to correctly adjust and wear a parachute. As my instructor said,

"One day your life may well depend on it so get it right." I had no idea how true those words were.

It is true to say that both our day and night flying was not without accident, and mistakes were made, as many aircraft were lost when training pressed on in some pretty poor weather. One day a dreaded telegram arrived at home with an OHMS number printed on one of the glued strips; the importance of the gram was initially lost on account of it being delivered by a young lad helping out at the Post Office. It materialised that he had first knocked on Vera and Bert's, and asked Vera if she could stay and comfort Mum and Dad after they had read the telegram. The news was what they both had feared: marked 'PRIORITY', it read –

> 'DEEPLY REGRET TO INFORM YOU THAT
> YOUR SON'
>  then stating my rank and name,
> 'IS REPORTED MISSING IN ACTION
> RAF STATION BODDINGTON ON AUGUST 7th
> LETTER FOLLOWS PLEASE ACCEPT
> MY PROFOUND SYMPATHY
> = OC. RAF BODDINGTON ++'

The impersonal words belied the significance of this brief message, explaining away the loss of their only son, me, in just six lines. Mother broke down and cried her heart out, Father tried to console her, but was hardly more together than she was. Vera brought the only immediate hope,

"It doesn't say he's dead, he's missing . . . it just says he's missing, soldiers go missing all the time!"

"That's right dear," Dad consoled, "our lad's missing, if he was dead they'd say so, so he's not dead." He stretched his arm around her and joined Vera in comforting Mother.

"They don't know what's happened to him anymore than we do, so we mustn't give up hope," Father shared in a faltering voice.

Minutes earlier life had been fine, well as fine as it can be in war, but now their world had fallen apart.

"The wretched war; why did it have to happen and why did he have to fight?" Her grief was turning to anger as blame had to be placed. "Those bloody Germans," she continued, "we should never have let him go."

"You say that Mother but you know as well as I that the lad's sights were always set beyond the streets of north London: he wanted to fly! And there was nothing we could have done to stop him."

Early the next day, duly delivered to home was one of my rare letters, sharing my latest adventures and signing off in my usual cheery manner. This proved too much for them to bare, so they got to a telephone and called Boddington Camp. After being transferred to different admin staff all was finally explained and within a few minutes I was on the line reassuring them that I was still very much alive and kicking. A couple of days earlier two aircraft were out on an operation, one tracking the other. The weather was atrocious and in the confusion, it would appear, the navigators got it wrong and the two planes collided, killing all crew. After the news of the crash sunk in, I didn't give it too much more thought: unfortunately in war there was always bad news. That particular day I had been assigned by the officer-in-charge to other duties, and hadn't thought it necessary to attend the full identity parade: this was when the actual victims could be identified. The mistake was recognised the following morning when I presented myself for duty, calling out my name and number I was greeted with disbelief and consternation by the officer. I was ALIVE again!

With a grand total of some sixty odd hours of daylight and twenty-five hours of night flying under my belt, my Visual Capacity and Altitude Tolerance Tests passed, operational training was behind me; I was ready once again to be packed on to yet another train.

By now Hitler was overstretching his German war machine, if he could succeed fighting on two fronts, Russia would be his new prize; Roosevelt, having announced to his people that 'America has been attacked', was now fully committed to this war.[26]

At the end of the year, the Japanese attacked the US Pacific Fleet at Pearl Harbour, Hawaii; the United States and Britain declared war on Japan; Germany declared war on the United States; everyone seemed to be at war.

# Chapter 18

Heading north, further north than I had ventured before, our long train crossed the border into the clan-lands of Scotland and on towards the wild, west coast. Journeying through the lowlands, little seemed distinctive about the landscape, but gradually that changed, giving way to deep wooded valleys and gorges overshadowed by steep grassy slopes leading up to rugged ice-scarred mountain tops: Scotland's glens and bens. Within the woodland forests, trees had now shed their bronze and copper canopies; the vibrant colours of autumn had long since gone and branches formed weird, wonderful shapes, leafless now until the turn of winter. Only the evergreens, the conifers, stood bolt upright as if guarding the sleeping forest until spring returned. Early haw frost had taken hold of the low lichen clinging branches, outstretched above the woodland carpet of decaying leaves. Nature was preparing itself for winter, a time of dormancy.

On occasions as we tracked westward, gorge would give way to loch and the mountains would discover their twin reflection in the cold, deep glassy waters. Late autumn rains cascaded down the hillsides into leats and burns, enlivening the many stone bedded rivers which weaved across the land, before refreshing the lochs, heading seaward. Lonely and forgotten sheep appeared as specks gathered high on the bald uplands in the craggy landscape, readying themselves for what the winter had in store. In the grey soulless villages along the way, amber light glowed from the small square cottage windows; wood and peat smoke drifted slowly upwards on the dank air, up out of the gable chimney pots, and danced this way and that on the breeze. The darkening sky dramatically told of changing weather, heavy smokey black cloud layers hung ominously overhead, lifeless patterns and shapes waiting to unleash another drilling downpour. The grey of winter was now upon us.

Nearing the coast, the landscape opened out to reveal breathtaking panoramas of wide open sounds and bays which were only broken by islets and isles, and the wake of lone fishing boats making for their home port. The air had a freshness and bite to it which belied the severity of what was to come. The highlands and islands of west Scotland could suffer some of the harshest weather in Britain, even though the sea softened the temperatures. Icy winds cut to the core, sweeping through this land with such force that all in their path were laid bare: trees arched, stunted and bent to the hills. This northern world seemed untouched by the war; no evidence of the devastating bombardment reducing to ruins towns and hamlets.

Through this wilderness my train steamed north, packed to capacity with service personnel, some like me heading for the Outer Hebrides; our journey seemed to never end. On arriving at the Kyle of Lochalsh, our train halted at the buffers on the pier's end, a bleak and lonely looking place, from where I was to embark on a ship which was to sail us to Lewis, way out in the Atlantic Ocean. The cool and moist climate, warmed by the gulf stream, was mild enough to maintain the coast ice free during winter months, even though it shared the same latitude as Alaska. Gulls dived around crying, and a distant hoot of the ferry echoed across the sound, as it readied to depart.

We sailed from Kyle of Lochalsh passing to our port the fertile islands of Scalpay, Raasay and the departing island of Skye, and on through the narrow Inner Sound. Majestic cliffs, clawed by the sea, rose up towering along the sea's edge alive with the shrieking of seabirds circling overhead. The MacBrayne's boat steamed on out into the open sea, northward to cross the waters of the Minch towards the Outer Hebrides and our destination, Stornoway. The wild ocean's swell broke onto the rocky reefs, stretching along Harris's magnificent shoreline; lochs and inlets cut deep into the steeply carved cliffs guarding its coast, holding fast against the rolling breakers; then onto Lewis where bays sheltered sandy beaches, with groups of white cottages staring out to sea. A curved spit of land ten miles long offered protection to Stornoway's harbour from northerly gales and provided sanctuary for the RAF station, where I was to be based. I will always remember the welcome we received upon docking after our eight hour boat trip: it was as if the entire island population had turned out to greet us.

One of the first revelations was to discover that the RAF station and airfield was still in the process of being built by the boys of the Royal Engineers, supposedly on the orders of Churchill: until recently the aerodrome was a golf links at Melbost! Officers were put up in the County Hotel in town, while some shared Lewis Castle with Royal Navy officers. The golf clubhouse was used as the flight headquarters and officer's mess, fortunately well stocked with wartime beer. Other ranks were billeted in the few Nissen huts erected by the links. The story went that one wild night a mighty storm blew all the huts away; that's why now the curved corrugated structures were guyed down with wire cables to anchors set in concrete, and the hangars were specially shortened to lessen the effect of gales. Accommodation in the huts was much the same as I had experienced on basic training, but each hut had only six beds: primitive to say the least! The pot- bellied stove in the centre of the hut burnt peat which was dug from the adjacent field; once alight it produced a satisfying heat.

Stornoway seemed very remote: little night life, few pubs, one cinema and a random bus service when the driver felt like it. It really wasn't a popular posting, not least because of the observation of the Sabbath: work, drinking and playing football were frowned on by the locals on a Sunday. The civilian airliner, a De Havilland Rapide biplane operated by Scottish Airways, flew each day, except on a Sunday: they said that even the seagulls didn't fly on a Sunday! When the airliner delivered mail to South Harris, south of Lewis, it would land on the beach: they didn't have a grass strip! The good news was that we didn't get involved in large-scale bombing of German cities and industrial sites with the inevitable deaths of hundreds of civilians. We also didn't experience the high casualty rates of Bomber Command; we just had to help patrol ten-and-a-half million square miles of Atlantic battlefield. And if that wasn't enough being miles from home I could hardly understand the locals: maybe that was their plan! In spite of all that morale was first class, as was the leadership and training. Stornoway Station was not a bad field, with no great hazards other than an eight-hundred foot hill due north which demanded extra care if taking off on tarmac Runway 36, when fully loaded. The obstruction, known as Sandwide Hill, was deemed to be a hazard too great later in the war, so much so that I heard the Americans imported earth moving equipment simply to remove it and seventeen houses from the landscape. The airfield had one long runway which was two-thousand yards long and had two shorter runways, each at just over one-thousand yards, orientated to provide safe landing in strong winds which would drive off the sea across the strip, lying only twenty-six feet above sea level.

New hangars were being built, as was the construction of an underground Battle Headquarters that would be a sanctuary should the field come under attack. A bomb dump was sited well across the field and in the latter days we enjoyed the benefit of our own pigeon loft and keeper; had the pigeons escaped they would have stood little chance against the local gulls which were always hungry. The field often suffered from strong winds, winds from all and every direction. Areas of the runway and perimeter track had been built over boggy ground, which would present a hazard for the larger heavier craft: there were regular bog downs!

By now the Germans were carrying out regular high flying reconnaissance flights, taking photographs over the harbour, town and airfield: it was the general opinion that all this was in preparation for their increased activity in the North Atlantic waters. Many feared that any attack might come from the north east following the fall of Norway to the Germans and their growing presence along its coast. Ports for re-stocking, repairing and harbouring the 'Kriegsmarine' – German Navy 'Unterseeboots' - were now ever closer to British islands and shores and our supply routes across the North Atlantic.

I could understand why cousin Oswald and Cara might well be concerned for their island's future.

The U-boat incursions were bringing us to our knees, depriving our country of essential food and supplies, just as they had in World War One. Whilst Coastal Command battled to turn the tide, there were those in the RAF and the War Office who felt the aircraft would be better deployed in bombing targets in Germany. Britain may have ruled the waves, but Germany ruled the depths.

Our convoys lacked sufficient cover from escort vessels and long range aircraft to allow them to travel via the Arctic route without suffering tremendous losses. Since the start of the war, over two-thousand vessels, thousands of tons of cargo and scores of seamen had been lost. I guess if you were a merchant seaman, the threat of U-boats struck fear into you, as they crept up under the cover of dark, attacking without any warning. For those that did survive attacks, they then had to face intense cold and storms.

I joined Group 15 of No. 48 Squadron, part of Coastal Command undertaking reconnaissance duties in the northern Atlantic. They had until recently operated Ansons, aircraft I was well used to, but now were replacing them with the stubby looking Lockheed Hudson, and were beginning to fly anti-shipping strikes off the coast of Norway. My first taste of operations was flying as part of a crew of six, patrolling over the waters between Scotland and Iceland on anti-submarine patrols, seeking out U-boats that threatened our convoys. The Minches between the Hebrides and northwest Scotland was a regular hunting ground.

The Hudson had three times the range of the Anson, which was quite appropriate as the Squadron badge was a petrel, which I was told was a far ranging sea bird! Although having said that, some of the later Ansons had extra gasoline tanks fitted, but this didn't help them go the fifty or so knots faster than the Hudson could achieve, nor gain its height. We were also equipped with more guns. Keeping these machines in the air fell to the ground crews, who provided round the clock maintenance and repair, often in the most extreme conditions, in freezing temperatures on our windswept field. The icy steel tools would stick to their hands as they fumbled with the most inaccessible nuts and bolts. They would work in their white polo neck sweaters, oil skins, thick socks and gum boots, with their field service caps buttoned under the chin worn over their balaclavas. Engine problems were a rare occurrence; usually everything worked, all the gauges and controls and guns. We had total confidence, we had to, our lives depended on it.

Our early intelligence briefings on base outlined the tactics being adopted by the U-boat commanders and the menace of 'wolf packs' preying on our convoys. Since the start of the war it was thought the U-boat fleet had increased ten-fold or more, with Hitler's blessing, giving sanction to Admiral Dönitz to 'sink on sight' all Allied shipping.

The lead submarine which identified the convoy would radio back to as many as twenty U-boats the convoy's exact location; our briefing officer said it was believed a hundred or more packs were operating at sea. They would form about the convoy, shadowing it until nightfall when they would wreak havoc, attacking from all sides and launching their punishing offensive. We were told that the German Type VII class craft was now the most common; it had a low bridge that made it hard for other ships to see when on the surface, even in broad daylight; at night, head on, it was practically invisible. Because their submerged speed on the silent electric motors was slow, two point eight knots maximum, they would usually surface to attack. The U-boats were most vulnerable when they surfaced to recharge their batteries for the electric engines, giving the crew a chance to breath fresh air again. They would spend much of their operational time cruising on their deisel engines in this way, hoping we would not spot them or that they would not be rammed by a battleship. It had been known for some more spirited commanders to surface mid convoy in full knowledge that the escort vessels would not fire on them, at risk of hitting their own ships. If under attack they would blow their ballast tanks, releasing air and filling with water so the sub would begin to sink into the depths. Passing neutral buoyancy, they would continue to pump and press to a greater depth to avoid the impact of depth charges; there they would wait on the sea bed, hoping that their hull would not implode under the pressure. The worst nightmare was that as they waited and hid on the ocean's floor, their oxygen would become exhausted and the crew of fifty or so would die from suffocation. The German submariners were a tough lot with strong nerves and plenty of courage, living and working as they did in squalid cramped conditions. The wake of their torpedo running was the best indicator of their position, so once fired they would change their course to avoid the inevitable counter attacks. A VII class with experienced crew could dive in under half a minute, then reach a depth of three-hundred and twenty-five feet, and cruising at four knots stay submerged for ninety miles.

Although the 'Mid Atlantic Air Gap', or 'U-boat junction', as it was known, was where convoys from North America, the West Indies, Africa and the Far East were not protected by our navies or aircraft, we could make a difference nearer home. I thought these sleek, semi-submerged hunters may well have had their day!

Stornoway's strategic position became increasingly vital as the war took hold; supporting and protecting the Western Approaches. Fleet Air Arm Squadron 701 flew the Supermarine Walrus flying boats from the harbour, keeping an eye out for U-boats as well as proving useful in air sea rescue along with the RAF Air Sea Rescue launches. Our training had not only talked through ditching procedures but instructed us in the art of parachute jumping. Many a thrilling moment had been enjoyed swinging on a harness from the roof of a hangar before releasing ourselves and falling onto a hard mat, collapsing onto the left shoulder at the point our feet touch the ground, before discovering exactly what we had fractured or broken.

The Squadron had its fair share of accidents, maybe more than its fair share. We would carry out flare dropping, loss of engine landings, practice bombings and firings, and 'wind finding' using flame floats. One of our number actually lost an engine at a thousand feet, just off shore, and decided to glide down towards the beach as he couldn't make the field. Taking down telephone poles in the process, he skidded across the shore, catching fire as he came to rest. Fortunately no one was seriously injured, well nothing a hospital stay didn't put right. Another chap had a near miss when landing his Anson as he swerved to avoid an old cement mixer left on the edge of the runway and collided with a sheep, killing it and smashing up the undercarriage.

We learnt the hard way not to fly too low and close over shipping: neither the naval escorts, nor the gunners of the merchant ships had ever heard of colours of the day, Verey Pistols, Aldis Lamps, nor had any idea about aircraft recognition. During one flight we fired, clearing our guns to check they were operating, only to be immediately on the receiving end of Allied so called "friendly" gun fire from those trigger happy navy boys who had us down as the enemy. It wasn't even dark!

We would see Harrow transport aircraft flying in on the 'Cabbage Runs', aircraft of 271 Squadron delivering to the island bases much welcome fresh vegetables. One weekend's delivery saw the five crewed eighty odd foot long Handley Page Harrow attempting to land in atrocious conditions with severe cross winds creating havoc for this old bomber; it over-ran the runway and came to rest in the boggy ground, where for a few hours it became the largest veg store on any island!

For peace of mind I had completed page ten of my RAF AIRMAN'S SERVICE BOOK; entitled 'WILL'. Having studied the 'specimen page' I wrote my name, rank and service number after 'This is the last will and testament of,' then concluded with, 'in the event of my death I give the whole of my property and effects to my Mother and appoint my Father as my executor'. Having duly signed and dated it, that was simply it.

Our NAAFI canteen was a comfortable place where all would congregate: it was warm! Oh, and beer was at a reduced price. The NAAFI girls, as we would call them, although most seemed like women to me, always appeared to be smiling. At the end of a long cold day it was a welcome that went down well along with the beer and the warmth! Coastguards were allowed to use the canteen along with us chaps, but only when they were on duty in the harbour. Many an evening a dozen or more of them would sit at the bar, smiling at the duty corporal who had no idea if they were on duty or not, and probably didn't care. One of the women, a plain but pretty lass with tightly curled dark hair and thin features, always seemed to raise a smile when she served me. They were a spirited lot, their banter and laughter rising above the sound of our idle speculation as we mused on what tomorrow had in store. Brenda, for that was her name, lived with her family in a traditional croft, near the settlement of Col on the Stornaway coast. Many of the local community were so friendly they would welcome us servicemen for a home meal and a chance to relax and unwind with their families. The young menfolk of many of these families were fighting the war far away in a very different land. More than seventeen- hundred of them left the island in the week prior to the outbreak of war. Dear Brenda was no exception to such hospitality and invited me back one weekend to meet her family. Spending time with them I realised how close knit these people were, and that the crofting culture was far more than farming and owning land: it was a way of life. We feasted on cullen stink, a kind of broth made from fish her father and children had caught, followed by their own mutton, potatoes and vegetables; all eight of us sat around a long wooden table. As we chatted after our meal sipping a locally brewed dram, it was clear a whole folk history surrounded their powerful community. Gone were the days for many when their grazing and five acres of land was sufficient to provide a living for a family; local employment now supplemented their meagre existence. Their ground was poor, and as they talked I realised they had to work tirelessly on the land which stretched from the coastal dunes – the macca, towards the inland hills - trying to improve its fertility.

The croft, barn and byre were thatched, their roofs perched on low stone walls which looked as if they may well tumble over at any time. An old lorry was dumped outside in a muddy spot in the yard, its box wagon had been boarded in like a shed with what looked like assorted driftwood and provided home to a family of pigs. The red cab, all that one could see of the vehicle, had lost its tyres and its battle with rust long ago and now sported a white door jammed closed with the *tushkar* – their peat cutting spade. On the bonnet in front of the split windscreen sat a cockerel; its mates clucked, strolling and pecking about in a carefree and nonchalant manner, the breeze ruffling their brown feathers as they searched for seed and maggots. In the cottage, small, white framed windows were sunk deeply into the stonework and the doorway was low, low enough that my head struck the timber doorframe. The fire smouldered in the black grate, whisps of smoke winding their way slowly up the chimney. I was unsure whether or not it was providing any great heat, and clearly others must have felt the same as the old boy stacked on more dry peat blocks from last year's digging: soon these were ablaze and fingers of flames flickered and danced.

The old chap and I retired to wooden carvers across from one another beside the hearth; he puffed on his pipe of used tea leaves, snuff and treacle, whilst I just stared. On the black wooden mantle over the fireplace the open seal oil lamp glowed, beside it hung the gun the old boy used to shoot the creatures. His silence was broken as he muttered,

"I know the war, the last war, and I knew so many who never got to the end of it; but I've forgotten many too, you do you know."

From the kitchen in the 'but' off room the black skirted and shawled maids were busying themselves clearing up and gossiping about everything and nothing; the weft of their Gaelic tongue flowed like music. For many the far islands, this last land on the edge of the mighty ocean, was not only a way of life but the only way they had ever known, never having been over the sea. As I bid my hosts farewell, thanking them for their island hospitality, a droning warplane flew overhead and for a moment the two very different cultures met. The long winter nights were now drawing in and the six or seven hours of day light had all but slipped away for another day as I steered my bike over the sandy track, then back the seven miles along the coast to the airfield, carefully balancing my precious gift of a dozen eggs.

Apart from the pubs and hotel bars in town, our main entertainment was the fortnightly dances, except that is, from the occasional fights which broke out at closing, often with the navy boys, which was entertaining providing you were watching and not involved. The Nicholson Institute in Stornoway was the place to make for if you wanted to pick up the local talent; there was a dance there most weeks and in the early days of winter it was positively heaving. I was warned by some of the old hands that many of the local girls wanted to get off the island, so if you weren't married, watch out! As the weeks went by I became more and more proficient at sitting out, with a pint as my only partner. The local lads were a great laugh but didn't move on the dance floor quite like the local lasses!! They had the physique better suited to playing shinty or rugby. One week I caught a glimpse of

Brenda's younger sister sitting at a table with a crowd of girls; I was certain she noticed me, so mustering all my courage, I asked her for a dance. Wendy, not wishing to offend I guess, accepted, explaining that she preferred to be known as Wend, then spent the next half hour guiding me around the floor, ignoring her mates as we chatted. Now this is what it was all about I thought. As I looked around I could see many a chap silently dancing, just being held tight by a woman, relishing the comfort in these uncertain times. Then came the ceilidh and my smug confidence was shattered by my pounding heart, nigh on nearly twisted ankle and total confusion; but we had a good time, and at the end of the evening she gave me a quick goodnight kiss. I saw a bit of Wend over the next few months, but probably our most memorable time together was a bus ride over to Westside and Ness to catch a glimpse of the seals basking on the Atlantic washed rocks. The old bus bore no resemblance to those in London; it looked more like a charabanc, or as I imagine one might look! Its seats were wooden; in fact planks were stretched across supports in the floor. Here all sorts of livestock accompanied the passengers: sheep, a goat and chickens – none of them in crates. As we stopped at the end of farm lanes, either deliveries would occur or the collection of yet more animals, resulting in greater noise and worse smells. Needless to say we had some laughs. I am not totally sure, but believe our average journey time was no more than fifteen miles per hour: never mind, the scenery was impressive when we got there and Wend's company proved great fun on the way. We saw a bit of each other after that, when I wasn't flying and she wasn't working. Brenda found the whole thing really funny, beaming every time she saw me.

Times off base were few, but when I could grab a moment I would cycle to the harbour and while away many an hour strolling around watching all the activity. Flying boats had been pulled ashore, up the slipway on wheeled cradles and parked on hard standing awaiting work. Once, after a really heavy storm, one of the seaplanes broke its mooring and when retrieved, the sad looking machine ended up in the yard to be repaired. Over time I got to know one of the engineers well and would meet up with him and his mates in town. Fortune came my way when he got the okay to take me up on a check flight in one of the Walruses they had partly rebuilt. What an experience as the old engine roared, pushing us across the harbour and finally, after what seemed an age, we and the wooden hulled biplane were airborne, circling high above Stornoway and its coast where I could just spot Col below and even Wend and Brenda's croft: I caught myself waving, but realised it was pointless as no-one would see me except for a smiling fellow airman.

Christmas of 1941 was memorable for a whole host of reasons – great dances, good drinking and not least, Mother's present. The high point was 'The Christmas Dinner' in the Sergeants' mess: a true feast and not a hint of rationing in sight.

| | |
|---|---|
| Cream of Tomato Soup and Rolls | Christmas Pudding with Brandy Sauce |
| Fillet of Fish with Egg Sauce | Cheese and Biscuits |
| Roast Turkey and stuffing Roast and creamed Potatoes Garden Peas Brussel Sprouts Brown Gravy | Coffee and mints Beer, Minerals, Cigarettes |

The real treats for many were the beer and cigarettes!

Mum's first letter and card to the Hebrides duly arrived, but unlike my earlier correspondence this was a parcel: not a very big parcel but one meticulously wrapped, taped and addressed. Her card explained the rationale behind this rather surprising gift:
*'I saved a few bob dear and thought that with the colder weather coming* (she'd never been north of the border so little realised

what an understatement that was) *I'd get you something, so I'm sending you a navy blue woollen balaclava, I hope the colour's alright.'*

Well the colour might have been alright but I wouldn't have been seen dead in one, and besides which, it itched like mad. I'm sure if I'd worn it for any length of time my face and particularly my neck would soon be so painful I wouldn't have been able to endure it any longer than a few minutes. Maybe the wool was too coarse or perhaps there were plain stitches where there should have been pearl stitches or vice versa? As I reflected on Mother's latest creation a brainwave came to me; the ground crew guys wore balaclavas all the time. My next trip to the harbour would witness an overjoyed Dave and a relieved me: I would hate to think of her well meaning gift not being used. That, however, wasn't the end of it: when I was next down at the seaplane maintenance workshop, a rather sheepish Dave admitted,
"I washed it because it seemed really itchy, and then found the darned thing wouldn't fit. I didn't want to throw it away so the other fellows found a use for it in the workshop." He beckoned me to go and see – and there it sat proudly atop their teapot. I had to agree it looked good and even more so when he added,
"Yes, and brown so you can't see any tea stains." I had never before realised he was colour blind!

Included with the balaclava, tightly packed inside it, was a book and as the volume was revealed, I had to smile: 'Biggles Goes to War'. She must have realised I was reading it when home and had inserted a note, *'Thought you could pick up the story when you find yourself not so busy luv . . . Mum x'.* She closed her brief letter by explaining that Father was busy with the allotment and his Home Guard duties, although he never really said much about it. He thought I'd be interested to know that a chap at work had heard from a mate that Adolf had started to drop 'secret weapons' off Southend. Some sort of new mine had been parachuted on to the mud-flats at Shoeburyness: the mine sweeping boys were down there sorting it out. Vera and Bert next door turned out to be a really nice couple and guess what, they played cards. The garden had been a picture and much to the delight of Mrs Harris, the much tended onions had cropped so well she'd offered them to all the neighbours including the odd couple upstairs. The whole close had been busy, she explained, raising money for 'The Spitfire Fund' and she had just collected it all together to pass on. Mother ended her letter with what sounded like a quote from somewhere,

*'Even though we live under the shadow of war, we must hold on to the truth that life is a treasure.'*

A bit unlike her really!

Oh, and a *'PS, Father's enclosed Oswald's latest letter luv.'*

Oswald's letter whilst long, enthusiastically described developments on the islands. Much of its focus was centred on the latest news concerning Steffan, the young Norwegian Oswald had met whilst working in the boatyard. He had finally safely returned from his latest trip on the 'Bus' run to near Molde in Norway, and was shocked to see how bad things were over there now.

Oswald explained –

"Many of the towns have been bombed to ruins by the Luftwaffe in retaliation for the people's obstinacy and refusal to surrender. Thousands of teachers and children marched refusing to become involved with the 'Hitler Youth', hundreds of teachers have been brutally treated, many being shipped to the frozen Artic North. The Church has denounced such acts of ruthless persecution and also the deportation of the Jews and workers. Many pastors have been arrested. Men of 18 to 55 have been seized and forced to work in slave labour gangs on roads, railways, airfields, naval bases and fortifications. Young women work in the German factories or in military barracks. Radio sets have been confiscated and sent to Germany, this is the only way they can stop the people listening to their Norwegian compatriots on the BBC from London.

It's hard to believe Ron, but still people fight back. Beneath German posters pasted on walls in the towns showing a large eagle with outstretched wings, with the globe in its talons are the words in German –

**'We are the Masters of the World.'** Underneath are daubed the slogans of the Home Front, **'Passive Resistance'** and **'Work Slowly and Work Badly!'**

German troop trains are derailed, power stations are blown up, Nazi headquarters and communication exchanges have been set on fire and bombed. Literally hundreds of stenciled underground news sheets spread the 'Home Front' message and news from secret wireless broadcasts throughout the land."

Steffan had said that some of the coastal Resistance fighters have been able to seize detailed plans of their coastal waters and shoreline, plans from German troops as they landed. A few Germans were interrogated by the Resistance who discovered that the plans were drawn back in Germany from photographs taken by thousands of German tourists sent by the German Nazi Government on "Kraft durch freude" ships before the outbreak of the war, just as the Germans involved in the Herring Export Trade had done here in Lerwick before the war. Many young Norwegians had volunteered to sail back with the British commandos after their raids on German coastal factories which were converting fish oil to glycerene for explosives. These men were to be the nucleus of the Free Norwegian Army in Britain. He was adamant that many Norwegians now knew what occupation was like and were willing to fight against it, even at the risk of their lives:

"The Children of Norway will have learnt one great lesson: 'that without freedom and truth, life has no meaning'."

Discarding the letters, I took up the book mother had sent and flicked past the pages and chapters until I reached where I had last read – Chapter X, COMBAT!

*'It was a bleak morning, with frosty stars twinkling in the sky and a raw wind blowing from the north, when, at five o'clock, the three airmen let themselves quietly out of the hotel and, with extra sweaters and their flying kit over their arms, made their way to the aerodrome.'*

The words and sentiment sounded so familiar!

It wasn't until my last operation out of Stornoway that I saw any real action. Our briefing talked us through the weather conditions: wind en route, visibility, cloud base and likely weather for our return. We would fly at a height of a thousand feet hunting out German U-boats shadowing our Northern Atlantic supply convoys. After our 'Ops' meal of bacon, egg, sausage and chips we collected flasks and sandwiches, then our equipment: parachute, Mae West and warm clothing. It was going to be bitterly cold up there so I wrapped up well with vest, pants, longjohns, shirt, trousers, thick woollen roll neck pullover, several pairs of gloves, scarf, flying helmet and my sheepskin lined Irvin jacket. Within the hour and almost before our fry-up had a chance to settle down, the smell of glycol and oil greeted us as we made ready for take-off. We climbed at about a hundred and thirty knots and headed on my course of zero10 degrees magnetic. This would take us northwest of Scotland and towards the northern waters of the Atlantic, between the Faroe and Shetland Islands, into the realm of the night. Having cleared the coast and testing our guns, we settled to cruise at around one-hundred-and-fifty knots.

Once we were on 'spot' we changed course and began our anti-sub sweeps, working across our designated search area. My job was to keep us on course, which was no easy feat: the cold was biting even though I was well wrapped up, making it hard to manipulate the navigational instruments. Feeling the cold I decided to pour my first coffee of the flight. Unscrewing the flask I filled the cup and took a gulp,

"Shit!" as I spat what seemed a boiling brew back into the cup. These flasks certainly do a good job: too good!

Forty minutes in and we made contact with a convoy, steaming southward. With the daylight fading to twilight, patches of grey mist blanketed, lingering below, blotting out large expanses of the ocean. Ships disappeared, swallowed by the swirling cloud, then with an eerie magic came back into sight. A weird sense of tranquility seemed to be all consuming: even the ocean appeared completely flat, its threatening seas momentarily becalmed.

Hardly visible below us, the U-boat rose to periscope depth: the German commander swept the sea several times to fix the convoy's exact position and, importantly, that of its escorts. This sleek undersea Atlantic warrior quietly broke the surface with just a thin white wake under the solid darkness of the winter night. The nights were long and black at this time of year, providing hours of uncertainty for the merchant men and escorts as to if and when the U-boats would strike.

As we executed our turn we spotted what it, partly submerged, to our starboard side, its fine silver wash trailing to its stern reflected in the moon's harsh glow. The German gunners scurried across the deck and under the eye of their commander in the conning tower, brought their .45 calibre gun to bear onto one of the vessels.

We banked, turned again and being cautious not to attract fire, lost height and brought our gunner within range. Before the sub had landed a hit, we opened fire. As our shots pierced the waters alongside the sub's hull, one of their gunners turned heavy machine gun fire upon us; an exchange of fire ensued.

A warship had changed bearing and was now steaming on a ramming course with the U-boat as it prepared to dive. The escort, intent on a kill, ploughed through the ocean, ready to disgorge its load of depth charges.

The U-boat shuddered, plummeting to the depths; that was the last we saw of it.

Landing at Stornoway, the aircraft was checked for damage, whilst we were de-briefed by the intelligence officer. After a hearty meal, washed down with a McEwans Scotch Ale, we crashed out.

I would long cherish many memories of my time in Lewis, where the wild winds and treacherous conditions out to sea would greet us as we headed into the open Atlantic and Arctic waters. There were times as the weather closed in, when it seemed as if I was living amid a huge damp cloud of sea mist. The amazing performance of the Aurora Borealis covered the sky with light, light that silently danced about the heavens, forever changing its colours and patterns. The dawning, as we returned from a cold night flight, glowed, colouring the snow covered mountains and reflecting in the little harbour of Stornoway below us. There was marvellous comradeship as we lived for the moment: I can still hear the haunting and magical sound of island lasses singing Hebridean verse in Gaelic.

Wend promised she'd write to me, but I knew I'd not hear from her. Maybe she did write and with all the turmoil of war I never got the letter; somehow I doubt it, probably she'd found another chap.
All in all it had been a tremendous time.

The Battle of the North Atlantic proved to be the longest of the war, and was to last four years.

# Chapter 19

Another important activity in which I was yet to be involved, was 'Crewing Up': the precise and scientific art of being selected and matched on a psychological, as well as a physiological basis with your future crew members. This exacting exercise was executed with all the airmen gathered together in one place; for us a large dingy hangar. We were given clear and comprehensive instructions – 'Just get on with the job of finding a crew!' and, amazingly, left to it. My flying colleagues were surprised at this concept, after all, the RAF is usually so meticulous in its instructions. Airmen of all shapes and sizes were represented in the hangar on that day, not to say all temperaments - and that was the problem. How would you ever know? Before the officer-in-charge departed he assured us that this was the best way of doing it and usually it worked well, with most becoming 'close knit units'. Nevertheless, this was largely our choice and, good or bad, we had to live with it. I imagined that instinct and gut feeling would play a valuable part in this.

By now I knew my immediate future was 'Heavy Conversion' and a chance to fly in those large, four engined bombers, so I buried myself amongst chaps who had a similar posting in mind. On first encounter I guess I tried to identify if we had anything in common with each other, aside of flying and, crucially, if I could get on with them. So it was that over the following hour, from what I initially thought was a totally chaotic approach, crews were born. I, once merely an airman, was now transformed into a crew member – not just any old crew member, but part of a bomber crew.

The first fellow who caught my eye was a flight engineer I'd flown with on a number of occasions called Harry. He was a mischievous chap with a wicked sense of humour, but there was no-one who knew engines better than him. He hailed from Hertfordshire, just north of my home town and, one of five, he was a born survivor; his dad had some high level job at Hawkers, Hatfield, and his mum sounded a gem. By now Harry had already teamed up with two others: Ronnie and Ken. Ronnie, a Canadian pilot who had not long since arrived from RAF Station Bournemouth had already got a reputation as an above average pilot. He was a bright eyed, dapper chap who at first glance seemed a bit of a lad; as I listened to them I couldn't help but grow to like him. He was probably all the things I wasn't and under his bullish exterior I concluded was a competent pilot and someone who would help our crew gel together. Ken, much the quieter of the three, was holding his own with just the occasional quip or observation – I immediately liked him and thought I'd found a kindred spirit. So with ginger haired Ken as our mid-upper air gunner – AG, and dispatcher, our crew was taking shape. After still more meandering and mingling we came up with a jolt as a tall wiry figure of a man abruptly stopped us in our tracks and confronted us with,

"Got a WOP yet?"

I looked at the others who then looked at me. Ronnie was the first to reply,

"Nope, are you offering?"

It was unclear whether the boldness of one matched that of the other but the lanky lad replied,

"Look no further, I'm Cyril and I'm your man."

"Great," remarked Harry, "only two to go!"

With our less than reticent wireless operator clearly having recruited himself, all that remained was our tail end gunner and bomb aimer.

We decided that the best plan of action was to split up to complete our crewing. I had a sense that Cyril may have seen it as a tactic to lose him, but he went along with it anyway. The scores of airmen talking themselves into crews was creating such a din it was hard to talk and even think. We agreed to meet again in fifteen minutes, with or without our gunner or bomb man. First back were Ronnie and me, both of us admitting to a fruitless exercise. Harry and Ken had enjoyed no more luck than us, but had got word from a senior instructor who said that if we were struggling there was a chance to make up crews at the HCU. Just as our hope of getting it together was fading, old Cyril turned up and promptly presented to the group, Reg.

"Reg here would like to be our bomb aimer if we want him?"

This time Ronnie piped up and spoke for all of us,

"Yep, sounds good to me boy; you want a crew and we need an aimer. Are you any good?"

A quiet self assured Reg immediately returned,

"Yes, I passed with a creditable eighty-four percent."

Ronnie hardly gave him a chance to finish,

"Then let's do it, you're in."

The rest of us, not totally reassured by Ronnie's simplistic confidence in need and necessity, agreed with one accord: our 'aiming' would be in the hands of Reg. Almost a crew, we would start our Conversion Training and begin the task of getting to know and work with one another.

No.4 Group Bomber Command was based and operated out of RAF Marston Moor, North Yorkshire. It was home to 1652 Heavy Conversion Unit - Bomber Training School and to us for the next six weeks; our beast would be the formidable Handley Page Halifax heavy bomber - a 'real' aircraft. Marston Moor, or Tockwith as it was known in its early days, had only just been constructed along with around fifty other new airfields across the country for Bomber Command. It boasted three tarred concrete runways, the longest approximately 5,600 feet. The widespread dispersal of bombers, apart from being essential, was a problem. Our dispersal area was badly placed from a taxiing aspect and to reach the active runway often meant taxiing around sharp bends and up and down slopes, quickly dropping our brake pressure. It also created difficulty in getting maintenance work carried out easily, a nightmare for Harry. Apart from seven hangars complete or under construction, there were few other buildings aside of the watchtower and bunkers.

Here we were tutored in the skills of flying the four engined Halifax that we would grow to love or hate and learn the art of working together as a novice aircrew; for Harry and the others recruited from ground staff, it was an opportunity to get more flying experience. This part of England was dotted with airfields, buzzing with activity from the early hours of the morning and resounding to the roar of these great engines. By now we had been joined by our rear gunner, Ted: a short, stocky Welsh boy who had got hopelessly lost on the train network and completely missed 'Crew Up'. On first impression Ted seemed a happy-go-lucky, bubbly sort of guy and soon became affectionately referred to as Taffy Ted: our 'tail end Taffy'. It crossed my mind, and that of the others, that it was a good job he wasn't our navigator!

The conversion flights would now give us the opportunity to learn about the new equipment we had to deal with. Our 'Circuits and Bumps' were flown conscious of the fact that the circuit of nearly every airfield overlapped with at least one or more other airfields. Consequently, all circuits were normally flown in an anti-clockwise direction, as to do otherwise would risk aircraft closing in on one another at 300 miles per hour. Our instructor made us fully aware of the fact that flying was a hazardous affair; not many come out whole from a crashed aircraft: he then let us fly solo as a crew. Night flying followed circuit work, as did two five hour cross country trips. There was also a need to keep up to speed on the Link Trainer, a flight simulator whose computation was operated by pneumatics; I could learn cockpit as well as fuel layout and switchings, should I ever need to act as second pilot. As well as mastering the chest parachute harness, essential for the crammed quarters on board, we also didn't 'escape' learning about survival and 'escape and evade' tactics. One of our evasion exercises was a wide game, in the middle of nowhere, and in the dead of night. We all got back, exhausted, covered in mud and hungry. Some whom the instructors had caught were 'DEAD'. I was alive and didn't get lost; the crew thought that this was a good omen, what with me being their navigator. Ditching and dinghy practice in the local swimming baths more or less completed our preparation.

We left 1652 Heavy Conversion Unit as a qualified crew, working successfully together and ready to take up our operational posting – wherever it might be.

We were now the new 'Glory Boys'.

# Chapter 20

Airframe BB225 was at the final stage of completion: our Halifax bomber was about to be born.[27] It had slowly taken shape in the London Aircraft Production Group factory, one of five in the country; Halifaxes were being manufactured at the rate of one every hour: a total of just over six thousand. The various parts and sub-assemblies were transported in from factories dispersed around Great Britain to avoid the Germans totally crippling production with their raids.

Wheeled out of the factory, the test pilot would then put our Halifax through its paces. Any problems were rectified on landing. The aircraft was then handed over to a pilot of the Air Transport Auxiliary Ferry Command and flown from Leavesden Aerodrome in Hertfordshire thirty-two miles to a small airfield deep in the Bedfordshire countryside. On landing our bomber and taxiing it along the peri-track to its 'D' (Dispersal) point, Audrey, an attractive young women looking no older than a girl and dressed in a very smart ferry pilot's uniform, her pilot's handbook stuffed down her boot, climbed out and reported to Operations to complete the handover paperwork. She then made herself comfortable in the mess waiting for her Anson 'Round-Robin' pickup at the end of the day.

The Halifax sat on the tarmacadam awaiting its first breath of action. Hundreds of workers across the country had put in more than seventy-six thousand hours to build this craft. I just couldn't get over how big it was. Its wingspan, at just around a hundred feet, was about twice that of the Anson and weighed seven times heavier – just over seventeen tons empty. Standing beside the undercarriage its scale was impressive: its tyres were the same height as me! It had to be about as big as it could possibly be and still just fit in one of the hangars.

The 'Halibag', as it was affectionately known, had only been flying for a few months yet already a growing number of modifications and variants were beginning to build its pedigree. Losses were high: maybe it was the speed at which it and its crews were thrust into the air, perhaps the inexperience of early trainee pilots, or deficiencies in the design: who knows. During the year, eight of our Halifaxes would be lost along with many chaps I had grown to like and admire. Most would not complete a tour of thirty missions, baling-out so to speak at about twelve or fifteen sorties. Although over time the odds improved this didn't help them! But these were the odds that awaited me and I had to be prepared to live with them.

Down a narrow side road marked 'This road is closed to the Public' was hidden RAF Tempsford. As locals sat, drank and jawed in the Wheatsheaf pub in the nearby village, they had no real idea what went on up there, nor for that matter in the countryside around.[28] They just witnessed the RAF personnel, and other 'different' looking men and women coming and going and thought little of it: after all strange things happened in the war. RAF Tempsford sat in a broad, shallow valley straddling the Cambridgeshire/ Bedfordshire border, more or less midway between St. Neots to the north and Sandy to its south. Originally intended as a bomber station, its location right next to the LNER's main London to Edinburgh railway line didn't appeal, nor did the idea of bombers taking-off in fog with full bomb loads heading towards Everton and the adjacent rolling hills. So it was that Churchill saw it as an ideal base to establish his newly formed Special Operations Executive – SOE Flight. He wanted the SOE to 'Set Europe Ablaze' by controlling and assisting nationals in occupied territories. Tempsford had become the centre for the most secret of activities - and my new home.[29]

Sited upon somewhat marshy ground Tempsford seemed to be undergoing continual expansion. Three concrete runways were built and around the peri-track were thirty-six hard standings, but this was now being increased to fifty. To the south lay the four hangars of the technical site and to the north the bomb stores. Close by, Gibraltar Farm House was used for agent reception and as a pre-flight preparation centre.

Hasells Hall at Sandy served as accommodation for our officers and its library was where our parachutes were folded. The domestic and sick quarters were dispersed, mostly south of the Everton Road, whilst other crew stayed at nearby Potton. WAAFs however were billeted in a separate camp at Everton – The Waafery, a barbed-wire fence offering security and separation! Across the fields, east of the airfield where we were accommodated, was Gibraltar Barn - 'The Barn'. Here prior to their missions and after their stint in one of the six local SOE training schools, agents would collect their equipment: arms, ammunition, radios, and other supplies for the resistance work before flying out.

Tempsford was home to No. 138 Squadron: originally a fighter and reconnaissance squadron based in Chingford, then reformed in 1941 from No. 1419 Flight as a 'Special Duties Squadron'. It was unclear to us new chaps what exactly that meant and what rôle we would take on, but it would not be long before we had some idea. The Westland Lysanders, unarmed 'Lizzies', were well established as the agents' taxis with their long range, belly fuel tanks and exterior ladders fixed to the fuselage for quick agent escapes! Putting down in some distant field, their pilots landed and retrieved faceless and nameless brave strangers under the eyes of the Germans. Wellingtons that had been stationed here were moving out to the newly constructed Bassingbourn base nearby. Tired and outmoded aircraft seemed to me to be the norm: maybe due to the reluctance to provide support from those in high quarters who had a distaste for our underhand work, or it could just be that Air Chief Marshall Sir Arthur (Bomber) Harris wanted to keep them all focussed on the *real* exploits of Bomber Command.[30] Our Squadron motto was 'for freedom', which seemed very appropriate as much of the flying appeared to be into occupied territory - from the Norwegian Artic Circle to the French Mediterranean shores as well as far flung Yugoslavia.

Hitler knew of Tempsford's rôle in the war describing it as 'The Greatest Menace', but although his forces were continually frustrated by its activity, the Abwehr (German Military Intelligence) was never able to precisely locate it.[31]

# Chapter 21

Cyril pulled the tan leather armchair that bit nearer the fire, then settled back to enjoy his pipe. Every so often he would remove the evil smelling briar from his mouth and sip a fine French cognac from a rather less than fine tumbler, courtesy of those Lysander Lads. Across the spacious ante-room, in the corner, stood an upright piano finished in burr walnut, its lid hinged up under the music stand upon which some well used score was propped. Above and to each end of the piano was bracketed an empty, swivel, brass candle holder. The stool sat awaiting its maestro, but none was about to tinkle the instrument's ivories this day. There was a record player on a table alongside, but tonight's entertainment was being provided by Taffy and Ken who were absorbed in a game of Trumps. A square veneered table had been cleared of all else, with the exception of their tankards and an ashtray for resting their smouldering Player's Weights. Harry was engrossed in front of an old wireless, fiddling with the dial tuner, and concentrating so hard on the broadcasts he failed to hear me greet him as I entered, or for that matter notice Ronnie perched at the end of the desk signing off his latest letter home. Seated across from Cyril was Reg, quiet Reg, so quiet he was asleep, legs stretched out in front of the blaze. I slumped into the deep, dusty upholstery of a Parker Knoll which, from the feel of the springs, had seen better days. There was an uninspiring gloom which well matched the décor and lingering smell of stale beer and tobacco. The glory days for this house had long since past. Ornate, framed paintings in dark, somber oils adorned the room alongside photographs of all shapes and sizes – of people, people who presumably meant something to each other.

Across the room another group of fellows was occupied reading newspapers or just dozing in the corner, seemingly minding their own business. One of them challenged in what appeared at first hearing to be a sarcastic tone,

"So you chaps want to zoom around up there at twenty thousand feet in an old metal tub eh, believing the bullets will bounce off yer?"

It wasn't directed at any one of us in particular and, as such, initially, no-one paid any particular attention to him. Reg was asleep, Taffy and Ken were totally engaged in cards, Harry was focussed on the whistling wireless set. That only left the other three of us and Cyril didn't seem to show any interest whatsoever. Ronnie was first to pipe up,

"Yep, that's about it!"

The airman chipped in again,

"You're a *Yank*!"

Ronnie gave him no opportunity to be disillusioned,

"No …. Canadian."

Ronnie greeted their assertion with disdain, clearly objecting to the idea of being born the wrong side of the US/Canadian border, after all he came from New Brunswick.

These were the Lysander pilots, the 'Lizzie Lads'. They were the men who would fly at night during the short 'moon period', over the Channel to occupied France, to land in torch lit fields deep inside enemy territory. They stayed only a few minutes on the ground, just long enough for their passenger to scramble out or to pick up an agent, a Resistance fighter or secret documents, ever wary of the Germans who could be lying in wait. These were the men of the 'Moon' Squadron that flew their clandestine missions night after night; and these were the men who got Ronnie's nationality so terribly wrong!

The card playing boys laughed: I am not sure whether it was on account of their poor hands or because they were amused at this verbal exchange. Cyril contributed a slightly nervous laugh and, with that, Ronnie joined in. Within a few moments the atmosphere had shifted from positively awkward to mildly convivial. The offending airman apologised, then continued,

"I am Giles," then turned to the other two, "this is Peawee Older," who sort of gave a wave, "and that's Terence," who then, not wanting to let the awkward moment go completely, concluded that they hadn't realised there were two foreigners in their midst.

"What do you mean," challenged Ronnie. With a mischievous air Terence gave a nod to Taffy, who, abruptly, in good humour replied,

"Yn Gymraeg, Taffy ydw i. My name is Taffy, I'm no foreigner, I'm Welsh!"

Everyone laughed.

Introductions out of the way on both sides, we spent the next hour exchanging experiences and learning more about life and times at Tempsford: the CO's lecture had given us a brief introduction but no detail. It must have been reasonably interesting because even Harry broke off periodically from his wave-length wanderings, unless it was the French wine they poured us that distracted him. Ronnie being teetotal stuck to coffee.

Although Ronnie had undertaken most of his pilot training in Canada, he had already experienced action on England's shores during this war. His action wasn't that of fire and flak, nor for that matter of raids and bombs, but of Mrs Peggy Darling, for whom the war had already taken its toll. Her husband had been lost in his first year of service as he waited on the beach for the 'Little Ships', and there was no going back to say a final farewell: Dunkirk and the Germans had seen to that. She and Ronnie had met at some do, he couldn't quite remember when or even where; he'd only known her for just a matter of a few weeks before he was transferred. As Ronnie put it, for Peggy war seemed to be full of goodbyes. He bemoaned his early days training over here complaining that when he first arrived he was given all sorts of jobs to do, including navigation: it seemed that, perhaps due to a lack of qualified navigators, or maybe bombers, you had to pitch in and do anything. I thought this sounded comforting: at least he'd be able to turn his hands to a variety of rôles if push came to shove. He passed out well, getting seventy-eight per cent but

154

spent his time either flying 'second dickie' to a more experienced 'skipper', freezing in a lumbering 'Flying Greenhouse' – the Anson as he described it, or sitting through lectures. Now qualified, Ronnie, a flight lieutenant of the RCAF, was ready to fly and skipper his own heavy bomber. He was clearly not going to be messed about: he'd have a laugh, but behind the controls he was a man on a mission - 'do the job and be the best'. And we as a crew realised and respected that. He couldn't wait.

Dear old Taffy had the most dangerous job on our kite; tail end gunner. When flying at freezing temperatures, his screen would mist up and smear with the prop backwash. Often the gunners would smash the Perspex screen to improve their vision and the temperature would plummet. Nearly half the tail end gunners were killed in action, being the first target enemy fighters would see. It was the loneliest, and the coldest spot. In many ways it was fortunate that he was short, although his stocky build didn't make it easy to squeeze in and out of the turret. As soon as he opened his mouth on the intercom you knew immediately who it was: he didn't need to sing out in his Welsh tenor voice, but understanding exactly what he was saying took some concentration at first. Beneath his bubbly nature ran a tough streak, a dogged determination which probably made him ideal for the job: he was a survivor. He initially volunteered for aircrew, to train as a pilot and thoroughly enjoyed his early days on De Havilland Tiger Moths, but as he progressed he and the powers that be quickly realised that as he stepped up to fly other aircraft his five foot something height meant he couldn't see through the screens, and his feet never quite reached the rudder bar. In a flash of inspiration, or maybe frustration, he asked how long the training would take to be a gunner. Just six weeks. It sounded appealing. He questioned if his height would be a problem: the answer was a categorical 'No'. So that was it. At gunnery school he spent his time either blasting away at long canvas sausages, as he described them, towed behind aircraft, or at ground targets; his tough attitude suited him well for this new found rôle. He was also one of the few who had been attacked by a Spitfire, wielding its 20mm canons and half inch machine guns. Whilst the pilot had to execute the standard evasive corkscrew manoeuvre, Taffy had to 'shoot' the Spit down with a cine-camera-gun. At the end of an exhausting day, he would fall asleep, dismantling and assembling machine guns in his head, or mentally processing profile after profile of enemy planes. At the end of it he was presented with his gunner's half wing, with the letters 'AG' mounted in a laurel wreath. With an 'above average', Taffy passed out as a qualified gunner – our 'Tail End Taffy'.

Our peace was shattered with the breaking news of an aircraft on its way back in trouble. It had been on a leaflet run over Germany, but on its way out lost an engine. Its navigational aid had failed so the crew had reeled-out the trailing aerial to allow them to transmit. They'd had an hydraulics failure and on return their undercarriage would not come down; they were heading for a belly flop, the undercarriage warning horn must have been blasting away. The hundred and fifty foot H.F. aerial lead trailing from the port side had not been reeled in, so it entangled with a nearby overhead power cable upon approach, and a fire broke out. As they landed, smoke bellowed from the ailing plane. The next thing we saw were fire tenders tearing across the field with an ambulance following closely behind. After what seemed an age, the ambulance sped away; we assumed the crew were safely on their way to the local hospital. We later learnt their undercarriage had been shot away and three of the crew had been killed in the crash and fire; others had later died of their injuries in hospital. One fortunate chap had walked away with only a sprained ankle, whilst a less fortunate was up for membership of the 'Guinea Pig' Club: a dubious recognition for those who had suffered extensive burns and undergone plastic surgery. That poor chap would never be the same.

For us intrepid aeronauts, our first tour was soon to begin: thirty operations and then a well earned rest for several months depending on your trade, eighteen or so for me, and then a second tour of say twenty or more ops. If I was to survive that, my war was over, unless I felt foolish enough to do extra ops on each tour, or another complete tour. Out of every one hundred aircraft of Bomber Command that went out, an average of ninety-six would make it safely home. I recall thinking that sounded pretty good, but then I failed to realise that that was only if you went once! After twenty-five ops you were fresh out of luck. The entire force of Bomber Command aircrew would turn over every twenty-five operations.

Funny how no-one ever told me that sooner.

Hugh Dalton, who was chosen as the new Ministerial Head of SOE, was reported to have written to Lord Halifax recognising the need for a guerrilla movement, comparable to the Sinn Fein in Ireland. He insisted,

"What is needed is a new organisation to co-ordinate, inspire, control and assist the nationals of the oppressed countries who must themselves be direct participants . . . "[32]

Whether it be through fate or fortune, we all now found ourselves part of *'Churchill's Secret Army, The Ministry of Ungentlemanly Warfare.'*

# Chapter 22

In what seemed to herald a final chapter in our formal training, attempting to fully equip us for that which lay ahead, our survival and endurance skills were put to the ultimate test. In a small blacked out hut the metal reels rattled as the 16mm film juddered its way through the projector gate; a flickering black and white image slowly came to life as we concentrated on the invaluable lessons contained within these 'RAF Training' gems!

In bold white characters, the title foretold us that soon we would know, *'How to get a pilot out of a ditched plane'*.

Reassurance came in the words:
'Calm and commonsense will get over most of the difficulties'.
The movie epic continued by explaining, in a scene shot over a pint in a pub somewhere, how you rescue aircrew from a bomber – now you're talking, I thought. It explained about a small sprung flap and extolled the virtues of an axe. Whilst emphasising that you must look carefully for each crew member, it cautioned that there is absolutely no certainty that you will find any crew member at their station; except probably the pilot. In short it is wise to carefully and quickly search what has probably now become a burning wreck. This rescuing job wasn't getting any easier.

The next film can revealed a far more encouraging subject matter, that is once it was threaded through the projector – *'Enemy Interrogation of Prisoners'*. If one felt at all concerned or worried at this stage, the film quickly reassured us with words like – 'Don't be downhearted; keep your mouth shut; you are still under RAF orders so all you have to give is your name, rank and number.' Well knowing that, and that the enemy will be happy with that too, certainly brings a real peace of mind! Plenty of good laughter rang out as the film whirred on.

This surprisingly gentlemanly way of conducting interrogation was not totally supported by the form AP 1548 which was handed out to us after the film. It is truly comforting to be cautioned:

- Not to believe anything you are told by the enemy or possible enemy sources. The enemy will impersonate British or Allied prisoners and mix with genuine prisoners: . . . so that's a don't talk to anyone, anywhere, anytime.
- Never to be downhearted if captured. Opportunities for escape will always present themselves.

Part five allayed any worries we might have by advising us authoritatively that any complaints one has as a prisoner can be directed to the Camp Commandant: so that's okay then. As we walked out, only the flapping of the RAF ensign in the gentle midday breeze aloft the station's flag pole distracted me from the parting words of our instructor,

"There is a fine line between courage and stupidity, but both can get you killed."

The spring day was bright and cool, the noon sun's heat warmed our backs as we stepped out across the grass to the hard-standing where our Halifax, 'NF-L', christened 'L' for Leather, awaited us. From the first moment I climbed on board a whole host of sensations affronted me. Inside the vast dark fuselage the air was cold and dank, the smell of fuel and oil lingered heavily in the atmosphere. As our voices echoed throughout the empty craft, I could hear other voices in my head: voices of airmen flying, fighting – scared, frightened, screaming voices, shouting over the intercom. And then, only silence.

In the whirl of it all I kicked the Elsan lavatory which was installed next to the Master Distant Reading Compass. One of the forty or so ground crew that looked after our aircraft had taken us on board: he stooped over, lifted the Elsan lid and revealed a cone ring inside the loo,

"This prevents splash back if you're enshrined during turbulence," he proudly remarked, then promptly closed the lid and chuckled.

Running along the inside rear of the fuselage, tracks supplied ammunition through the rear, amoured bulkhead to the gun turret. It was explained that the armouring of the bulkhead was to stop gunfire travelling the entire length of the aircraft. This is Tail-End Charlie's office or in our case, Tail-End Taffy's; once settled in, the ground mechanic explained, Taffy won't find it easy to get out in a hurry, nor for that matter will any enemy fire". No comfort to him I thought. He'll sit clear of the tail-plane and fins in the E'turret with some ten thousand rounds in total, in the tracks and reserve ammo boxes behind him: in all only two minutes of continuous fire from the four Browning machine guns, twenty rounds from each gun every second. Immediately forrard of the portside crew entry door was mounted the flare chute and flare stowage. A ladder led up into the mid-upper gun turret, with its twin Brownings and in this confined contraption Ken would ensconce himself, scouring the skies above us looking for the enemy. The ground mechanic, that was with us, pointed out to Harry the storage area for ropes and stakes, explaining the picketing of the aircraft. Grabbing the starboard handrail we stepped over the rear spar; massive stringers and struts crossed this way and that supporting all the framework for each of the forty or so foot wings which supported the engines and fuel tanks. Just ahead was the main spar, the strongest part of the structure, creating in the middle of the plane a secure crew rest bay, with bunks, along with hydraulic accumulators and rather pathetic heaters that would duct the hot air from the engines. Above was the second of the escape hatches, which the ground engineer commended to us, explaining it was for ditching,
"Only for use on the ground, not when airborne". This was the safest place in the whole plane, in the event of ditching or crash landing, and the bracing position if you could get there in time. During take-offs and landings Reg, Harry and I would tend to hold there whilst Taffy would stay in his cosy turret. Forward on the port side, bracketed high in the corner, was a golden brown coloured rectangular cane basket with slot openings to its sides. This was to host our two pigeons: in the instance of us needing

rescuing the pigeons would head home with our message, or last position attached to their legs. We also had onboard a waterproof screw top container in which to store the birds should we ditch – wet feathers and they can't fly! But we had had impressed upon us that there was only enough air in there for them to survive forty minutes. The mechanic related to us that one Skip had experienced problems keeping the aircraft on an even flight when one of the pigeons got out of the basket causing the WOP to run up and down inside the fuselage trying to catch it! We looked at each other and were unsure if we were being wound up.

Throughout the wings were located twelve fuel tanks, about one thousand eight hundred gallons in total. For take-off the inboard tanks are used, we burn eighty gallons, then switch to outboard tanks and burn some two hundred and twenty gallons, before switching again and topping up the inboards. When we approached target we would go to the inboards to keep fuel close, which reduced the risk of damage to fuel lines or the tanks from enemy fire, and the loss of our homeward supply. This was all in the hands of Harry, who found himself standing much of his time, staring through the above fuselage Astrodome for sitings, or at his control panel below. At the head of the engineer's panel were the four cylinder temperature gauges, the cylindrical oil pressure gauges and oil temperature dial gauges. Everything appeared quadrupled, a set for each engine that is with the exception of the fuel gauges: there were twelve of those arranged below along with four fuel pressure warning lights, two port, two starboard, one for each outer and inner engine. The lower panel housed a bank of engine start buttons with booster coil switches, Gill's position indicators for cooling and other controls and switches for pumps and motors: a right old confusion it looked to me!

Harry Anthony Wills, the baby of our crew, was our flight engineer and the technical brains of our crew: his job was to understand everything on our aircraft. He had been a car mechanic before the war in a specialist garage, Allen Autos, near

Woodford Green. Here he learnt to strip and rebuild engines, panel beat and weld metalwork and master the finer skills of vehicle electrics. There was nothing he wouldn't have a go at and consequently was constantly in demand to help out the inexperienced motor shop boys. If there was a part needed and they couldn't get it, give him a workshop, the materials, tools and time, and he'd not come out until it was made. He cut his teeth in a maintenance unit repairing everything from Tiger Moths to Spitfires. At first he was trained as a wireless operator, but after a brief spell he was retrained as a flight engineer at St. Athan, one time claimed to be the largest RAF Station, and then RAF Cosford. Within such a short space of time, Harry had moved from repairing cars in Essex to being thrust into the sky over Europe and responsible for a bomber! He would start the engines, initially control the centre mounted throttles, and in flight, get the wheels up, trim the flaps and continually eye the instruments, especially the fuel gauges which were rarely accurate. He was almost a co-pilot, but with one control column that wasn't possible; if anything happened to the pilot it was practically impossible to get him out of his seat in all his flying gear anyway. Harry's mind would be filled with thoughts of fuel levels, engine performance, rates of consumption, mechanics, hydraulics and electrics: in fact everything to do with the workings of the plane. His flying hours were minimal during training so when he exclaimed,
"In at the deep end again" you knew exactly what he meant. With the technical complexity of these big bombers we were all grateful we could leave it in Harry's, or I should say, Sergeant Wills', hands.

Now it started to feel really cramped: as I passed down the starboard accessway I pictured the pilot perched above the WOP, ahead was my desk as navigator and in the nose, the bomb aimer/nose gunner would lay on his couch, face down. WOP Cyril would sit surrounded by all the main electrical controls as well as the wireless receiving and transmitting sets for hours on end. For him it was to be a lonely existence, straining to listen to the faint signals in his headphones, over and above the white noise of atmospheric static. Physically and mentally he was by himself, concentrating fully as he tapped out messages at the rate of one word every two or three seconds. He undertook his Morse and wireless training, familiarising himself with RAF gear at a Signals School rather unusually located above a Woolworth's store. From there Cyril moved to a Radio and Radar School for signals training, then AFU to practice point to point wireless work where he got his Morse reading up to an impressive twenty-six words a minute. The Percival Proctor, a single engined, four seat trainer of No. 4 Radio School, gave Cyril his first experience of airborne wireless training at RAF Madley, in Hertfordshire. From there came the long journey to Evanton on the Cromaty of Firth in Scotland, and three months at No. 8 Bombing and Gunnery School flying in the twin engined Blackburn B-26 Bothas. He returned nearer to home to Gloucestershire and underwent night flying training in the good old Ansons. Cyril's boldness was only matched by the sharpness and dryness of his wit, which we were all soon to discover.

Ronnie, our Skip, would be perched directly above him, nearly twenty feet off the ground on his own, commanding a full view forward of the props and the inboards blades which seemed perilously close to me. On his right side was a folding seat for a second pilot, trainee sprog, or the engineer. To Ronnie's left, on the inner port fuselage, were arranged the main controls of the Autopilot, good old 'George'; as well as the fire extinguisher buttons, his HF radio set, which detected the 'squeaker beacons' attached to friendly barrage balloons and provided bearings for 'homing', and the covered destruction switches: the loss of an aircraft carrying secret equipment could not be risked. To his right hand below the engine speed indicators were throttle levers, propeller speed control levers, mixture and supercharger controls. Above these was the bomb jettison handle and to the side, the elevation trimming tab control, flaps and undercarriage levers.

Directly in front on the instrument flying panel was arranged a plethora of gauges and switches. Ahead was his control column, rudder pedals and a master compass along with a repeater display of the aft distant compass. A real mass of instruments and controls for anyone to get their head around! As if in an attempt to make sense of the whole mess, the ground crew had stuck a card on his panel stating  – 'The engine is the heart of an aeroplane, but the pilot is the soul'.

I stepped down into my domain and could imagine myself settling in; a chart table was positioned to my left facing port side and packed with displays and instruments: altimeter, airspeed indicator, dead-reckoner and compass. I also had to hand an air position indicator, which would enable me to read the latitude and longitude of our air position, relative to our air speed and compass bearing, the information of which would be fed into the unit. An oxygen and intercom plug set was mounted side by side, along with chart and pencil racks. On the formica chart table was a pantagraph plotter, and overhead a projector which displayed images of the night sky onto the chart.[33] The only other light into my windowless world was that from a small, bright angle poise lamp. At one time it had been assumed that we observers would also take on the role of bomb-aimer, but studying brilliant white maps, plotting routes, made it very hard to adjust one's vision to cope with accurately spotting a target in an otherwise inky blackness. So the bomber aimer was born, so to speak.

Ahead, beyond my black-out curtain was all light: the nose of our Halifax was bisected by a massive oval Perspex dome that strengthened it and created optically flat oval panels so the bomb-aimer could view the target accurately. Here Reg would lay prone on his couch, straining his eyes, adjusting his computer controlled bomb sight, inputting wind strength and direction, barometric pressure and the bomb load velocity. Our height, course and speed would be processed automatically, making fine adjustments to the motorised bomb sight, the 'church cross' on his screen. To the starboard side was mounted the bomb release arrangement and 'Mickey Mouse', a clockwork rotor arm which controlled 'bombs away'. When times got tricky his couch converted into a seat so he could take control of the twin forward facing Browning machine guns, and join in on the action.

We looked on, keen to get in the sky, knowing this war wasn't going to wait for any of us.

# Chapter 23

The next day was our first mission. Having devoured a hearty meal, I attended the flight briefing, and systematically we covered the key information: confirm routes outward and return, identify the colours of the day for signalling, the modus operandi, the meteorological report, our wireless procedure, and check we haven't any identifying items on us. If all okay, then off to get dressed up.

Our raid was over Germany, perhaps the first of many in our bid to change the course of the war. But our view quickly changed when we learnt our load was millions of printed propaganda sheets. We were flying on a 'Nickel', a leaflet raid as 'Courier de l'Air.' Harry clutched a bundle of brown paper parcels and in the depths of the dark, noisy fuselage, ripped off the wrapping. Blocks of leaflets like mint banknotes were tied tightly together. When lifting off the hatch covers to drop the untied leaflets to thousands of Germans below, the sudden in-rush of air sent the sheets flying throughout the aircraft, like confetti. Harry was clearly unaware of a chute provided for the job. To us it seemed like serving up Jerry with free toilet paper, which had a message from General de Gaulle. However our scepticism was marginally allayed when we learnt it was a vital part of the propaganda war and provided a valuable opportunity to practice long range navigation at night.

As we climbed to fifteen thousand feet, the temperature dropped to minus 30°C and was still falling – it was bitter; there seemed to be a continual draft right through the aircraft, and from the way my black-out curtain was moving, I think the front turret, although sealed, was still leaking. At high altitudes, ice would form on the aircraft and break off hitting the fuselage, creating an alarming cracking noise, much like being hit by gunfire. I wore my pyjama trousers, three lots of longjohns, a long sleeved silk and wool vest, a polo neck jersey, four pairs of socks and my flying boots. My lined tan boots I could cut off at ankle top, to end up with what looked like suede shoes, so if I had to bale out and make a run for it I didn't immediately look like a British airman. I wore my Irvin insulated flying suit, over which was my Mae West life jacket, and then my parachute harness. On my head I had a 'C' type leather helmet with intercom set and a pair of Classic goggles and of course I had to be able to wear my oxygen face mask. It would take six or seven minutes to complete my navigational calculations and to do the plotting. I then tried to warm my hands on the heater behind me and get my silk gloves on to give my hands a chance to warm up before starting the next set of calculations. The others had three pairs of gloves – silk, wool and leather. Ronnie had some sort of electrically heated suit. Cyril, tucked away in his cosy wireless cubby-hole underneath Ronnie, had the warmest spot and the benefit of a small window on the world when we banked to port. He'd taken an extra jumper in case we ditched but I don't know how on earth he ever thought he'd get it on in a hurry. Ken in the upper dome would have been fine if the sun had been out, but as unusual as this night was, the moon was just not hot enough. Our primitive heating system on board did little to fend off the pending frostbite, of which we all had a taste over time.

Our load away, we headed back to be greeted on our home turn by distant searchlights and puffs of flak bursting way out to port: clearly a gun had got something in its sights, well so we thought. Before we let loose a single round, Ken cried over the intercom, "There're other birds up here, loads of 'em to our port and heading east into Germany: more of our chaps." This time the shots were not for us. On our return we were to discover that ours was a diversion exercise, known as a 'Bullseye'; the real operation was taking place elsewhere.

We quickly got into a routine with our operations, and to me as the navigator and the 'granddad' of the crew, each op was much like the last. I went to the briefing, did my flight plan, climbed into the plane and my seat, pulled the blankets around me, concentrated on the same charts and instruments, and that was more or less it every time. By now we were regularly into France; at dusk we would leave the coast of England, climbing often into thick cloud covered skies, and as we climbed through the cloud we would break into the clear, bright evening. Midway across the Channel, night would fall and under the cover of darkness we would cross the French coast. I would hope and pray that no searchlight or gun positions had spotted us; as I plotted the 'fixes' identified by Cyril on the wireless, I would calculated our course, to the drop target. Taffy in the tail and Ken mid, both frozen and cramped in their turrets, were keeping their eyes peeled, constantly scanning every inch of the dark sky for fighters which would often attack from below in our blind spot, targeting our belly which was completely vulnerable, or strike from above seeking to take out old Taffy, or our engines. Ronnie would have to fly straight and level leading up to the drop and the 'run-out' after. As we approached the target Harry and Ken would prepare the containers and packages and Reg would concentrate on his end of the job, lining up the drop. Once delivered you would want to 'get the hell out of there' as they say, as quickly as possible. The longer we hung around the greater the chance of being spotted and shot down.

Whenever we went on an op we were provided with flying rations of chewing gum, two bars of chocolate, barley sugars, a tin of orange juice and a thermos flask of coffee. On one occasion the latter proved a painful wake-up call for Taffy, who was quietly going about his business. He had poured himself a cup of coffee to fend off the chilling air and lodged the flask to one side in his turret. With a shout from Ken at mid upper over the intercom, "Fighter ..."
Taffy swung the turret and, elevating the guns searching for the gun flare of the fighter, heard a graunch as the breach end of the Browning crushed the thermos which he had stowed clearly in the wrong place!

"Bloody Hell," was cursed over the intercom, as piping hot coffee soaked his suit and legs.

A 109 was very close, climbing away to our port and before Ronnie had a chance to say anything, Ken screamed,

"Coming down from 5 o'clock." Its guns now blazing Taffy was on it, trying to make each round count as he delivered them into the dark abyss, towards the 109's fire. Taffy hollered,

"Corkscrew … to port, Go!"

Ronnie responded immediately flinging the aircraft downward with the engines screaming at maximum torque, but perhaps due to the severity of the banking, soon lost control and the Halifax started to spin. Most of us were able to brace ourselves against nearby struts or spars, but Harry was not so lucky: he took a bit of a tumble but fortunately suffered no ill effects. For several minutes Ronnie struggled to regain control as we twisted and spun erratically through the sky. Reg, bracing his feet against the instrument panel, helped Ronnie heave back the control column. Our altitude saved us and we eventually levelled out and resumed flight; we had all been badly shaken including our attacker, who I imagine, thought we were lost to the sea and had made off.

Heading directly for Tempsford, our thoughts firmly focussed on the odd pint or two at the Wheatsheaf, we landed only to discover we had sustained serious damage to our tail plane, now partly fractured from the fuselage. We were to learn that this outcome following a corkscrew was not unusual, and in one recent incident that exposed this alarming vice of the Halifax, the crew had not regained control and ended up in the drink.[34]

There were a couple of pubs in the village, the Wheatsheaf being favourite among the Lizzie Lads. Our introduction to the local watering hole proved the first of many visits, and in turn provided a rare opportunity to familiarise with the rarely accessible members of the WAAF. The joint tenanted landlords were a husband and wife, Nigel and Mandy: more convivial hosts you'd struggle to find. They ran a warm and friendly house which was welcoming to us service chaps as well as the locals. We would while away many a pleasant hour when the weather was so duff we couldn't fly, or our kite was in the workshop, with a round of cards or at darts, downing a pint or two, reliving that last op, that moment when nearly all went terribly wrong. Often we would just sit in the corner of the private snug and listen quietly to the tales those Lysander-Shagbat boys had to share – of secret flights into France and their hairy landings and escapes. "Everything depended on the moon" they would say: they only had eight days each month around the full moon when they could drop and pick up. They would fly out with a map across their knees, navigating by only the moonlight. This was a lonely and perilous job, they had no armaments, no fighter escort. Their navigation had to be precise as they looked for that small field, their landing site. They didn't need it to be long: about 600 yards was enough. They would watch for the L shaped arrangement of torchlights, the flashing morse code signal, then land along the leg of the L and gunning the engine, turn around at its base ready to take-off again. The cargo was never known, nor its purpose: they would stay on the ground for as brief a time as possible, maybe just a couple of minutes, all the time watching for the Wehrmacht and the Gestapo. Once the partisans had exchanged the agents and supplies, they would adjust their trim and be on their way home. Peawee made it sound all very exciting but also extremely risky, but they seemed to thrive on it. Peawee, in a kind of whisper, emphasised the danger further by adding,

"It's nerve wracking if you get to the field and their Morse signal is wrong."

"I got to one landing site," Terry contributed, "to discover, as I did a fly through, there were great rocks at one end; I could see them in the moonlight."

"What did you do, abort?" enquired a disbelieving Cyril.

"No, not a chance, I had an agent on board to be landed; I passed over two or three times, there were no Germans in sight, so I signalled for them to find another landing field and quick! Anyway, I finally got her off and away safely."

Some of us chaps stared at each other, probably thinking that something like this was in store for us.

The door of the public bar creaked open, three women strolled in. Although they were in civvies the fact that they were WAAFs was clearly evident by the manner of dress: I don't know if it was their stride or maybe their matching shoes, whatever, they were definitely WAAFs. I never cease to be amazed at the range of shapes and sizes that young women come in. One of the things I'd noticed at the dances was that the girls of a similar appearance don't seem to congregate together. These three looked like 'toughies' to me, the sort who would refuse any airman's invitation.

The shorter of the three strode confidently to the bar and, gaining Mandy's attention, ordered what appeared to be a sherry. She allowed herself the opportunity, while she awaited her drink, to look about the bar, and noticed an old boy who was perched on a stool, leaning on the counter studying his paper and pint, as he did each evening. His bushy jet black hair partly masked his facial features, maintaining an element of mystery about him. A man of few words, this was John, or as locals would refer to him, 'Wis'. Every so often we'd buy him a pint of local brew, which as we suspected, kept us on the right side of him and the locals.
'. . . that's the lot thanks Nigel; oh, and a top up for Wis,' we would order; Mandy would usually pour his and, as she placed it in front of him would comment in a matter of fact way,
"This one's on the boys Wis!" and glance towards us. He'd look up and then across to us, smile and chant,
"Nice one, good on yous," then go back to his paper.

The petite one noticed my gaze, and sort of half smiled, then was disturbed by a call from one of her mates across the bar. Her friend, with the fuller figure and sporting rather a large case, was giggling with the other dark haired lass and shouted across from where they had chosen to sit, ordering what sounded like two

171

shandies. The smaller one looked somewhat irritated, but ordered anyway: the other two just carried on jawing away. They all settled with drinks in the corner, well away from us, chattering, maybe about us, as occasional glances in our direction were hardly disguised. Realising I'd been staring, I looked back to our group, wondering if any of them had noticed. The last thing I needed was to be ragged by the lads. On a number of future occasions we would notice the young women always seated by themselves, until one evening when Ronnie, who had already had a couple, invited them to join us. It was hard to tell if they were keen, certainly there was no stampede. The dark haired one who introduced herself as Georgie, seemed the most eager, replying that it was kind of us and introduced her friend Marion who just laughed, whilst the slighter one Jude, who seemed more serious, showed little reaction at all. That was the start of a passing friendship: such friendships are relatively easy to make in war and even easier to lose.

The following morning we woke to a glorious summer's day: the air was heavy with perfume from the blossom and across the field an engine chugged as a small tractor ran up and down, cutting the long damp grass. It was a perfect day for flying with cloud cover light and hanging high in the breathless sky. For once our talk wasn't of last night's trip to the pub, nor our hairy flight over France, but why the flag was at half mast. Almost casually Ronnie spoke,
"We must have lost a crew during the night . . . "
Up until now our flying had been straightforward, fairly carefree with only the rare incident, but Reg soon brought us back to reality,
"It's the war, you can't get away from the fact that many have, and will die . . . and that includes us."

In the mess was the usual pungent smell of cooking; the heavy mixture of old frying fat and bacon comforted my senses, but the atmosphere was not the usual buzz of chatter and laughter. A somber mode lingered, undoubtedly on account of the loss of one of our planes. As we ate and surveyed the nearby tables trying to determine who had copped it, Taffy joined us, breaking the news, "Frank's gone . . . it's Frank, not one of the kites!"

For a brief moment I cast my mind back: there had been good times and bad times, and somehow war binds together those of us who have been caught up in this all consuming battle for survival, carrying us through those times. For many of us we began as boys, with little or no concept of our mortality, and after an experience few of us would wish to repeat, we emerged as men; for others, the ones not so lucky, they would never reach manhood.

On the previous morning, Frank decided he would go into the village and, amongst other things, send a parcel. Much of his conversation during the previous week had been centred around his mother's birthday later that month: what would he buy her and about the party the family were organising. Not only had he decided on a special present, but he had bought it and now wanted to ensure it would arrive on time. Leaving the station, he climbed onto his Triumph Tiger 80 motorcycle and headed directly to the village Post Office where he dispatched the package and a Greetings Telegram to his mother. After buying some bacci and Swans in the store he grabbed a paper and started back. A local farmhand was ditching alongside the lane and heard the bike approaching. Suddenly the engine sound changed from a blurt to a roar as it raced, over revved and finally stopped. It was discovered that as Frank was motoring along, there was a dip on a bend in the lane which partly obscured his view of oncoming vehicles. Two young boys were coming the other way, riding their delivery bikes abreast in the middle of the road, and in swerving to miss them, Frank's front tyre caught the verge. He must have lost control and was thrown against a tree, his body crumpled against the trunk, smashing his head on impact. He suffered massive head injuries, a seizure at the roadside and was rushed to the nearby hospital in Bedford. There the doctors fought hard to save him, but the accident proved fatal: he died later that day.

The lads on base joined the mourners and the family to bid farewell to Frank. We realised then that it was wrong to think we would all die in combat.

The station chaplain commenced the service by saying –
"I'm sure that many people would be surprised at the genuine sense of faith which exists in the vast majority of our young RAF officers. Many, before they seem to casually take to the air, facing all sorts of dangers which they take in their stride, offer up a silent prayer. They know their Lord will protect them in their going out and coming in. I know that Frank was one such officer, he told me so; it has been a privilege to know him. In the book of books we can read that God speaks of Jerusalem 'as birds flying'. Whatever the defining interpretation may be, be it angels, or today aeroplanes, there is no doubt that aerial defence against the forces of evil is meant. We read of how the Lord, exulted in Spirit said, 'They that wait upon the Lord shall renew their strength: they shall mount up with wings as eagles.'"

We finished the memorial service with the Psalm, whose words read -
*'The Lord shall preserve thee from all evil: He shall preserve thy soul.*
*The Lord shall preserve thy going out and thy coming in from this time forth, and even for evermore.'*
and sang together the rousing hymn that many of us knew –
'Abide with me'.
The last verse seemed particularly poignant, mindful of Frank's tragic death and the missions ahead of us –

'Hold Thou Thy Cross before my closing eyes,
Shine through the gloom, and point me to the skies;

174

Heav'n's morning breaks, and earth's vain shadows flee:
In life, in death, O Lord, abide with me'.

Frank's fiancée, family and close friends huddled close beside his burial place, sobbing and crying; as a sign of our respect we men 'Slow Marched' from the entrance of St. Mary's Church where on its south wall, a stone gargoyle appeared to silently scream at this terrible loss. From some way down Church End an airmen fired the green 'Verey Pistol', signaling that Frank was going home . . . he would not see the dawn of another day.

The Wheatsheaf was a friendly little inn, far cosier than the Anchor, or our austere mess. Wis, as usual was up at the bar, his hat next to a half empty pint. Beside him, perched high on a bar stool was a Ladybird that none of us knew: they appeared to be deep in conversation, but she was doing most of the talking. After our cursory glance and wave to Mandy, who was busy pumping up beer from a new keg that Nigel had just changed - she liked to keep him busy, we settled in our usual spot. The girls arrived shortly afterwards and when they joined us, we got the drinks in. Mandy lined them up on the bar for Harry and Marion to bring across; I don't know what Harry was saying to her but she had trouble not spilling the drinks for laughing. They parked themselves on a couple of hard wooden carvers and their laughter continued. After about twenty minutes and my pint, the WAAF with Wis made a move to go; she glanced to Jude and Georgie and smiled.
"Who's she?" fired Ronnie, wondering what Wis was up to.
"One of yours?" pried Taffy.
Georgie was quick to fill us in,
"WAAF Officer Burnett, she's IC Training and keeps busy on station, chair-bound with cipher work; she's firm but fair, and they say a bit perilous, like a fire cracker. Ronnie struck up again, this time directed at Wis,
"So, all this time you have been chatting up a WAAF officer behind our backs, no wonder you don't say much but just smile!"

The old timer turned, raised a broad beam upon his whiskered face and muttered,

"Her; she's a Little Tinker."

With that Mandy giggled aloud; Nigel, who by now had extracted himself from the cellar, roared with laughter, and Georgie couldn't hold back a smile. This rather familiar description even brought forth a laugh from Jude, a rather nervous laugh but nevertheless a laugh. I was seeing a side of her I'd not seen before.

For the WAAFs on base, work was often long and hard: office work in the Operations Block, work in the parachute section and helping in the mess. They would also act as drivers, being seen in their blue gabardine coats and berets escorting officers, resistance workers and 'Joes' (SOE Agents) about the field to and from flights, under the shroud of secrecy and darkness; and on occasions they would drive agents to London for their de-briefing. When aircraft returned after 'ops', they would meet them and guide them along the runways and peri-tracks. On the wall in Flight Control a large chart showed all the crews that were on 'ops'. A column showed each crew's expected time of return, a column for those that were late, and another column for those who had not returned. Jude said that when she got back off duty, girls would ask if their boyfriend's plane had returned:

"It was hard not to tell them when they were late or their plane hadn't got back. It was so sad to see their faces when they realised what had happened." Jude paused for a moment, unsure whether or not to say anything else, her face full of a wistful, melancholic expression.

"It seems as though the only way to cope is to have a certain unreality about life." Lifting her glass to her mouth, Georgie, with a gentle voice, explained,

"Do you know we are told on no account are we to even look at our passengers in the rear seats of the cars, and definitely must not use the rear view mirror." With a genuinely sweet note to her voice she spoke of Frank,

"I knew him you know . . . Frank, he seemed a really nice lad. I would give him lifts on base and he would often share about his girlfriend and home. When I heard the news, I was so, so sorry." The atmosphere around the table had become sombre as for a brief moment again we all thought of how easy it was for life to be snatched away without warning.

At that moment into the pub, and I perhaps should add, into my life, walked a rare beauty: a woman wearing a dress instead of a uniform. She looked lovely. Rather surprisingly she was all by herself as she went up to the bar. I strained to hear her voice as Nigel began to serve her, but quickly Mandy came to his aid, much to Nigel's annoyance! Grasping courage and my empty glass, I went and stood beside her on the pretext of asking Nigel for another. Wis, whose head was now well and truly into his paper again, hardly seemed to notice her as she glanced his way. She turned and caught my eye. As I related earlier, people come in all shapes and sizes; she to my mind was the ideal combination. Before I could surmise what she did or where she came from, she asked,

"What do you do around here?"

At times people ask me what I am doing, what's happening on base, and why is the RAF so secretive. They are naturally interested and wonder how the war is going - it is no more sinister than that; if I thought it was, I would have to report them. Anyway there was little point in anyone asking me, I really didn't know much! Not wishing to let the opportunity pass, I quickly told her,

"Aircrew … bomber, up at the base, I'm a navigator; these are my mates;" as I gave a passing recognition to our table, where by now it was evident that no one had missed me. "What about you?" I quickly added wanting to continue the conversation.

She didn't look like someone involved in the war, but what looks prove is that they can be so wrong.

"In the army" Well that truly was a surprise! "Oh, and by the way, I am Felicity."

Felicity was in the army alright, but her army's battle was on the land, our land.

"So what do you actually do in this army of yours?"

"It's not my army," she said with a hint of cynicism and laughed. "Well," she carried on, "we work over 50 hours a week, milking cows, ploughing with the tractor, weeding, hoeing, mucking-out and spreading and harvesting. Just occasionally we get extra special jobs like rat catching." She paused for effect.

"Bligh," I said rather pathetically, "that sounds like hard work?"

"Of course it's damned hard work, but we do get one week off a year," then grinned and laughed, inviting me to join in. "And some fabulously sexy clothing – green jersey, brown breeches, cotton blouse and felt slouch-hat."

"Um!" I responded without thinking as I eyed her up and down; I couldn't imagine her in that get up looking half as good as she did now.

"What are you staring at?" she asked, re-arranging her dress.

"I . . . I was? Sorry, I was just thinking." Once again a lovely smile swept across her face,

"Well, the farmers say we look sexy, but if you saw some of their wives you'd think a cow looked sexy!"

Harsh I thought, but then as I reflected on the only farmer's wife I knew in the Westcountry I had some sympathy with her opinion.

"We rarely see a pretty young lady out of uniform in here." She looked at me, half smiled, and in a cheeky manner said,

"I should hope not, that would hardly be decent," then placed her hand on mine. Immediately aware of my discomfort over the ambiguous remark that I had made, she slid her chair closer to the bar, leant forward towards me and beamed,

"Only joking." I thought this one was going to be a handful, but an enjoyable handful! Within a few minutes we had struck up a friendship, one which both Nigel and Mandy found amusing; the lads hadn't noticed, well so I thought.

"Who are you navigating your way around?" was the direct, and far from subtle question from Ronnie across the room.

"Is that them?" she enquired.

"Yes, THAT'S them alright; um . . . the girls are WAAFs we've got to know from the base."

Getting up from her stool she declared that we should go and join them.

"So who's this beauty?" explored Taffy, not noticing slightly scornful glances from the two girls. Marion was still so engrossed, chatting and giggling, all else was passing her by!

"This is Felicity," I knowingly explained. "She's in the Women's Land Army," and before anyone had the chance to think of a reply, Cyril interjected,

"I can see that," quickly appreciating her beauty.

"I've signed up for the ruddy wrong service," Taffy shared, much to the amusement of the boys. The girls kind of smiled but rather grudgingly.

"How many maids like you are there in this army?" Taffy went on.

Felicity, totally unphased by the reception, replied wryly,

"Several thousand!"

"Are there by gum?" was his reaction.

For some reason the mood became slightly serious. Felicity was next to speak,

"I was asking what you did." A moment passed as clearly they were considering what to say, then Ken broke the silence,

"How about giving her a demonstration? Let's show her what it's like on a bombing run," and looking at Reg, "what do you say?"

And so it was, a complete re-enactment of a live bomb run was performed before her eyes, complete with radio and intercom. In a flash of inspiration, or maybe because there was no fighter buzzing around and he felt redundant, Taffy did the sound effects, and all were amazed at how realistic they sounded. Harry had to break off and get involved for take-off and, give him credit, Wis joined the others in the bar and applauded at the end. If only all flights could be quite so easy.

Nigel turned on the radio and the sounds of Glen Miller's Orchestra played throughout the bar: little did we know that Jerry

would be listening to the same BBC broadcast throughout France
– the Germans loved Glen Miller's music!  We said our farewells,
Felicity looking at me strangely,

"Why are you looking like that?"  I asked out of curiosity.

"Well, are you going to ask me out or not?"

Harry, who had been fairly quiet throughout, picking his moment
after she left, shared with us his well considered and articulate
assessment of Felicity,

"She's smooth as milk stout, and much tastier."

# Chapter 24

By now our bomber force was building in strength, its improved accuracy and effectiveness bearing down heavily upon the enemy.

The night, Saturday May 30th 1942, at an RAF airfield somewhere in Eastern England; over the meal little is said, airmen were preoccupied, the telephone continuously ringing. At the briefing that followed information is imparted to the crews about that night's big raid. The room is packed; Old Nige, along with Ronnie, was crammed up against the back wall with other chaps and an apprehensive air is all pervading. The squadron commander comes in followed by the navigation and intel. officers, with this the chatter subsides and the crew men stand; then as they settle down the briefing begins. The Battle Orders, listing aircraft and crews had been posted earlier, but the target had remained a closely guarded secret: fuel load being the only indication - 1,700 gallons. The primary object of tonight's raid was to destroy Germany's industrial heart, de-house its workers and break the morale of the German people: a raid of utter devastation, an approach that British people were beginning to question.

The weather was unsettled out over the sea and into Europe, bringing about a delay to the planned start of the operation. Ops could be scrubbed at anytime, sometimes almost immediately after they were laid on or while the lads were enjoying their last smoke before boarding. It had even been known to recall the aircraft after take-off.

Before climbing aboard preliminary checks are carried out and, once satisfied, onboard checks begin. With everyone at their station, they wait their turn to prime and start their engines. The starter and booster coil buttons are pressed and gradually, after warm up at 1,000 rpm, engine tests are carried out. Finally, the pre-taxiing checks are completed and they are ready; static crackles over their headsets as their skipper, in a confident voice, asks,

"Ready for take-off?"

"Ready Skipper" comes the confirmation from each in turn.

The pilots open up the engines slowly, re-checking readings; as the engines roar the flight engineers systematically ran through their check procedure. WOPs confirm signals equipment, generators, batteries and electrics are all fully functioning, as is radio contact with Tower. The navigators prepare the charts for that night's still unknown final destination.

The bombers, one after the other, turn onto the peri-track manouvering for take-off order. Each aircraft's ground crew - the fitters, riggers, electricians and armourers - run clear of the engine's slipstream, knowing now, that there is nothing more they can do; the lives of the crew rested to a large degree on how well they had done their job. As the aircraft move slowly to the runway, the ground crew give their pilots the last 'Thumbs Up'. The aircraft sit, engine straining against the brakes . . . then they are away: one by one, creeping at first, then building up speed they hurtle down the runway, and sluggishly climb into the air under the weight of their fuel and heavy bomb load. Their tails now high off the ground, the aircraft waver slightly, this way and that, as the pilots keep their nose dead straight. The ground crew stand watching the exodus, waving as every ninety seconds one after the other takes off, until the last plane was away, above the grass and crossing the hedges, climbing into the distance. At the very last moment one of the bombers develops engine problems with glycol leaks on port and starboard inner engines, and is unable to take-off with the others. In the dark, the long job of unloading its bomb load would begin. Winches whine as armourers begin lowering the bombs on to trolleys and tractor them back to the dumps. On the 'Aircraft Movements' blackboard in the Control Tower, 'R for Roger' was scrubbed from the 'Departures' listing.

Circling high above the aerodrome for one last time, its buildings and lights becoming fainter, the bombers reach the open sky, lit by a dramatic red sunset. Their route takes them over the English coast, crossing the North Sea and on to the Netherlands, their final destination still unknown. They had not been flying very long, keeping a continual look-out for enemy fighters, before they found themselves in thick cloud. Radio silence now operated; their next communication was on rendezvous over Southwold with the main bomber force, which had departed from fifty-three airfields spread right across Britain. This day 161 Squadron would fly high, not their usual *modus operandi* of 1,500 feet or below. The convoy would need to climb for level bombing of their heavy loads. At twelve-thousand feet the crews would begin to suffer with plummeting temperatures, creating a degree of slowness in their thinking and reasoning. To confuse the enemy's primitive detection systems, some of the planes would disperse bundles of 'window' – strips of metallic foil. It would be hard to imagine the remarkable scene, 'the armada': the awesome spectacle of over a thousand heavy bombers in formation, lights switched off, attempting to avoid each's slipstream, creeping across the sky, flown by trainee pilots and instructors alongside existing crews - in fact anyone who could fly. Nige, anxious and exhausted after endless ops, was up there piloting a Wellington and even Ronnie had been roped in to pilot a smaller crew of four other fellows so their crate could carry a full bomb load. Neither of them knew the exact details of this night's raid. The convoy stretched seventy miles; ahead of them went fifty fighters to do battle with any attacking Luftwaffe. This was the horrific reality that was soon to befall the German people. Bombers spread far across the sky, moving in formation at differing altitudes towards their target. Sparks from exhaust pipes would shower down on groups of aircraft below as they cautiously nudged nearer, under the cover of darkness.

Their target was now clear: Cologne, one of the oldest settlements in Germany and its third largest city. Nestling on the banks of the

Rhine to the far west of the country, was the industrial centre of the Ruhr Valley, ironically Happy Valley, and the Germans' Military Area Command Headquarters for District VI in Munster, and the home station for the 211th Infantry and the 26th Artillery Regiments.

Their mission was known as 'Operation Millennium'', the first one-thousand bomber raid by the RAF in the war. There was nothing particularly magical about the number of a thousand aircraft, it didn't have any strategic military importance, but it was hoped it would grab people's imagination. Churchill, with a great sense of theatre, gave the idea his full support. Getting all one-thousand aircraft was another matter; the Admiralty, under pressure and exasperated at what they saw as gimmickry, refused to let Coastal Command Aircraft be diverted to the operation, so Harris had to find the aircraft from Bomber Command squadrons in Operational Training Units.

A grey nothingness stretched out below them with only the occasional small cluster of lights, bright searchlights or flashes from guns. They pressed on deeper over the German countryside, the largest force of aircraft Britain had ever assembled: a threat that could not be ignored. Searchlights pierced the cold gloom, fingers of dazzling light stroked the sky seeking out their foe: the British bombers which had come to unload their deadly cargo. Bursts of wild flak whimpered and erupted about them, sending out clouds of smoke as the artillery barrage tried to pick off the leaders, the pathfinders that guided the way to the target. Once a searchlight cone had captured a plane in its beam, it would stay firm on its prey, concentrating the enemy's fire. For the bombers, they had to hold position at four-thousand feet in spite of attacks and losses; the aim was for all the planes to strike in three parallel groups within an hour and a half.

Nige was fighting hard to hold his aircraft in formation. They were packed so tightly that any mistake could prove disastrous;

this was not the way to fly. It was very easy to identify the city: the shimmering Rhine and its bridges weaved below, and the twin towers of Cologne Cathedral were silhouetted by the blazing incendiaries. The sheer mass of the force proved more than the ground defences could cope with. To Nige, in the last group, Cologne was visible at sixty miles out: a dull red glow engulfing the city. As he drew closer the flames reflected on the aircraft: they appeared to be on fire as tongues of red flames danced up and down their wings. It took nerves of steel to stay on course amidst the aerial bombardment, whilst the bomb aimer lay prone, fine tuning his sights on their final approach. The bomb bay doors groaned open and, in a sequence that was designed to do the most damage, the bombs were released causing the aircraft to momentarily buck up as the bombs were away.

At 12.47am, on 31st May, the first bombs and incendiaries were dropped: the last fell at 2.25am, one every six seconds. Three-thousand tons fell in ninety minutes! Eight minutes after their bombing the aircraft would set course for home and nine minutes from the coast the crews took a last look back at the city fires which resembled distant volcanoes, erupting and spewing forth fire. That night, around eighteen-and-a-half-thousand buildings were destroyed, nearly five-hundred civilians and soldiers were killed, over five- thousand injured and almost sixty-thousand left homeless. Forty bombers did not return with the loss of eighty-nine instructors and pupils. In all, twelve- thousand fires raged, a foretaste of what was to come, the start of strategic bombing of whole areas, the birth of the bomber stream!

For those who returned there was the de-briefing, and a glance at the board to see who was missing; but they wouldn't know for sometime whether they were prisoners or dead. It was often the resilience of youth that allowed them to face the evening meals when they moved up the large 'T' shaped dining table to take over the seats of those who would not be coming back. On some bases

185

it would only take three weeks to move from the bottom of the table to the top!

The word was that a Whitley didn't get back with the others: it became separated from the fleet in the bad weather, and the plottings of its inexperienced navigator was out. Low on fuel they landed in what they believed was a suitable French field, only to be astonished when they were welcomed by German speaking farm workers. Fortunately, realising their mistake, they were able to restart their aircraft and get off before the arrival of German troops. They were just able to make a British airfield, spurred on by their near fatal mistake, and were guided in by someone on the ground operating an Aldis signal lamp flashing a welcoming 'Green'. The next day their air gunner, Martin, was taken ill and Doc reckoned it was German measles and must be as a result of their brief stay in Germany! One of the bombers just made it back, seriously damaged: over the target, a Lancaster, positioned in the formation above it, released its load and it got a bomb right through its wing. The crew had to hand crank down the undercarriage: after all 'take-off is optional but landing is compulsory!' But according to Fred, their bomb aimer, they still hit Jerry.

Ronnie's plane didn't make it back: after three-quarters of an hour flying its outbound leg it hit major engine problems. Soon after the port-inner went the oil pressure on the starboard outer engine dropped, then overheated and caught fire. His WOP put out an emergency call advising they were going to be forced to ditch, detailing that they had observed a Navy convoy eight miles off and said Ronnie would aim to end up in the 'drink', as close as possible to vessels. But life doesn't always work out like one's plans. Ronnie ordered the jettisoning of their bomb load as they limped over the water and although now inevitable, ditching was not going to be easy; crashing into the sea was one of the worst fears for bomber crews. The WOP was just able to send a final SOS call before communication was lost.

The aircraft skidded and yawed sideways for a short distance before its nose dipped, the Perspex nose fairing braking up as it dived into the ocean waves, cold water gushing in. They were down in one piece despite the bomb doors only partially opening; they were floating, for the present, several miles off the Dutch coast. Those of the crew who couldn't get into the ditching position braced themselves against the spars and internal structure to help reduce the impact of being thrown around and the risk of serious injury. One of the crew was able to release the dinghy and all inflated their Mae Wests. After a scramble they cleared the bomber having but a few minutes as it was by now starting to sink rapidly, beginning its last journey, this time to the bottom. Struggling through the freezing waters, Ronnie and one of the crew righted the inflated dinghy which had overturned and all but one of them clambered onboard. Instantly the drogue sea anchor was deployed to help reduce their drift as they made attempts to reach their floating crew member. The airman bobbed about, this way and that in his Mae West, his arms frantically beating the water in a valiant attempt to make for the raft. The waters were cold and hostile, survival was measured in minutes. Even if he made the craft the chances of a successful rescue were still unknown. At last they were able to get a rope out to him and dragged into the raft one exhausted and petrified airman, suffering from severe 'cold shock'.

Their sprawled, exhausted bodies sank deep into the air bags of the dinghy, staring at one another, glad to be alive. Water collected in the dished centre of the craft caused their feet and legs to be continually soaked and freezing. In the sea they seemed to move with each wave, falling, then a moment later, rising, their bodies leant and swayed with every swell, the rolling movement bringing on nausea. One tried to bail out what water was in the raft but with no real success: as it was thrown over the side the wind would blow it back. The cold was biting into their bodies, numbing their extremities, but Ronnie knew that they mustn't sleep, they must fight it: they were too fit, too courageous and too young to die. For some, now was the moment to pray to a God whom they believed in but had had little to do with recently. The clouds lifted as the sun's first light dazzled and sparkled on the water.

In the chaos they were able to grab one of the pigeons, the other must have flown or drowned; with a message written in a shaky hand and their last position attached by thread from their survival pack, they let it free, not knowning if its instincts would get it back. Several hours later an Allied aircraft patrolling these waters, responding to the SOS, spotted them and radioed their position, confirming that there was no German shipping evident in the area and a message was relayed to the headquarters of 277 Squadron Walrus flight at Martlesham Heath on the Suffolk coast. Shortly afterwards two Walruses were airborne and heading to pick up the crew. When they were within a few miles of the dinghy the stranded Ronnie fired the Verey pistol, putting up a red flare. While circling low overhead, one of the Walruses dropped a series of smoke floats to get an indication of the wind direction and strength; the sea was now taking a bit of a swell and landing was not going to be so easy.

The Walrus, a strongly built wooden hulled biplane of the 20's, was powered by a single Bristol Pegasus pusher engine, and had a cruising speed of 95 mph – it was built for conditions such as this.[35] It was crewed by three 'web-footed' boys, a pilot and two others, who were responsible for getting the 'customers' aboard. They could carry . . . well, as many as they could get in and still get airborne! With a swishing sound the little flying boat splashed down and settled in the water; once close by, the crew of the Walrus managed to 'hook' the dinghy and pull it towards them. Soon three of the men were onboard the amphibian, their wet, cold bodies wrapped in blankets and sipping hot coffee. The second Walrus had put down nearby and drifted close enough to throw a line to Ronnie and his mate, who were now waving their arms frantically. The gunner of the Walrus, standing in the nose hatch, let them drift along their fuselage, under the lower wing to the rear hatch. Here the second gunner hauled each in turn onboard, wary of how little free board there was in choppy seas, eighteen inches or so, then they would start to ship water.

The two Walruses, one following the other, taxied, then after what seemed an endless time bouncing and being tossed across this hostile sea as the pilots worked hard to keep the sea planes heading straight, their engines roared, breaking free they took to the air. The sea had been cheated and would not take these men on this day. Approaching home they could see the thin line of the coast, glistening bands of water swirled about as the wind lanes moved on the surface. The surviving airmen wondered what the beach looked like and if the tide was in, breaking onto the sand, and if anyone was on it who could hear or see them. Wide open fields lay below where sheep, oblivious to their plight, were peacefully grazing. The lads began to think of the Mess back at base, a cosy armchair and pint, and were grateful they had been saved from certain death.

News of the rescue had been broadcast throughout the station over the Tannoy system. There would be five more aircrew for Mr. Robertson of the 'Goldfish Club' to welcome as qualified members, 'escaping death by the use of an Emergency Dinghy'! Pilot Officer Percy Prune had been heard to say:
'Your dinghy drill, ensure that you have studied or else your hopes and dreams of rescue are well and truly flooded.'
Jolly good job the ditched lads had taken heed of these wise words!

Ambitious proposals had already been considered for a twenty-four- thousand strong force to be ready for the invasion of Europe.[36] This overseas force would be recruited, trained and mobilised by agents who had been infiltrated into the occupied territories, people who had been attracted by the appeal 'for young men and women who were fluent in a language other than English and who were willing to volunteer for an "adventurous" future overseas'! They weren't told the nature of the adventure or for that matter, how adventurous it would be.

Such a force would require regular supplies, equipment, wireless sets, weapons, ammunition and explosives: all the hardware a secret army would need. That now was our job and lives, including our own, depended on how well we did it.

# Chapter 25

Ken had decided to keep a diary of his 'wartime exploits'. He'd bought for the purpose a little black Woolworth's notebook costing all of a tanner. In this he was going to record the finer points of each of his flights, the highlights of day to day life at Tempsford and undoubtedly occasional comments about us chaps. He would refer to us all as 'The Saintly Seven': I am not at all sure where he got that idea from. Maybe it was because of the altitude at which we flew, perhaps the irreproachable lifestyle we all led in the air force, it could even have been to do with the way we all joined in singing when Taffy's tuneful rendition of 'Guide me Oh Thou Great Jehovah' echoed over the intercom. Whatever it was, we certainly found it amusing: totally inaccurate, yet amusing nevertheless.

Ronnie had now returned safely from the freezing waters of the North Sea, so once again The Saintly Seven were back together as a crew. We congregated in the Mess to celebrate over a meal and were astounded to see as we went through one of the ante-rooms, an olive green Austin Seven parked on the carpet. Not the usual or best place to park one's motor!

"What on earth made Dave park it there?" Ken exclaimed to us, and whoever else was within earshot. One of the boys, catching Ken's puzzled enquiry shared with us the story.

"He didn't, and he's not aware it is there. You know his crew clocked up twenty ops and had been rewarded with three days stand down. Well, he and his oppo Benji decided to take off to London and because his mate's car was more reliable they went in that. Dave had left his Austin parked alongside the ante-room doorway, out of the way! Well, his crew had decided it was in the way, and whilst the other three were unscrewing the double doors into the room, Dan and Sam removed some of the external bits on the car that would have got in the way. Having carefully pushed it in, they placed an old newspaper under the sump and rear dif to protect the carpet, re-fixed the car parts and re-hung the doors to

191

the room." Having to get the car open to steer it, the final touch was to sit Dave's mascot, Bluey, in the driving seat, its hands taped to the steering wheel. Dave might go to London without Bluey, but he'd never fly without it stuffed inside his flying suit. After Dave's initial anger, discovering on his return that his car had, to his mind been stolen, he saw the funny side and with the others returned it to the real world of roads again. Ken got fair scribbling that night! He told me sometimes he couldn't get to sleep his head was so full of what he needed to write. He confided in me that as the war progressed he was determined his diary wouldn't become a chronicle of death and despair, it really worried him; unlike many of us he joined up out of a sense of duty, not as a bored young man desperate for action.

Reg had just received some sad news about his older brother, Albert, serving in the North African Campaign who had probably been taken prisoner of war by Rommel's Afrika Korps on the surrender of Tobruk. Reg, understandably, became even more introverted and thoughtful than usual, and we all decided to give him a bit of space, whilst being aware that he needed us, but not letting him mope for too long.

My date with Flic was to the village of Sandy, and its cinema – The Victory. She stood beside one of the pillars in the shadow of the entrance portico, and as I approached I remembered just how beautiful she was - slim and tall in a casual kind of way. She had short shoulder length fair hair and hazel eyes that shone and laughed even when she herself wasn't laughing.
"Hi," she greeted me.
"Hello," I managed to utter, still marvelling at my good fortune. We settled down in the large first floor auditorium to watch 'Road to Zanzibar' with the all singing and dancing cast of Bing Crosby, Bob Hope and Dorothy Lamour. If she thought it was going to be a serious film, she didn't let on, giggling at many of the ad lib gags.

Before the big movie filled our screen, the latest Newsreel flickered images from around the world, the accompanying voice upbeat and reassuring, encouraging us to believe we were doing well.

"US victory over the Japanese in the battle of the Coral Sea delaying the enemy's plans to invade Australia".

A frightening vision of hundreds of sailors leaping off the American aircraft carrier Lexington into the sea as it was being fired on by the Japanese flashed up on the big screen.

Then a quietness fell throughout the auditorium –

"Tobruk captured by Rommel's overwhelming forces: 25,000 taken prisoner. To the accompaniment of a terrific air bombardment, heavy tanks crashed through the perimeter, followed by masses of infantry and more tanks". Whilst the scenes were unfolding a distant voice, maybe Monty's, demanded, "The Middle East must not fall to the German Reich." Gaumont News film showed the first pictures taken over the ruined city of Cologne, a sanguine reminder of what our boys can do: who knows where next? The newscaster announced that the US was in final discussions regarding the detail of a "formal establishment of a European Theatre of Operations for the United States' forces", and with little or no pause he declared,

"Britain puts big freeze on ice cream!" To a general murmur and lively giggles around the cinema he shared that the demands and needs of the ice cream trade were too great to bear in wartime – from September 30$^{th}$ ice cream would be prohibited.


One thing I hadn't appreciated was that a couple of Flic's army mates were with their fellows in the row in front. At the end of the movie she introduced me to her two girlfriends, Fi and Dom.

"How is it you've all got short names?"

She looked at me quizzically and smiling said,

"Upbringing silly, we're all meant to be posh!"

I couldn't leave it at that, as we bade farewell to her girlfriends and their 'whatevers',

"And how did they get hold of nylons, there's no Yanks about here?" hoping I hadn't led her to believe I had a leg fetish!

"Well," she began as we walked towards her car, "even though they're Land Army girls they want to be seen as being fashionable and, as you said, it's not easy to get stockings, so they coat their legs with a paste that gives an impression of wearing silk stockings," she paused to check I was keeping up mentally as well as physically, "and trace a dark line down the back so it looks like the seam!"

I was speechless, that was news to me.

"Let's go for a meal," she proposed.

"Why not?" I heard myself saying.

We walked across the square to a small restaurant, well somewhere that did food, albeit a limited menu. Flic insisted she'd pay for the meal before we went in, quite abruptly brushing away my offer with a toss of her head.

"If I choose to treat you that's up to me, it's my money!"

I agreed with a slightly self-conscious laugh. I couldn't remember when I had last had such a great time, not that the meal was fantastic or anything out of the ordinary, but Flic certainly was.

We made our way back to her car, a 1936 Morris 8 which she thought was wonderful,

"Dad bought it for me, I can't really remember why."

I thought he probably didn't need a reason. She moved a pile of blankets and a hot water bottle off the passenger seat and threw them in the back. The engine sprung into motion just as a light drizzle started to cover the screen.

"Will you do the wipers for us?" she asked, and demonstrated so there was no doubt in my mind of what to do. We headed back to the airfield, down the country lanes, our masked headlights picking up the rain reflecting on the road. Drawing closer to the base it appeared like a city slumbering, awaiting a sudden call to action.

As we were saying goodnight, I had an eureka moment: I realised who she reminded me of – Jane, the bright young fun girl that appeared, sometimes every part of her, in the London Daily Mirror cartoon strip. Before I had considered what I was going to say and how I was going to say it, she broke my train of thought,

"What is it?"

"You remind me of Jane in the Mirror."

"Is that good?"

"Oh I should say so," I affirmed.

"But I haven't got a dog . . . and isn't she saucy?"

"I suppose so," I admitted, continuing to smile affectionately at her as she confronted me,

"So have you found your Jane? It sounds as though you're in love."

We kissed and cuddled and kissed some more; on parting we vowed to meet the following night; but then I didn't know what was in store for me.

# Chapter 26

The day started in much the same way as any other day. The shimmering, azure June sky stretched from horizon to distant horizon, flawed only by the lingering cumulus which signalled that there might be change on its way. A gentle warm breeze played on the grass, flicking it this way and that, never certain where it was coming from nor going to. High bows, their branches filled with the wind, gracefully drifted from side to side then came to rest, awaiting the next blow. Across the trees, bands of glowing sunlight moved with the passing of the clouds, creeping slowly with the changing sky. Today was going to be a day full of surprises.

Ronnie got us together late morning in preparation for what lay ahead,
"Right lads, if you've seen the board you'll know we are ops tonight, we're doing our Night Flying Test - at two this afternoon." He eyed each of us in turn, checking we understood, "Make sure you're ready chaps."

Across the field the dedicated ground crew had already been fussing over our Halifax, 'L – Leather', for the past few hours. They really loved their own allotted aircraft, and whilst it was us aircrew chaps who had the stories and any glory, they were the ones who kept us up in the air. If we brought her back peppered with holes following a run-in with Jerry, we were the ones who got it in the neck. On our return from an op, some of the ground crew would always be there regardless of the hour or weather, to greet us back. Their faces said it all as we climbed out exhausted, relieved we were back in one piece and the kite still flying. After each op one of them, usually Les, would proudly paint a roundel with a stencil on the nose, port side under the pilot's canopy.

On that particular day all initially went well, as for an hour we circled around the airfield, testing everything. Taffy, Ken and Reg would test their guns; Cyril his sets, Harry his controls and instruments, as well as with keeping an eye on the engines; Reg, his auto bomb sight and bomb release mechs, and Ronnie his controls, undercarriage, brakes and so on. All readings were what we expected and she handled well, except for problems with one of the props. When down, Ronnie reported that one of the airscrews didn't respond between coarse and fine pitch to the governor, which automatically controls the propeller blades to the engine revolutions. The daily inspection had shown nothing, so the engine with the faulty prop was test run, checking for all the possible faults. Nothing could be found, even the squadron engineering officer and 'Chiefy' our chief engineer couldn't get to the bottom of it, but there wasn't a spare prop in the maintenance hangar, so it was decided we'd fly as we were.

We all got together in the NAAFI for our pre-flight meal, much the same as our feast on return, except no rum in our coffee! There was an atmosphere of sleepy stupor as we entered the hall, the only noise coming from the kitchen. I pushed through the double swing doors into where the activity was; a WAAF looked at me amazed,
"Sir," she addressed me and, looking at a chart, enquired, "is it seven early suppers sir?"
"That's it," I confirmed as I asked if we were the only ones away that night.
"As far as we know at the moment; you be sitting down Sir and we'll bring it over."

The dining room was deserted at this hour so we had plenty of seating options. It had been no more than a few minutes before an amply built WAAF came in, not the lass I'd spoken with, this one was much more formidable. She carried a tray stacked with plates of food which she placed upon our table.
"There you go Sir," as she slid the plates in front of each of us in turn.

"Thanks," we said, totally concentrating on the astounding spectacle of two back rashers, three overweight sausages bursting at the seams, a positive gaggle of fried eggs and two hefty slices of fried bread. Somewhere amongst it all were two tomatoes and a slice of some sort of pudding. The whole lot was further furnished with her next tray of accessories in the form of a couple of rounds of toast, marmalade and jam as well as lashings of hot, sweet tea. I looked up and offered her congratulations,

"A true banquet!" to which she smiled and returned to her hot stove.

My nostrils had long since been exercised in this way and as for my taste buds, they were already salivating at the sheer thought of what was to come their way. Ken's air sickness nor his nose bleeds ever stopped him enjoying his food and today was going to be no different. If ever he was sick on a mission he'd tell the ground crew when we got back; they were understanding knowing that this usually merry wisp of a man couldn't help it. Although he never knew his old man, a World War One pioneering pilot in the Royal Flying Corps, his mother told him he'd always been sick before he took to the air.

En route back from our feast, I was able to catch up with Georgie and asked if she would get a message through to Flic, explaining that we had been given a night op at short notice, but on my return I would meet up with her. Georgie was more than happy to do the explaining,

"I really like Flic you know, we'll all catch up in The Wheatsheaf when you lot get back," and then, as if her afterthought was too important to forget, continued, "I hope the sortie goes well, and take care of yourself."

"Don't worry Georgie, tonight's a piece of cake."

Georgie didn't see Flic until late that evening and by then I had already flown out on my night's trip over France. To Georgie it was just one of those routine 'cloak- and-dagger' missions. She didn't know what we were flying into, nor did we; she certainly didn't know exactly where we were going – we weren't allowed to say. The weather was far from ideal and none of us had any idea just how out of the ordinary this mission would prove!

The ground crew were still busy preparing 'L – Leather' for that night's operation. Twenty C-type containers about fifteen inches in diameter and five-foot-nine inches long, were being loaded on, destined for the Resistance; four of them would lift the container carefully into position, each weighing in at a tenth of a ton. C-type containers hardly ever broke on impact where as the H- type, five drums stacked one above the other, often did. The various compartments inside each container would be crammed packed with equipment, supplies, first aid, food, money, weapons - Piats, Stens, Brens and hand grenades, and ammunition. Occasionally the explosives would explode on hitting the ground, probably because the detonators had been badly packed but we never had that problem, thank goodness. Wireless sets had to be packed in special kapok parcels to avoid damage: broken radios were no good to anyone. We could carry a maximum of fifteen containers which were loaded into the aircraft's bomb bay and released by the bomb aimer, much in the same way as bombs. We could also drop packages and panniers through a large yard-wide hole in the Halifax floor, which was located amidships and covered by two semi-circular doors.

We assembled an hour and a half before take-off for our briefing for tonight's flight. Our briefing was a fairly lonely affair, just as we suspected no-one else was flying this night. Briefing Officer Gush entered the room, along with a rather quiet intelligence officer, and began to outline tonight's mission,
"Take-off 22.40. Heavy load, containers and packages, all up weight 59,500lbs. Tonight's special mission, central France, west of Limoges – 3 separate Resistance drops."
He then proceeded to detail our route out and preferred return route, operational altitudes across the channel and over occupied territory, as well as dropping heights, speeds and anticipated flight

duration. We were issued with our code letters for each drop zone and ETAs. The QFE – altimeter adjustment, is one, zero, zero, four, and then he proceeded to tell us the colours of the day.

"Collect and study your charts well," he insisted, finally focusing on me.

The intel officer Lewis-Bowen was next to hold the floor. Lewis-Bowen was a chubby, ruddy faced man with curly hair and large ears; he coughed for our attention as he stubbed out his cigar and addressed us in an accent that originated from one of those public schools, probably Harrow.

"Www..ell chaps you sh..should be aware th..that we've only jjj..just st..started drops in..into F...Free F..France." We concentrated hard on his important words and not his inflicted stammer. "The w..w..word f..from the Maquis is th..that Je..rry is more active int..tercepting communications and exp..panding their netwo..work of collaborators. Over th..the last two we..eks in the area Gestapo have b..been laying in wa...ait on our supply drr...ops and our Lysanders have had to...oo abort an agent delivery alto...together and sh...shift the DZ in another inst...ance. The evidence suggests we...ee need to be on our guard chaps, they arr...re getting more ingee...nious with their intel gathering and t.t...torture techniques." He paused, sipped a large glass of water-like liquid that was golden brown in colour and hosting clinking ice cubes. "The Luftwaffe night fighters are buggerrr..ring us about again and se...eeem to be concentrating about northern Bisss.....ccay; damn nuisance really. Their ground base detection is bee...ing developed all the time and their Freya n.n.network is now extenn..nsive and expp...anding, keep low and use your 'winn..d.dows' chaps, jolly good luck boys." None of this was news that surprised us, but it wasn't good to be reminded.

"Oh and ch...check your pockets, labels and p..p..paaapers before you leave here . . . just in case yyy..ou are captur..rured, and if you are, keep absolu...lutely mum," and with his usual postscript signed off, "don't f..f..forget lads N..N..oah used air recon...nnaisssance as a source of intelligence, so if you see anything, tell us. Make it a saa..afe one lads;" then he toasted us with his cold tea drink as he took his leave.

Our rather matter of fact Briefing Officer now ran us rather superficially through the Met Report –

"We are expecting the westerly front to bring more unsettled weather, but nothing too severe. Cloud cover five-tenths at 10,000 feet, storms are doubtful although there may be spells of heavy rain nearer to the French coast. Expect a tailwind, 30 -40 knots, 2 – 5 – zero over Biscay, crossing the west coast." The information, as general as it was, ended there. "Nothing much to worry about, is the kite all okay?" He sought confirmation,

"A-okay sir," returned Ronnie.

"Excellent . . . have a good trip chaps, I'll see you for de-briefing in the morning."

"Thank you sir," came our chorus.

Ronnie nodded to me and we did our usual: he never fully trusted the skimpy weather reports so we would go through to the Met boys and get a complete run down. Corporal Bristow, as usual, talked us through 'what the heavens have in store' for us. The depression crossing us was building slowly and may take several hours. A cold front was expected, with deteriorating weather conditions at its head, strong veering winds, choppy seas, emanating from the west – Sole and Finisterre. By the time you cross Biscay and the French coast expect the possibility of storms, thunder doubtful but not excluded. Rain and hail clouds building to 20,000 feet, snow over 20,000, icing level 12-14,000 feet. Accompanying strong up and down draughts. He re-iterated the wind speeds, direction and cloud cover albeit uprated somewhat, and told us what the glass was doing. As he smiled, he wrapped up with,

"Well that's it chaps."

Ronnie, catching his throwaway line curtly replied,

"Ideal!" with a humour that was hard to appreciate at times. As if, as a word of comfort, Bristow's parting shot was equally flippant,

"Rest assured, no one has ever collided with the sky!"

Bristow didn't know that his forecast on the front was a hundred miles out! The evening sky filled with long, fast moving mare's tails, stretching high and wide, signalling the likelihood that bad weather was on its way; maybe even a gale. We weren't in control of the weather so had to be sure we were in control of our Hali and, in those conditions, it certainly wasn't going to be easy.

We gathered in the mess for a last cup of tea and conflab, then headed for the crew room where we collected together our kit, donned our flying suits, then boarded the lorry and headed for dispersal. Unloading our gear and, having time to spare, we laid out on the grass which was still warm from the fine summer's day. The WAAF driver called from her cab, wishing us a safe trip, then swung the truck about heading towards the main block. Harry didn't normally smoke but he would always have a cigarette just before a flight: he said it helped calm his nerves, but he never seemed nervous to me. Perhaps it worked!

One by one we boarded the kite: Ronnie first so he could start the checks. I slid up backwards into the aircraft then swung my legs around; once in I grabbed the kit as it was passed to me - it would all need sorting and stowing. The bitter cold and stink of the aircraft struck me: this was nothing new but hit me every time. Harry was already up front on the flight deck with Ronnie, so the rest of us started to move and pack away the gear, pigeons *et al*. I made my way up to my station to order my charts and double check everything was together for tonight's trip, leaving the boys checking the containers and their loading, as well as the labelling on the packages showing the Agent code name, ready for the three deliveries.

Taffy shouted out to me and the others who were within earshot, "No need to worry about me boys, I've got a book with me so I shan't get bored, nothing ever happens on these trips!" Ignoring him we busied ourselves knowing full well that if there was anything up in the air, Taffy would have spotted it. Taffy moved down through the bulkhead door to his 'office', where before he tested the turret or guns, or did anything else, took a small stuffed toy from inside his Irvin flying jacket and tied it with cord to the side of his seat. Ruffles was a rather tatty cream teddy bear, no bigger than his hand, given to him by the ladies of Llandovery WI as a good luck mascot. I don't know what Ruffles thought about being stuck in an icy cold turret, no coat on, night after night without so much as a sip of coffee. The ladies said it was to be a symbol of hope for him against all odds: a chance for magic to prevail!

For me, I placed my trust in being well prepared: the words of one of my training officers, who was always aware of the risk of being captured rang true – "The best way to escape is to avoid capture in the first place and to always fly fully equipped to travel through enemy territory." I learnt over time to prepare myself for such an occasion: a folded tie was always in the pocket of my jacket, and in the haversack that never left my side, was an old peaked cap. About my person, or in the sack, I stored my RAF 'ration box': a collection of survival aids: a sterilizing outfit – tablets for my rubber water pouch, twenty Horlicks malted milk tablets for sustenance, four Benzedrine tablets to overcome tiredness, glucose sweets and chocolate, silk maps of France folded small and wrapped around my Heliograph, a device for signalling using the sun's rays, all residing in a small, brown, waterproof wallet. The Emergency Flying Ration was treasured as a vital bit of kit, as was the First Aid Outfit for Air Crew, and Tubunic Ampoules - Morphine Syrettes. I hoped I'd never need them but if circumstances necessitated their use, they would probably be invaluable. I always wore a casual shirt and lounge suit trousers underneath my flying suit. My pockets would be stuffed with all sorts: a razor, cream soap, toothpaste, a phrase card in French, German and Dutch and of course my 'Escape Kit'. This contained a plethora of things which I thought valuable: button compass, matches, wax needles and thread, fishing line with hook, a length of wire, a ribbon saw . . . the list went on; all the things I gathered that I thought would be useful, providing they were small and light. My penknife would be clipped on a lanyard to my flying gear, a second smaller knife was stuffed into one of my CT6 fur-lined flying-boots.[37] The great thing about my boots was that I could cut the stitching around the top of them and turn them into shoes in an attempt to fool the enemy should I encounter them.

We were fortunate tonight: unlike previous evenings, the field was not cursed with lingering fog - the wind had seen to any chance of that. It was not clear, however, as to what might be in store for us on our return. The boys were trying out a new idea, FIDO – to help avoid the risk of fog closing down the base. Pipes were run down both sides of the runway and pumped full of petrol; once the fuel was ignited the heat generated burnt off the fog. This fuel guzzler could consume well over 1,100 gallons per minute through its extensive pipe work, but in extreme circumstances did seem to do the job! We wouldn't be needing it tonight.

Ronnie called through the cockpit window to the ground crew manning the external accumulators that started the engines,
"Clear . . . Contact." The port inner engine started to turn, sluggishly at first, the propeller pulsed into action coughing and spluttering. With a sudden roar resounding through the fuselage the engine came to life. Ronnie throttled back, dropping the engine to idle then began the task of starting the other three. When all four were running and up to temperature, each in turn was run up to speed and the magneto tested. Ronnie now ran through the pilot's checks ensuring he was happy before signing the 'Chiefys' 'form 700': then the aircraft would be ours!

In the dead of night the noise from the Merlin was unmistakable,
"Tower – 'L for Leather' request Radio Check and Taxi Instructions – over."
"Tower – 'L – Leather' radio strength 5.
Cleared to taxi Runway 25, check QFE 1004, over."
"Roger 25 – 1004 – set."

We slowly moved along the peri track making for the end of the runway.

"Compass on NORMAL, Pitot heater ON, Elevator trim set, Rudder Neutral, Propeller Control fully UP, flaps 20 degrees DOWN." Ronnie concluded his procedure,

"Engineer check fuel contents and selection.

All crew call in, check instrumentation and respond." We duly did. The final checks were complete and we waited for our signal.

Taffy was firmly in his turret, possibly reading his book; Ronnie was in his seat at the controls with Reg seated alongside helping him; Harry was immediately behind studying his bank of dials, whilst Cyril, Ken and I braced ourselves between the two spars.

"Tower - 'L for Leather' request line up Runway 25 – over."

"'L for Leather' - Tower – clear to line up.

Surface wind 2-7-zero degrees, 15 gusting 25 knots – be advised no aircraft traffic in vicinity."

Ronnie's final words to the tower followed,

"Roger Tower, lining up.

Tower - 'L for Leather' ready to TAKE-OFF."

A distant monotone voice replied,

"'L – Leather' clear to TAKE-OFF."

"Stand by for take-off," Ronnie's laconic tones relayed over the intercom.

The Halifax's engines roar a full-blooded cry as the whole aircraft strains, held on its brakes like a wild stallion trying to break free; we only now await the flashes from the green Aldis lamp. With the release of brakes, the aircraft suddenly jolts, and the huge bomber begins to lumber, rolling down the runway, slowly at first but fast picking up speed. As the tail veers, Ronnie corrects, utilising the throttles and then the rudders. The machine trembles as its tail plane gradually lifts and smoothly we leave the ground and fly.

We were airborne at 22.45.

As we climbed and circled wide of the field, Reg shouted over the intercom,

"You can see 'Tempsford Two' well lit up tonight." Laying to the west, more or less midway between Great Barford and Bedford, was a decoy airfield, hoping to distract any enemy aircraft from the main field.

"I see her," returned Taffy in his familiar Welsh lilt.

"Well let's hope it's not needed tonight chaps when we get back." Ronnie offered.

As we continued to pick up our course, Ronnie completed his checks,

"Under carriage UP, flaps RAISED, 160 knots indicated – fuel booster pumps OFF." He called us – "Now turning to port onto 360 degrees, climbing to 2,000 feet."

All was silent except for the usual quip from Taffy to Skip which Ronnie found impossible to ignore,

"What do you mean you hope my landing is better than my take-off?!"

"I'm surprised you noticed Taffy, it can't be a very good book," came the observation from Cyril.

"You might as well take the night off," added Ken.

"That's enough chaps, let's just keep our eyes and ears open."

"Right Skip," was the unanimous response.

Up in the main control room of the control tower the WAAF flight sergeant stood at the local control desk waiting for 'November Foxtrot Lima – L for Leather' last words over the radio. She put her hand to one of the earphones and pressed it slightly as she heard Cyril over the airways. This would be our last radio contact; radio silence would now be adopted until our return, unless something went drastically wrong.

Heading for the south coast, we levelled out at 2,000 feet and Ronnie eased off the power. The trip down country was uneventful, nothing much was seen. At the coast, reaching our turn point we set our course from a beacon and started to climb to 6,000 feet over the channel, and a potential watery grave. The visibility was deteriorating, and positive identification for navigation was now impossible; we cruised on. Occasional breaks in the cloud opened up dim windows on the world below: endless sea, as we floated overhead. Nearing the coast we lost altitude to about 500 or 600 feet, in an attempt to gain visibility and to avoid radio detection. We were now all at our No. 1 Stations; on longer trips some of us would rotate duties, but not this night.

Taffy slid into the tail turret seat: it was no easy job as there was little room and plenty of things to clout. Letting go of the grip handles he sat upright, trying not to bang his face on the breaches of the four machine guns right in front of him. He would close the door behind him, making sure it was fully shut: the last thing he wanted was for it to open when he tried to turn the turret! Alternatively, as he wasn't strapped in at all, there was always the possibility he could fall out . . . when he didn't intend to, for this was the only way Taffy could abandon the craft if all went wrong! He turned the turret full beam, left then right, testing its free movement and the guns elevation up and down using the control bar, moving in the rising and falling seat as he did so. Taffy reported to Ronnie,
"Rear Gunner to Skip, turret okay, permission to test guns."
"Okay Taffy, and you Ken and Reg," Ronnie affirms.
Having got permission, bursts of fire rattled from the gunners into the empty sky; we all now knew they were working as the whole aircraft shuddered.

My time was spent head down, concentrating, working out every detail of our route, needing to take account of enemy defences, fighters, wind and weather, as well as trying to fix our three DZs and finding our 'reception committees'. We had 'Gee' on board, which was equipped at my desk. It was early days for this VHF technology, but it was already proving valuable in helping us fix our position, taking signals transmitted from three ground stations in an arc 100 miles apart. Once I had got the readings off the unit I could plot these Lattice Values on my special Gee Lattice Chart and fix our position in Europe within 6 miles. Tonight it should prove reliable as there weren't many other aircraft on our route at this time to interfere with it.

Reg, having vacated his seat beside me, would be flat on his belly now, scanning the scene below trying to spot the torches or bonfire markers, and the code letter flash of the Resistance. It was no easy job, if only he could get a clear view through his optically flat aimer's panel; he would push the wall spray canister to coat the screen with anti-freeze to stop it icing over and marring his vision. The weather now had deteriorated, the depression deepened; this was the muck we had been warned about and it was appearing on cue. There was very little time left before midnight would arrive.

The French coast passed below, hardly visible, a grey shadow of land kissing the faint moon-sheened sea. The pale moonlight glinted on our canopies as we cruised up and down the coast, hoping to get a pinpoint or else to see searchlights in the distance which would help ID our exact location. The Germans were now successfully jamming our Gee System set and causing us real headaches. This was a nervous time as we were within Jerry's night fighter belt; we were well and truly on our mettle. Ronnie from time to time would give us each a word over the intercom, but only briefly: when crossing enemy territory we would keep the chat to a minimum. Reg could just see from his turret, menacing clouds scudding across below. Somewhere down there three groups of Partisans were waiting the arrival of our aircraft, laden with supplies for their communities.

On this humid, cloud covered night, in June of the third year of the war, eight people gathered, taking up their places on a field somewhere in France. These were members of The Resistance who, whilst holding down jobs, fought to free their country from

208

German occupation. They had crept out during curfew, under cover of dusk, from their villages, risking identification by local Vichy police or arrest by the Germans. Some had managed to make the field on foot, others by bicycle and Le Boucher in his unmistakable van; all were ready for a long, silent wait. The farm hand had an old and unreliable shotgun he had hidden away, which had a split wooden butt bound by electrical tape, while the teacher from the local school had mustered a wooden bat: hardly adequate to defend them against the occupying forces. The men of the group used their torches as marker lights, whilst the woman signalled with hers to the anticipated British aircraft. All concentrated, awaiting the sound of the approaching aircraft engines from the west, or the threatening arrival of military vehicles and Gestapo: they could never be certain that somebody hadn't collaborated with Germans and given them away. Disappearing into the thick undergrowth that bordered the field, they lay in wait, the rain starting to fall now, heavily, soaking their outer garments.

Half an hour passed and still there was no sign of the aircraft. The foul weather seemed to be set in for at least the remainder of the night.

Approaching the third and last target, according to my navigation, we throttled back as we crossed the release point at 350-400 feet at about 140 mph. The weather was worsening with every minute. The first two drops had gone well: flying low and slow the consignments were successfully dispatched, but no signal was identified from the third drop zone. We flew over the area twice more, but didn't see any sign of our reception. We needed to find the drop zone and unload the cargo quickly to stop it being scattered far and wide. At times the Partisans would delay their signalling in order to establish the identity of the plane – but this night there were no late signals, no evidence that they were even there. We couldn't risk another circuit.

"Skip to crew, I am going to 'skate off' boys, we can't chance being spotted by Jerry. Yep, I am heading back. Skip to navigator, give me a heading." I had a warm feeling knowing we were on our way home. As was his custom on our homeward leg, Skip called each crew member in turn to check we were alright. We all gave an okay to Ronnie, all that is except Ken.

"Cyril," called Ronnie, "see what's happened to Ken."

"Right Skip," came the reply. After a few minutes of investigation a voice scrambled over the intercom, then clarity returned,

"I say again, WOP here Skip, Mid Upper been indisposed, enthroned on the Elsan and flying high, he's on his way back Skip."

Clearly Ken's malady had returned with the usual vengeance and was giving him a 'run' for his money!

The forecasted tailwind had now developed into a nasty headwind of some 60 knots and the rain was lashing down. All in all Ronnie was having a struggle to keep us in the air on my bearing.

"Skip to Engineer, any ideas on what we can do to make more headway, it's filthy up here?" Harry had been frantically checking all his instruments and diving periodically to the fuel cocks, forward of the rest seats, to control our fuel tanks and supply,

"Engineer to Skip, suggest we cut back on throttles and dip nose one degree or so and see how it goes for a bit."

Out of the night sky, machine-gun tracer lashed past us; Taffy from the rear turret screamed 'FIGHTER!' over the com. The Luftwaffe pilot had seen the flames of our engines; 'L for Leather' was now firmly in the centre of his sights. More tracer blazed passed; the fighter, which was dead astern and high, was diving towards us. Ken and Taffy let rip simultaneously, rattling shell after shell at the marauding night fighter. As the Focke-Wulf 190 over flew us, Reg had positioned himself in the front turret ready to line up his gunsight, emptying the single machine-gun on the passing fighter as it came into view. Ronnie by now had the old kite banking and climbing steeply in an avoidance manoeuvre, turning, changing our heading. Our giant bird seemed to hang on our propellers, shuddering with every ounce of power, pulling us skyward. Reg's final burst of fire peppered the fighter's port wing and hit its straining engine. The relief at seeing him run was short lived when we realised how badly we'd been hit. We all in turn reported in to Ronnie, we were 'A OK' and gave a damage report. "Keep your eyes open boys, that may not be it," demanded a stressed Ronnie but a fighter pilot had enough experience to know that a smoking Halifax didn't need a second attack.

The fighter's closing fire had wreaked havoc along our port side, filling our fuselage with shell holes. The next few minutes were anything but calm as we tried to fully assess the damage; smoke was bellowing from behind Harry's instrument panel. The whole trip we had been bedeviled by appalling weather and the rain was driving through the punctured window frames and shell riddled fuselage panels, drenching our equipment and electrics. A cold draught was now whipping through the aircraft, the maps and logs being blown about the fuselage.

Harry had been back amidships, switching the fuel cocks, to maintain the aircraft's centre of gravity; scrambling forward he snatched an extinguisher and returning to his station sprayed the panels with the methylbromide, subduing the fire for the present. Shrapnel from the shells had pierced the port inner engine housing and we were now experiencing problems with its smooth running. A burbled message burst over the intercom from Taffy,
"Oxygen out, need . . .," his intercom went dead. By now our port engine had failed, the propeller blades becoming visible, spinning ever slower and more jerkily, until still; the problems were beginning to mount. Ronnie announced that as well as some electrical systems down our hydraulics looked as though they'd taken a hit. Our fuel gauges, according to Harry, were registering zero, as did our oil pressure gauges; we were still flying, but for how much longer? Maybe we were running on fumes. Still we had no contact with Taffy,

"Get back Ken and see what's happening to Taffy, quick as you bloody can!" yelled Ronnie as he kicked in the extinguishers.

Cyril had lost all radio contact, along with his wicked sense of humour, whilst endeavouring to keep the few electrics that were okay, functioning.

In what seemed like no time, Ken's voice rang over the com,
"It's no damned use I can't get through to him, there's a blazing fire against the rear bulkhead."

I guess Taffy thought the chances of making it were slim, what with the bulkhead on fire and his oxygen supply problems; little did he know of the other disasters befalling us. As it happened he'd swung the tail turret round to the beam position until the steel doors, through which he entered and left the turret from the fuselage, were now facing out to the open sky. He wrenched Ruffles, his teddy, from its anchorage, opened the doors and threw himself out backwards, praying that the parachute and the French Resistance would both work to save him.

I was never to know what happened to Taffy!

We were losing height fast and now, in spite of the draught fair blowing through the plane, the acrid smoke was beginning to fill the fuselage and our lungs; in fact the draught was now fanning these very same fires. Our outer port Merlin coughed and misfired, Reg cried out,

"The outer port engine's a smoker."

Ronnie tried the engine extinguishers but to no avail. He was already using extra power on the two starboard engines, but these now were overheating and we were still losing height.

"What the hell do we do now?" came someone's voice over the com.

"Glide," yelled Cyril.

"No ruddy option left I'm afraid chaps but to 'ABANDON HER'", yelled Ronnie as he tried to hold her steady. I knew that the aircraft could not remain in the air for very much longer and,

as if I or the others were in any doubt, Ronnie calmly and clearly confirmed,
"Bale out boys, bale out!"

When you suddenly find yourself in a life or death situation, you hope you will make the right decision. I found that the uncertainty of what might happen next frightening. Of course this is all happening in what is but a brief moment and, as I started to do things, I began to focus on improving my chances: escaping the doomed aircraft safely, being rescued and making my way back to England, home and freedom.

As we clipped on our parachutes, Ken had already climbed to the escape hatch. With the opening of the hatch a wind ripped through the plane, sending papers, charts and anything that wasn't fixed down flapping in all directions. As he flung himself through the hatch and started to plummet he realised his parachute pack had not been hooked to him properly: the pack swung up and hit him with a tremendous clout in the face, causing his nose to bleed, the impact being like nothing he had felt before. Descending at a frightening speed he drifted in and out of consciousness: it seemed to him like a dream over which he had no control, as he headed finally home!

Cyril, cleared the plane well just as Harry had done, but for some reason seemed to delay pulling his rip cord. I never saw his chute deploy but then it was a filthy night and none of us were sure at what altitude we were.

Falling through the air, Harry felt his intercom cord, which was still attached to his helmet, brush his face, whipping about in the turbulence. In spite of this irritation he was surprised to feel no sensation of falling, he just seemed to be hanging in the sky. He felt horribly alone having seen Cyril bail out the Hali but not seeing his 'chute open. He considered there was just a chance, a slender chance, he would survive to smoke another cigarette.

213

Having watched the remaining crew, all that is but Reg, drop away through the escape hatch and disappear below, I clambered back to Ronnie to report,

"Everybody away Skip except Reg, and Cyril set the detonators before he jumped." He turned to me briefly and with a weird matter of fact manner, acknowledged with a nod and thumbs up.

"Are you alright? Shall I go now?" I asked, knowing full well that Skip would be the last to jump. He nodded again and in a shrill voice uttered,

"Go, get the bloody hell out of here."

As I fell, I instinctively ripped my glove off, pulled my rip cord and hoped it would open, many of them didn't. It seemed a long while before I heard a whomph as the canopy opened and spread wide above my head and, with the noise of cloth going taut, sharply jolted on my shoulders and crutch as it did so. I could hear only silence apart from the ever fading sound of 'L for Leather' as it hurtled towards the earth. I seemed to just hang, suspended indefinitely in space, safely in the harness hardly descending, just swinging in a black abyss. It was almost like being in a dream, or watching a movie, not knowing when it would end. Although I couldn't see anything, there were no lights, no shapes or forms, no flak, no firing, just more eerie blackness; I had a sense that I was fast approaching the ground. Gripping the canopy lines, I tensed my whole body, frantically straining my eyes to see where I was going to land and when, but even in my worst imagination I could not have visualised what was to befall me.

Reg, standing alongside Skip on the flight deck, concentrating on the behaviour of the instruments, felt Ronnie grab his arm and, turning, heard him shriek above the din of the engines,

"Jump, damn you."

Even to Reg, who'd held on to the last, it was apparent there was no hope in hell in getting this beast down in one piece and that Ronnie wouldn't go until he had jumped. But as Reg prepared to jump, the rip cord of his parachute got caught on a mangled piece of framework. It wasn't clear what it was but it didn't really matter, for within a few seconds his parachute had opened, and in the gale blowing through from the hatch and fuselage, the canopy was bellowing inside the aircraft, wrenching Reg this way and that, as the cords cut into his palms and fingers. Reg was never going to jump clear and with the onboard blaze spreading to the dry silk 'chute as it whipped about the fuselage, Ronnie's fate was also sealed.

In the pitch black of this freezing June night, deep within the Bedfordshire countryside, a woman in WAAF uniform stood by herself, straining her eyes and ears for any sign of the returning Halifax. It was now long overdue and without any word, things looked grim. A corporal cycled by, turning up early for his ground crew shift, and stopping, asked her if she was alright. She, in a rather shaky voice, admitted she wasn't really,
"I'm waiting on 'L – Leather' and they're late." He, attempting to comfort her, lied,
"There's still time, don't give up hope," and with a reassuring smile cycled off.
Georgie knew full well it would take a miracle now to bring us safely back.

# Chapter 27

Gliding down in the blackness on my flapping 'chute, something seemed to suddenly rush up to meet me, but unfortunately it wasn't the ground. Literally, only a few seconds later, I was plummeting and buffeting through what seemed like tree tops, with branches clawing at me as I fell. Just as suddenly there was an almighty rip and jolt as my 'chute caught above me, violently halting my descent. And that's really the last I recall of the whole thing. Hardly a text book landing but there again our instruction of long ago was anything but extensive. When I came round the only thing I could think of was the pain in my head and back, every time I tried to move a stabbing pain shot down my spine, and when I took a breath I got discomfort in my chest. Clearly my last minute prayer for survival had worked, but I forgot to be specific about the condition of my survival! I knew now that in spite of my suffering I had to get free of my parachute and down, out of this tree, but I had no idea how I was going to manage it. The rain was incessant and the mist swirling just above the ground, fortunately engulfing me in its shroud: a blessing if Jerry was searching the area.

Stretching my arm across my chest I hit the quick release on my harness, a foolhardy action causing me to jerk from the discomfort, as I precariously slid out of the contraption. Grasping firmly the bough and tree trunk upon which I was now perched, I contemplated my climb down – in the dark: my immediate instinct was to get to the relative safety of the ground, but it probably wouldn't prove easy. Moving very cautiously and with some difficulty I began to explore the tree, feeling for a way down; all the time spasms of pain shot through me. To my great relief I had but grappled down a mere few feet before I found myself treading on the dank woodland floor. With a sudden realisation, a flood of relief and exhaustion overtook me and I collapsed; slumping against the tree trunk I fell asleep.

I awoke with a jolt, my body rigid, but not from injuries, and for a few seconds I didn't know why; and then I heard them, some way off I thought, although it wasn't easy to tell exactly in this gloom. As the rain had stopped thank God, I could now make out what sounded like a German patrol. Jerry was on the move, probably out searching for the crashed aircraft, my Halifax. I could distinctly hear the rumble of their vehicles and a mumbling of voices. Fortunately for me they seemed to be heading away; if captured it would mean a German prisoner of war camp and an uncertain future - I really didn't believe that any interrogation would be a gentlemanly affair! It wasn't possible to make out any vehicle lights either, so I was comforted to think they wouldn't see me, well not at least until sun up. I am a bit hazy about what exactly I did after that – it must have been my head injury, but I do recall making a valiant attempt to scramble up the tree at first light knowing somehow I had to get my 'chute down. The idea of capture spurred me on. To my relief its entanglement didn't look at first glance to be too bad: maybe the heavy rain had played a hand in shifting the canopy, or perhaps my weight suspended from it for who knows how long had helped, anyway, whatever it was, I thought if I could overcome my suffering I stood a fair chance of pulling it down. Slowly I was regaining better control of my battered body, and the pain seemed less severe, maybe I was getting used to it, perhaps moving about eased it in some way, or it might be a sudden rush of adrenalin, I really didn't know. After much tugging and tearing the majority of the 'chute was loose, loose enough that with a hard tug from the ground it would come down. Clambering back down I gave my harness and lines several hearty pulls and was relieved when the 'chute tumbled on top of me. Having noticed earlier a drainage ditch by the edge of the trees, I used a piece of stone to scratch out a hollow in the soft, damp soil beside it, the excavation of which proved easier than I at first had imagined. The bottom of my hollow was loose enough to clear with my bare hands, which were already cut and bleeding but not badly. I ensured that I could make it a sufficient depth in which to bury my bundled parachute and Mae West jacket: never before had I realised just how big they were.

As the sun began to rise in the early morning I could just glimpse smoke drifting from the horizon into the lightening sky. It was hard to judge its distance but looking across the open landscape, was probably three or four miles distant. I remember thinking that more than likely Ronnie and Reg were already dead by the time our Halifax plunged to the ground: out of control, probably skidding across a field, a blazing victim of bad luck and the Luftwaffe. The wreckage must have burnt for the rest of the night, unused ammo exploding, hopefully keeping Jerry at bay. Until they could get close enough to inspect the fuselage and surrounding area, they would not know how many British airmen had died, trapped inside this burning inferno. And more importantly for me, how many escaped the plane before its crash; I needed to get as far away as possible and quickly before Jerry started to scour the area. I was uncertain where we had precisely come down but my best bet was to head south. Studying my silk survival map and compass I experienced a blurring of my vision, this was not going to be easy. I sucked on my Horlick's tablets then nibbled two squares of chocolate which had come to hand in my search for the compass. Still soaked and cold, I longed for the warmth of the rising sun to drive the chill from my bones. According to my watch it was still the early hours of the morning and, deciding to partly disregard what I'd been taught, I concluded that if I was cautious I could spend a couple of hours hiking before I needed to hide up. Taking the tiny knife from inside my flying-boot, I trimmed off the gaiters, the stitching doubling as laces, making them resemble shoes, then packed my kit, checked my clothing, donned my old cap and headed on my way, whichever way that was. This was obviously going to prove easier going than it had in the dark, tripping over sticks and falling down holes each incident resulting in more agony. Still aching I skirted round the edge of the trees keeping to the undergrowth: if I should be spotted I thought it would be possible to run deeper into the woods and take cover. After a short time I came across a clearing on the woodland edge where the trees had been felled and logs were stacked. Damp sawdust lay in piles on the ground and bundles of twigs and branches had been discarded. An old rusty saw lay wrapped in a dirty, black coat, stashed in one of the log piles. After a brief moment's thought, I slid the saw back into the pile, put on the coat over my flying gear and, hoping I was dealing with an absent minded forester, made off.

The woodland gave way to open countryside and hedge lined fields, broken by the occasional clump of trees. I carefully considered my best route. An old disused path followed the hedge line alongside an overgrown ditch, this seemed to offer the best bet if I wanted cover close at hand. The going was harder than I imagined as I crouched low to the ground, tangled brambles ripped at my clothes and hands, hands that were already cut up. The wet grass soaked my legs, water running down into my boots, chilling my feet: wet feet were bad news. By now I had managed to find a small, fast running stream and, conscious of the downpour the night before and the seeming absence of animals, took a chance and drank. Along the way a primitive bridge crossed the stream, an ideal shelter under which I could rest, water to hand, and regain my strength during the day until nightfall. It was becoming too dangerous to journey any further in this light. As I half dozed I pictured my mates back on base in the mess with a sizzling fry-up, maybe writing home about their recent exploits or cuddling up to a pretty girl in a matinee cinema performance before they took-off on another night time mission. Your mind can play funny tricks when you're tired and feeling low: mine was going into overdrive I concluded; but as I thought of what dangers I had escaped from, I drifted off to sleep.

My bouts of fitful slumber were disturbed by a whistling; it was 1630, 4.30pm, and the tuneless whistle was not far away. Very slowly I raised my head from my hiding: 200 yards ahead of me I saw the head of a German soldier gliding above a hedge, a rather strange appearance, and for a moment, more comical than dangerous. As he passed by a gate I glimpsed his old bicycle half hidden by a long greatcoat. Fortunately for me he was concentrating on getting somewhere fast, head down, steel helmet strapped tightly, rifle slung over his back. He passed by still whistling. The rest of that afternoon and early evening I dozed, being troubled by little other than my ailments. The sun dropped below the horizon on a clear but chilly evening. Filling my rubber water bottle and adding sterilising tablets, I prepared to set out on my journey and escape. Muddy tracks, undergrowth soaked with the dew and a dropping temperature held no delight for me, but I needed to press on. I am not sure whether it was the exercise or the copious amounts of water drunk, but frequently I needed to stop to pee, and used those moments to take stock, gathering my thoughts. I fixed on a prominent landmark that would serve as my heading in the half light and when crossing open land and lanes was extra vigilant, stopping to listen for a long while first before taking the risk. After several hours of arduous struggle behind me, crossing ditches, climbing fences, battling through thickets and possibly hiking several miles, I came across a small hut in a coppice. The hovel showed no signs of being used and to my overwhelming relief offered a safe sanctuary for a brief few hours. In the pale light of the moon I could just make out the silhouette of trees crowded around by bushes, their dark shapes seeming to come alive all about me.

In the early light of morning this hiding place seemed unreal – dilapidated, smelly and riddled with flies, but that night it seemed like a blessing. As I lay, back propped against the side of the hut I contemplated my lot, only to have this worthless exercise almost instantly interrupted by a voice: that of a woman talking to a young boy. Careful to make as little noise as possible, I peered through a gap in the hut's boarding towards the direction of the disturbance. They were chatting away, leading a few cattle along the track that I had arrived on, far too busy to be aware of me. Their progress was slow, their country ways reflecting little of the impatience of war. Finally I could breathe again and, slumping on the hut's floor, sighed as if in gratitude for my crude shelter. My route so far had kept me well clear of any villages or habitation, now, however, I must be on or at least near a farm. Soon after I heard the two of them coming back, without the cows but the woman still full of French chatter as they passed by: this spot was proving to be busier than I had anticipated. If that was not enough, the young lad quickly returned, without the woman this time, herding a bunch of porkers. Every so often their ramble halted as the pigs foraged in the tasty earth; a thwack across their hindquarters from the boy's stick was sufficient to move them on, well at least for a while. To my horror he corralled them into the coppice within which was my hut, my sanctuary, and with blinding realisation, my 'pigsty'. A couple of swine made straightways for the hut and pushing their way in started oinking and squeaking angrily as they nosed about my body. It took little imagination to realise that my situation was quickly becoming untenable as more pigs were attracted to the hut by the disturbance, and even the boy was now beginning to show an interest. It was only a matter of time before my presence would be revealed. The sack door ruffled, this time not to herald the entrance of another pig, but the boy who gingerly peered inside: the game was up.

I cursed my bad luck, but it was too late. He paused for a moment as we looked at each other, trying to weigh one another up. Then an amazing thing happened: he put his hand to his cap and saluted me; I don't know what I was thinking of but rather than speaking I responded by saluting him back. My safety now rested with a young French boy who was a stranger to me. He leant across to me, shook my hand and, tapping my shoulder, pointed for me to stay in the hut. Then he was gone as quickly as he came, driving the swine outside as he went. I didn't think I particularly looked like a British airman, so I could only assume he had heard about the plane crashing nearby. I waited, not knowing what was happening; the pigs had discovered a hoard of windfall apples which were already being devoured by maggots, and had completely forgotten about me; and I wondered if the boy had too. He couldn't have been more than twelve or thirteen yet seemed to have a mature head on his youthful shoulders, with hands as coarse as a rasp, probably caused by his daily, farm duties. His friendliness seemed genuine as did his concern, but then I was hardly in any position to judge.

Within the hour he had returned, alone, hiding a bundle under his jacket. Wrapped in an old hessian bag was a chunk of bread spread with a greasy fat – a bit like dripping, two or three cold, cooked potatoes and a beer bottle half full of warm, thick milk. As he slid them across the wooden floor to me he smiled, then crept away leaving me once more on my own. My hut mates were now snoozing contentedly, shading from the noon sun under the overhanging boughs of the trees, following a morning full of routing and excavation. The food and drink was truly welcome and whilst devouring the provisions, I attempted to fathom my future prospects. None of the boy's actions impressed me as those of someone who was about to turn me in, in fact quite the contrary, his watchful nature belied his years. During that afternoon he visited me twice more, as I rested my damaged back, regaining my strength, each time with a few more meagre supplies, for which I was most grateful.

With the coming of nightfall I wondered what would be in store for me; should I make a break for it and head on my way whichever way that was, or hold out trusting in human nature and see what happens? I needn't have concerned myself because right on cue I heard a voice whispering outside. Lifting the corner of the sack hanging across the doorway, there facing me I could just see the grey figures of the boy and with him an old man holding an axe. Climbing out of my 'safe house' I burbled,
"I'm a British airman and I have just bailed out of my aircraft which crashed over there," and I turned and pointed into the distance. By now the pigs were beginning to get restless,

disturbed by our activity and not as peaceful as they should be at this hour. The old man grabbed me firmly by the arm with one hand and swung the axe with the other as he led me and the boy, off along a path through the woods. Glancing down towards the boy I could just make out his reassuring smile as he recognised my uncertainty and fear. We seemed to walk for ages in the dark, but it probably wasn't actually very far before we came to a group of buildings. As we drew near a dog started barking a little way off threatening to wake the whole neighbourhood, if not the whole of France; almost instantly a nearby voice yelled out and the hound stopped. From the direction of the noise I could make out a dull light through a window of a house. Crossing the yard, the old man kept looking about, eager to make the door as quickly as possible. Throwing the latch, he thrust me inside, into the gloom. The sheer force of my entry caused me to miss my footing; tumbling to the floor, I took a crack to my head on the way down and remembered nothing more of my arrival.

# Chapter 28

Waking, I found myself lying in a room in half light, hiding more than it revealed. Across from my bed seated in a shady corner I glimpsed a woman, the old woman who had the day before tended the cows with the young boy. It was difficult to see in this light but she painted a strange picture, sunk in a high- winged chair, her apron pulled over her face. The crone dozed, her laboured breathing occasioned with a rasping wheeze that came and went; every so often she fidgeted which disturbed her sleep and caused her to change her position in the chair. Nothing else stirred, the room was at peace, warm and restful. Heavy drapes across the window appeared to exclude all but a slender beam of light which found its way between the curtains, piercing the gloom, coming to rest on the floor, touching the edge of the bed upon which I was outstretched.

I lay completely still, my eyes exploring the surroundings, but there was little to see. Nothing of the comforts of home in England greeted me, no furniture or ornaments, pictures or possessions; the room wasn't even that large. A single oil lantern hung suspended from the ceiling, its cracked mantle dark with soot. Attempting to move myself up in the bed, a discomfort in my lower back caused me to recoil and slump back down. A headiness accompanied my movement, a feeling similar to that which I had experienced before, the morning after a drinking session. It didn't over bother me but clearly I wasn't a hundred percent. My attempt had disturbed the old woman, she wriggled, shifted her legs then, pulling the apron from her face, stroked a hand over her wispy hair a few times and stared at me. Realising I was now awake she smiled, revealing a toothless mouth. She resembled a thirties horror star but I couldn't remember who; I thought these French women were meant to be beautiful? Maybe I was being unfair to this elderly dear. Not a word was exchanged and yet I experienced the same reassurance I had felt when the young boy had discovered me. She hoisted herself out of the chair, smoothed down her dress and apron then shuffled to the door. My inquisitive nature deemed I speak but something held me back, probably the uncertainty of being understood or more than likely because I still didn't know who these people really were and what they would do with me. She left the room and standing in the doorway called out,

"Henri, ici."

I heard no reply, perhaps none was needed; she turned and arched in the doorway, fixing me with a penetrating glare. Stout footsteps resounded from outside the room, my impression was of someone slowly climbing a wooden staircase; I imagined it would be Henri. A tall grey haired man, wiry in stature, entered the room, easing his way past the woman; it was hard to distinguish fully his features in this light, but maybe this was my 'wild axeman'?

"Don't be afraid," I blurted, "I am British!" and feeling this was hardly sufficient went on to explain, "my bomber crashed, I have just bailed out!"

He replied in an authoritative tone which showed no signs of apprehension or anxiety.

"I see you are English, not German, by your voice!"

Well that seemed comforting if I was to believe him. He strode over to me and taking a cigarette from his top jacket pocket, put it in his mouth, lit it, then placed it between my lips. I coughed and choked, wasting no time in removing it from my mouth. The old girl chortled as she muttered something to Henri. For a brief while he and I attempted to communicate, I with my pidgin French and he with broken English, both of us using hand gestures as an aid to our understanding.

It seemed that the Germans had discovered the plane with the remains of only two bodies. He was uncertain but had heard an English airman had been caught nearby and was being sent to Germany, this man had broken his leg when he parachuted down. He knew nothing more other than the Germans were still looking, but not yet here. To me that sounded as if it was only a matter of time. His words were confident but seemed to suggest concern.

"You rest now," as he pressed his hand on my shoulder; he looked puzzled as he gently touched my temple, "you fell in the night and went to sleep, and had many bleedings and your back is no good." I nodded, having little alternative and thanked him. He concluded with comforting words,

"Here you are safe, for a time." They both left me, latching the door behind them; I couldn't be sure but it sounded as if a key turned.

My head was in a whirl, questions and thoughts bombarded it from all sides and in the mayhem I fell back to sleep. My sleep was fitful, disrupted by pictures in my head, disturbing visions of blazing aircraft, men in flying gear - screaming, then scouring soldiers' faces, German soldiers, their faces shielded by steel helmets. The restlessness I suffered must have woken me. The room was just as I remembered it earlier but it now seemed airless and I found it hard to breathe. Casting back the bedding and sliding my legs out, my feet rested firmly on the timber floorboards ready to take my weight. Steadying myself, conscious of the discomfort in my back, I carefully pushed myself on to my legs and shuffled across to the window. Gathering back the thick drapes, dust filled my nostrils: I wanted to sneeze but didn't. The panes revealed a moonlit night, dirty with a swirling mist choking the air. As I eased the steel catch on the half casement of the window a crisp freshness chilled my face; I felt alive again as I stood there, my eyes closed. An urgency to relieve myself became all consuming and in looking about the room for a solution to my predicament I observed a pot slid under the bed, just visible in the moonlight. Sliding the half-full, lidded vessel back under the bed frame once I had finished with it, I climbed back between the covers and returned to my rest, feeling exhausted.

The young boy entered and sidled across the room, a glass of milk and a chunk of bread in his hands; it was daybreak. He looked

226

pleased to see me awake and thrust breakfast towards me! This was the lad who had secretly kept me fed these past days and thankfully continued to do so. The day appeared to have got off to an altogether murky start, the boy deciding to half shut the window on the very early morning.

"Thank you, merci," I offered him.

A broad beam filled his face; his eyes smiled brightly. He left as quietly as he had arrived. The repeated squawk of a rook cut across the morning's otherwise silence and soon the dawn call commenced its accompaniment. A distant dog's bark could faintly be heard, incessant for a while, with the crow of an agitated cockerel; the countryside chorus was beginning to be performed. In time I was conscious of noise within the house: doors, footsteps, muffled talk – their day had begun.

Again I attempted to move, believing my earlier pain would probably have passed, but quickly I discovered that not to be the case. My cuts and bruises troubled me little; however, a deep-rooted discomfort emanated from my lower back. Some movements were more painful than others and there appeared to be little logic to this; my discomfort resulted more from the way I moved rather than what I moved. A stabbing sensation to my chest at times still accompanied my deep breaths or if I twisted my upper body; I concluded that the possible cause was a cracked rib or two, the only cure of which I knew was rest. I began to feel deeply frustrated, confined to bed unable to make my escape from France and the Germans, unaware of what my future here would hold. So far these folks were kind and understanding but I needed to be on the move again and heading for home. Dangers awaited me in such a venture I was sure; equally I was certain I was not totally safe here and, the longer I stayed, the more dangerous it would be for my hosts.

The noise outside the room drew nearer; the door opened and once again Henri entered, dragging the chair across the floor, its legs scraping the boards. He pulled it up to my bedside, clearly wanting to talk as he made himself comfortable. I noticed more in this daylight than I had the night before: the man's gaunt features, his boney cheeks and jaw, an altogether weathered, haggard look. His thinning hair was greying, greasy and brushed back flat across his head; deep-telling inset eyes stared at me as he spoke. Henri, in a lethargic, gravelly voice, began to explain what I must do; his strong French accent made it difficult at times to understand his every word as he laboured to speak in English; his message however was abundantly clear. I was sorely tempted to aid him in his endeavours at times, but resisted in case this might appear offensive.

I must stay here at 'Ferme Verger'; it was too dangerous to wander far; I would be at risk from the soldiers. Anyway he was defiant I could not travel until I was much better, my back healed and my head mended! No more dreams; from what he was saying, during my first day I had called out and talked in my sleep and been very restless. Certainly he was right: I could not consider going it alone while I was in so much pain and my movements so limited; regarding my nightmares, I had no knowledge of these. I started to interrupt him, questioning the danger for them should they hide me: they faced certain death if caught helping me. But he was having none of it and talked over me.

"You stay here until Le Maquis can get you away. Hm, you understand?"

I had little option but to agree, this being the response he expected and the only reply he was prepared to accept, acknowledging in a more relaxed manner,

"Tis good!"

They would need to find me a better hiding place: a refuge which would not be discovered should the Germans search the farm, or one known by any collaborators. Meanwhile, it would be best if I tried to exercise a little: maybe this, along with the country air would help me sleep better. It would do me no harm if I took it

228

easy I concluded, and stayed out of sight. But I must change my appearance: old clothes, his coat and one of his hats; my boots were good but I needed different trousers. All these his old mother brought me and, under her watchful eye, I dressed. She then bundled my old garb, taking it away to burn outside.

Gingerly descending the creaking stairs, both feet coming to each rung in turn, I grasped the stair rail tightly; the last thing I needed to do was to fall. The smell of old floorboards mingled with pungent, cooking odours which lingered from the downstairs kitchen. Evidence of breakfast was spread in a muddle about the kitchen table, stacks of dirty pots and pans filled the sink. A cat lapped at something in a dish on the stone floor, pushing it about in an attempt to empty it. A black, cast iron stove proudly stood filling an alcove at one end of the room awaiting fuelling for the next hot meal of the day. Chopped wood for the night, dry sticks as brittle as glass, lay piled in a stack against the wall. The kitchen was dark; shadows created patterns about the floor, walls, table and benches and added to the dormancy of this place. Nothing here murmured.

Venturing out of the farmhouse and into the morning air, it was clear that unlike home, summer had been here for sometime. The early mist had lifted long before I was out to disturb it; all about were signs the season had long since turned. In the days earlier I had been so preoccupied with evading capture that I had little noticed the countryside I had fled through and sheltered in: the grass was at its greenest, vegetation at its richest, great tangles of plants tumbled from the hedgerows. The bird song was bright, bringing an excitement to the hedgerows and trees as the sunlight played and glimmered through their foliage. Fruits were ripening, growing plumper and soon would be ready to pick. The heat of the day seemed to satisfy the most demanding of the farm hens as they clawed the ground one foot after the other, scratching in the dirt for anything they thought could be regarded as food. Somewhere beyond the orchard, the hedgerow and trees lay the countryside, the lush fields and meadows - nature's sanctuary, and the villages and towns now haunted by German soldiers.

Weary from my countless steps about the sun drenched yard and orchard, I was all but done in and rested awhile on a rustic bench aside the house, my back against its warm, stone wall. The air smelt sweet; drifting clouds of summer pollen hung on the season's fair breeze, sparkling in the golden light. The sound of a bicycle starting along the gravel drive startled me; I couldn't see it being tucked out of sight of the road behind a gangly bush. As it grew nearer I cautiously peered between the leaves and was surprised to see a young woman pedalling for all she was worth, a galvanized bucket swinging from her handle bars. My natural instinct was to withdraw back into the foliage and wait for the visitor to go. The bike came to a stop and was propped against the wall, the bucket clattering. It was not now possible to leave the bench to take refuge inside the house without being seen. Suddenly a sweet voice addressed me, as the woman lifted back a branch,

"Je suis Brigitte."

Her voice was comforting and reassuring and, as I gazed at her, I sensed she was not shocked to see me.

"I live with my family here," she explained. At first I found her English somewhat unnerving. Having gathered my presence of mind I started to explain who I was and how I got there, but was interrupted in mid flow when she simply exclaimed,

"I know," smiled and continued, "I have just been to take a message about you to Le Maquis!" I sat gazing at her, this attractive woman in her early twenties who knew so much about me. As if sensing my confusion she beamed, sat beside me and in a gentle voice said,

"So tell me about your family and home."

I gathered my thoughts for a moment then began to describe our maisonette and London, quickly realising that maisonettes and underground trains might be a total mystery to her, as was the idea of there being no farms in London. She impressed me with her interest, asking question after question, and soon I found myself talking about Mother and Father.

"What will they be feeling?"

"What do you mean?" was my thoughtless response.

"Well, now you have not returned" she went on to say. With everything that had happened to me I had failed to give them a second thought. Without doubt by now they would have received a telegram, a second telegram! A 'Regret to inform you telegram', but now it would explain I had 'failed to return from an operational flight against the enemy'. Little chance of confusion this time! They would have no idea that I was alive, how I was or where I was; Mother would be distraught. The fact that I couldn't tell them greatly upset me as I knew that each day their papers would be full of news of more war disasters.

When I'd finished what I was saying, we both exchanged an affectionate glance, then sat in silence, comforted by the warmth of the day. Neither of us felt any urgency to end the peace and quiet. After many moments Brigitte spoke,

"It is hard for me to understand what is happening in this war of yours; life is so, so different here now to what it once was before this war and all its killing. I hate it, I hate everything about it; I hate how people have changed, how I am different. I hate how it is now so hard to trust people, even people we know, those we work and live with. Now with so much evil forever about us, forgiveness seems hard; grotesque actions have been excused in the name of oppression and freedom, greed and sacrifice, rights and wrongs. No one wins a war." She paused for a moment, "How can it be that hate can be more powerful than love and grace?"

Her profound concern caught me completely unexpectedly, I had no idea. It seemed almost inconceivable to me that the war had so dramatically touched her life here in this peaceful French countryside. Brigitte, soft of voice, murmured,

"Is this how it's going to always be? If only it were a dream and would end . . . we should go inside now, just in case."

She collected the bucket full of berries and plums from her bike, then led me into the kitchen where she set the pail on the board beside the glazed sink. Resting across the table from one another I glimpsed a tear in her eye: slowly it rolled down her cheek. I realised then how special a woman Brigitte was.

"What of you Brigitte; what was your childhood like?" As she reflected, a beautiful warmth shone from her face,

"I remember my Mother so clearly, she was amazing, just what we children needed. After the chores, she would wander with us for miles and miles through our French countryside, playing with us, talking about the wildlife and telling us stories; her English was not good but she tried to teach us as we lay in the long lush grass of the rolling fields, or amongst the fresh hay that we'd gathered in. We would take a little food with us from our kitchen and collect berries, then by the babbling river we'd feast and lay under the sun. To me as a child they were wonderful times, times that should never end; when you're young like that your childhood seems as if it'll go on for ever. The war had snatched away our Grandpapa, but Grandmamma was marvelous; she loved being with us all, she adored the animals and the countryside. It was paradise for us all.

"My brother Matthieu was four years older than me and much more serious. Nicolas, being five years my younger, like me adored our outdoor life; full of fun and mischief he would be up to everything and anything. For Papa, family life seemed to be idyllic: he had his farm and animals, his health and youth, and was surrounded by his growing family; but above all he had Mother. One day, when I was fourteen, all of that changed. By then our family had grown and my youngest brother Émile, who was nearly two years old, was beginning to make his mark. For Mother his birth had been anything but easy, and afterwards her health slowly deteriorated. A few days before my fifteenth birthday, Mother became seriously ill and died: what seemed to be our perfect life was shattered. Papa became dark with depression finding it harder and harder to play and talk with us as he once had. Grandmamma would spend hours with us whilst caring for Émile, but her son, Papa, grew further away from us all. Life for our Émile was going to be very different than it was for the rest of us, as we soon discovered. The shock of mother's sudden death had been more than little Émile could bear, from that day on, he never spoke another word. Somehow with Mother's going she had left behind a gift that was so precious, a young life that would, with time, fill Papa's heart with love again. Over the years our little family would come once again to know joy, to laugh, and whilst remembering our mother, be grateful for our love one with each other.

"My life was filled with a love for the countryside; we would walk down the lanes leading the cows as they chewed on the lush green grass, the sweet aroma on their breath. Papa would perch little Émile sideways on top of one of the cows for a ride; their udders would hang and swing as they journeyed home.

"My memories are full of moments when I would paddle in the river shallows, the thick, gritty mud oozing between my toes, the oceans of green grass all about us and the stillness of the woods, dappled and dark. Fires that Papa would painstakingly build between apple and pear in the orchard would smoulder for days on end as he piled on more dying leaves, and the smell, as it lingered, heavy in the air. I learnt how to build stooks of corn and which mushrooms to collect and take home to our kitchen; the boys would bring back rabbits and pigeons for pies and stews. I still remember the first smell of sweet new hay in the barn; the ramshackled, tumbling barn that smelt of horses, their sweat, and leather. I recall sitting in a patch of warm sunlight and, as the rays crept slowly along the ground, I would move, keeping away from the shadows. There were times on hot, summer afternoons when it was if the countryside would go to sleep. The garden was silent and even the hens stopped clucking.

"One of the things I can remember is that as well as times together as a family, I was able to do things by myself: I didn't always need adults – the countryside was so safe. I got to know wildlife: the birds that would nest in our hedges and the flowers that blessed us with their scent and blossom. I imagine there was nothing spectacular about our countryside but it was what I knew and loved. I would walk and cycle endlessly, exploring the fields and river, the woodlands and villages: my world, which only ever seemed to grow bigger. To some my childhood might appear one of solitude, but I cherished every moment of it and would have that time all over again. I loved to look from my bedroom window early on a summer's night and watch the yellow radiance of a full moon shining through the treetops, filling our garden with a brilliant silver light; or the darkness of the sky in autumn revealing the stars, hundreds and thousands of them twinkling their mystery; and the feeling of going to sleep, hearing the sound of rain splashing on the roof tiles above my head.
I had a special childhood."

# Chapter 29

We sat together silently as she remembered. In what was such a brief time we had learnt so much about one another: our lives, our hopes and fears. Already we had an understanding of each other and a trust, a simple trust but one which allowed us to feel safe.

Émile ran into the kitchen, bubbling with excitement and ignoring our mood, he seized Brigitte's hand, pulling her to follow him. Across the rear yard mounted on a rickety, wooden frame was a pair of hutches, and in each hutch was a plump grey rabbit: that much was apparent. What wasn't so obvious was that one hutch was now also home to half a dozen young. In amongst the straw, curled tightly in a corner were six, furless, baby bunnies. Their ugliness seemed lost on Émile who was already trying to feed them with leaves and grass he had just picked, hoping to satisfy their newborn appetites. The proud doe relished the treat! Brigitte explained that from the outset, Papa had been quite clear with the lad as to what the final destination for these creatures would be, but that, it was evident, hadn't stopped Émile treating them like pets - and I didn't envy anyone trying to take them away for the pot! Brigitte shared, philosophically, that with so many wild ones around, Papa had more than enough rabbits for the pot. We all laughed at the sight of these blind, naked lumps as they wriggled about; Émile, silently laughing, probably hadn't considered that when fat, these babies undoubtedly would find their final home to be the kitchen, all skinned and prepared!

That night I slept soundly, unconscious to the world around me, tucked away as I was in the house, at the far end of the attic. My hiding place was plain yet comfortable, its existence unapparent even to the most prying of eyes. Sunlight did not visit where I slept, no window allowed the dawn to play upon my bed; but faintly I could hear the waking call of the cuckoo, the coo of pigeons and the early chorus of the birds in the fruit trees announcing the dawn. While I was still drowsy I began to feel the heat of the new day's sun beating down on the roof. That morning when I rose, all were out about their work except the old woman who was busy shuffling about the kitchen and stooping over the stove, her bent back probably a result of hours working on the land. The others returned, we settled around the large table whereupon the old woman, in turn, filled our bowls with a large dollop of what looked like thick, steaming porridge. The water in the kettle boiled and bubbled on the stove demanding to be removed and made into coffee. The old woman obliged as she went on busying herself with breakfast, hardly sitting, eating crusts of bread which she dipped into her porridge. A lively chatter between the three of them accompanied the meal; I, being able to grasp only the odd phrase and word, hardly understood their meaning. We feasted on black bread spread with white, soft, creamy cheese or thick, gooey treacle, together with an egg from the large eartheware *cruche* jar, all washed down with mug after mug of strong coffee. The food was good but very plain and clearly, considering the difficulties with rationing, they lived on what they could produce themselves or find close to hand. About midday we'd feast on more bread, this time dipped in a bowl of vegetable soup – there seemed to be no end to the soup. A large plate of potatoes was served up with *rutabagas* – turnips or leeks. Some days we might have a small amount of meat, often ham or slices of salami, but sometimes a sweet tasting mince of sorts for all to dip into. A creamy sauce occasionally helped to make the meal more palatable and different, along with a salad made from mashed corn which Brigitte and the old woman would cut fresh from the field. Regardless, there was always a rather bitter coffee to finish! The evening meal, after all the day's work with the livestock, seemed to be an opportunity to use whatever food was left, finished off with coffee, or on rare occasions, red wine. My body wasn't used to so much liquid in a day and so the pot slid under my bed was essential: I'd never have made the outside 'loo shed' from the attic in time.

At first I had hoped to leave within a week or two, but as the time slipped by it became obvious that this was not to be. My back at times still caused me some pain and greatly restricted my movement, although gradually, as my stay lengthened, it got easier. The time was proving far from unpleasant, as I was treated like one of the family and, to be honest, I was becoming more and more captivated by Brigitte. Visitors were few and infrequent: on one occasion an elderly, moustached man called to examine me - I was told he was a sort of doctor who was willing to treat injured airmen who were evading the Germans. His visit was brief, just long enough to include a chat over a drink with Henri. The rudimentary treatment prescribed for me? - Rest! When visitors did call it was usually only to collect eggs or milk, stopping no more than a few minutes; then I could hide away in the attic, or at the back of the barn where I would lay snuggled in the sweet smelling straw, warm and feeling safe. Once or twice I was introduced to close members of the family, but this felt most disconcerting as I knew little of what was being discussed: except for one who asked me lots of questions, and at first seemed most suspicious of me. I later found out he was with the Resistance and that it was not unusual for German agents to disguise themselves as crashed airmen. The Germans rarely called, but when they did it was unannounced, their cars screaming down the drive, scattering the gravel as they skidded to a halt. I had to be forever ready to dive into hiding, knowing capture would lead to me being arrested as a prisoner of war, at best. However, the greatest fear was for what they would do to the family – death was most likely and for Émile, if he should survive, life would be so hard. I couldn't bear to think what they might do to Brigitte.

Some while after I had arrived, the Germans came visiting: I was ill-prepared, resting in the open at the back of the house. I was still not completely familiar with the farm at that time and not sure where I could go to avoid them finding me. They sounded furious and impatient as they set about searching the farmhouse and buildings, brushing Henri and the old woman to one side. In the panic, the only haven to hand which I thought was safe, was a narrow ditch completely hidden by a web of brambles and twigs. I dived in. The sensation was like a hundred needles scratching me all at the same time: a torture which I had to silently bare. I scrambled deeper under the dense thicket, trying to make as little noise as possible as I arranged the undergrowth over me. There I lay for what seemed like hours, concentrating on every sound, every movement, waiting for the car doors to bang, its engine to start then growl as the vehicle raced out of the yard. Still I daren't move: I couldn't be sure they had all truly gone. Increasingly I became aware that my careless dive into the ditch was not without its cost: my body was riddled with pain; my back which for a moment I had disregarded, seemed frozen, rigid, seized; I was in agony. In time I could hear the voices of Brigitte and Henri, evidently in their search for me, but my hideaway was discovered by Émile, who, crawling, caught a glimpse of my pale face, now running with blood from the gashes on my forehead. Slowly they got me out, wrenching back the tangle of undergrowth about me; helping me inside, they eased me, half walking, half carrying, stumbling up the stairs and finally to my bed. As Henri removed my filthy clothes, Brigitte, dabbing my wounds with a damp piece of cloth, whispered,

"They were not looking for you; they had come for food, to steal our supplies so they could feed their hungry stomachs!"

Overwhelmed and exhausted, I slept.

With the passing of the days I became more and more besotted with Brigitte. To me there was no question of her beauty, the naturalness of her charms, her rare spirit and grace, her generous, reassuring manner and the way she comfortably wore her fair looks. Brigitte was all that a woman should be: vivacious, intelligent, an adventurer, a delight to be with, a woman I could feel at one with. Émile, her youngest brother, loved her: you could tell by the way he looked at her and helped her around the house. Poor little Émile had suffered some sort of damage to his brain and the nurse thought this was the cause of his 'lost voice'.

Brigitte said her mother was beside herself with grief. Brigitte's middle brother, Nicolas, was away fighting for France in Algiers whilst Matthieu, the oldest, had been deported to Germany to work in one of the armament factories: a move which resulted in many young Frenchmen deciding they would rather fight for France, leaving their families and friends and joining The Maquis. Over the months that followed the family had heard nothing from either of them.

All my days at La Ferme I spent with Brigitte. Life was easy; I rested, slowly regaining both the strength in my back and my movement, but every so often I would be reminded that all was not well with it. I continued to be haunted by violent dreams: tension and panic became my bedfellows as I tried to sleep. If my nights were frequently troubled, my days, aside of the throbbing headaches, were bliss: strolling with Brigitte about the farm, ensuring we could not be seen, talking endlessly or just spending hours wistfully together as she went about her chores. At first Henri was quiet, seemingly uneasy about our relationship, whereas the old lady made no effort to disguise her objection, and became abrupt and offhand with me: fortunately I understood little of her drawl. Émile proved as much of a friend as ever: I would see him silently working away at the woman, trying to bring her round.

The farmhouse was large and substantial, built of stone whitewashed walls and towered three storeys high; interlocking terracotta pantiles covered the steep roof, providing a home beneath for birds and bats. Its grandeur belied the poverty of the household which lingered below the surface. Shutters, for keeping at bay the noonday sun, hung beside the ground floor windows, peeling paintwork partly hiding their rotting woodwork. Any movement of them it seemed would cause their final collapse. There was evidence that other windows once had boasted shutters: corroded hinges were secured about their frames, white walls beneath stained with rust. A rambling bush weaved its outstretched branches over and around the corner of the house, veiling the windows, its close leaves proving a haven for insects and birds which happily mingled amongst its blossom. Reaching out it formed an arch with a giant oak tree which overshadowed the yard and water trough, beside which was the well. Here, twice daily, Émile would labour, filling buckets which he then carried into the kitchen. At least once a week he would ferry extra water indoors, which when heated on the fire, shallowly filled a small tin tub for bathing. The family order of washing was strictly adhered to, and for me, being the last, they half emptied the tub, topping up with fresh water. Needless to say my experience was decidedly cool! As I grew stronger my contribution on the farm became greater, sharing some of the jobs with Émile and Brigitte. Chasing the gawky hens, fluttering and screeching back into their coop at nightfall became a right old game; the horses to be visited, fed and watered; and then there were the cows, backwards and forwards every day to be milked. But the real antics were performed by the pigs and very much appreciated they were. Brigitte and Émile would fall about as the swine snorted, slobbered and rooted deep into the soft loam in search of the choicest morsels. With the shortening of days, so we would spend wonderful times wondering about at dusk: in the twilight, gathering wild green damsons, fattening plums, black sloes and crab apples, all destined for pies or preserves, stored behind the pantry curtain under the stairs. Brigitte would know where wild cherries hung ripening, and if she collected enough her grandmamma would delight in making a cherry pudding. During the day the kitchen always seemed quite dark, its small windows affording little sunlight to brighten and warm the drab room. Of an evening a tall oil lamp was placed on the table and once the wick was warm and drawing, its light filled the room, casting weak shadows in the glow of its pointed flame which flickered playfully with every draught. Émile fetched sticks from the barn and soon Henri would have flames roaring up the stove chimney as the twigs cracked and blazed. If the oven was not being used Henri would stack wood in it to dry for the morning. Boots and wooden clogs were lined up beside the cooker and when the weather wasn't fine the old woman would hang the washing from the *lavoir* to dry. Off the kitchen was a gloomy corridor from which a large wooden door opened into their best room: a room that was usually kept closed, and as I opened the door a current of cold air hit me. An impressive communal dining room, some twenty by thirty feet, filled with heavy, dark wooden furniture, any elegance that had once existed had long since faded. This was the room that would sit all the family, relatives and friends, around a table which dominated the room. An old sideboard clung to one wall prominently displaying the family valuables and treasures: pride of place, amongst the statue of the Virgin Mary and framed photographs, was given to a lovely porcelain *'Bon bon l'iele'* sweet bowl. Everywhere and everything was covered in a thick deposit of dust. An ornately embroidered, white, linen cloth lay over part of the table, looking tired and creased. Candlesticks stood like sentries in a line down the centre of the table waiting to be lit so they once more could bring life to this dreary room.

The room that surprised me most was Brigitte's parents' bedroom, because it still retained all the personal touches of her mother, nine years after her death. Her clothes hung on pegs alongside those of Henri, mother's hairbrushes and combs were arranged before a mirror, the reflection of which was partly marred by a web of black on its coating. On a shelf unit in the corner of the room was a shrine to the Madonna; central on the lower shelf was a framed black and white photograph of Brigitte's mother, slightly faded but still quite clear. A kindness seemed to shine from her face which was attractive in a plain way, holding the most wonderful of smiles. Her curly hair tumbled about her neck just kissing her shoulders. Her dress was simple and black but somehow the photographer had managed to capture something of her mother's charm and innocence, the same charm and innocence I saw in Brigitte. I stood in front of the photograph for several minutes, gazing, just wondering what she was like.

241

Making an early start, we took the family horse and cart and headed to market, weaving along roads lined with chestnut trees, through the rolling countryside, the river threading its way alongside for much of our journey. Finally we arrived at the edge of the small village of Cousion-sur-Cherane, once I am sure delightful and full of charm but today a village fearful for its future under the Germans. This tiny world of peace and tranquility deep within the so called Free French countryside was now on the edge of this miserable war.

Our wagon rattled around a bend in the road which skirted below a wooded hill rising steeply in this pastoral landscape; we crossed the village bridge over La Cherane, its waters flowing gracefully through the surrounding countryside, and started a gradual climb into the village. Looking back I could see old men sitting at the water's edge, concentrating on their rod and line, endeavouring to outwit the cunning fish. A couple of washerwomen were crouched at the far bank scrubbing their laundry, white sheets spread wide about them, laid on the grass and bushes to dry. As we rode up the hill towards the church and cottages, an old dear with her washbasket full, hobbled towards the bridge. Down the road, as if chasing her, clattered a tram, its passengers peering about as it hurtled for the bridge and onward to the distant city of Limoges. To our left, trees from the Catholic Presbytery hung overshadowing the road; here the priest lived in his shuttered home nestling below the magnificent church with its remarkable roof resting on four carved columns, a brass ball gleaming on the highest spire. Pigeons roosted on the tower and circled high above us dipping and climbing. Aside the road was the market place where a variety of stalls were set up, already frantic with activity. An abundance of flowers cascaded from a stand beside the road, their colours a rich mosaic of bloom. All manner of folk rested on wooden benches, chatting, enjoying the warmth of the sun. The pungent aroma of coffee lingered heavy in the air. Henri, pulling the cart into the square, told me to be on my guard: there were no Germans in the village that day, but Vichy police could arrive at a moment's notice. He had already explained to me that his visit to the village was vital so he could meet with contacts of the Resistance and the Maquis, and for them to see me, even though I was disguised in Henri's old clothes. Brigitte clasped my arm as she led me away, leaving Grandmamma and Émile to return to the market, and Henri sauntering off towards a café. On a board displayed clearly for all to see, was an official German notice, dated **'Paris, 22 September 1941'** and signed, **von Stülpnagel, The Military Governor of France.** It's message was plain:

> **Any male person directly or indirectly helping the crew of enemy aircraft landed by parachute or having effected a forced landing, or assisting in their evasion, or hiding and helping them in any way whatever, will be shot immediately.**
> **Women guilty of the same offence will be deported to concentration camps in Germany.**
> **Any persons seizing crew members having effected a forced landing or descended by parachute, or who, by their attitude, contribute to their capture, will receive a reward of up to 10,000 francs. In some cases this reward will be even higher.**

I looked at Brigitte and demanded of her why she and her family should take such risks in helping me. She uttered not one word . . . but just smiled.

Children from the Kindergarten gathered in the square, chasing round the fun fair roundabouts which had been towed there just before the outbreak of war, now dejected and silent, except for the children's raucous noise. Soon a crowd of more enfants joined them, refugees of Moselle, from the Lorraine School in the village Brigitte explained. As we walked about the village, Brigitte shared with me her childhood days and experiences, the memories of her youth. Older children would go to either the boys' or girls' school in the village where her mother had been taught. The boys' school was opposite the tram terminus and here, late on summer afternoons young people would meet and talk for hours on end, stealing kisses in the shadows. On special occasions Papa would take us to one of the cafés, usually The Oak Tree Café on a Sunday after Mass, whilst Mother and Grandmamma would do their last shopping for Sunday lunch. Here we would be treated to a drink of lemonade surrounded by local men drinking and playing cards, whilst noisy town folk arrived from Limoges for the day, starving, hungry and thirsty!

"Pardon Monsieur," came a voice from behind us. We turned fearful of who it might be. Before I could determine exactly who the man was who was facing us, a sense of relief swept through me as I realised he was not wearing uniform.

"Ah, bonjour Brigitte," he went on. Her uncle, a stocky man with a weather beaten complexion, was dressed in his best, evidently on his way to share a Pernod and pipe with old friends. After pleasantries and a knowing smile cast my way, we headed back to the cart, keen to return to the safety of the farm.

The stark, silver sunlight shimmered on the cottage roofs, dimming as passing clouds masked the sun. A few farmsteads resting along the skyline, presented a hazy silhouette, the sky behind dirty white as grey tinged clouds tumbled above the horizon. Pulling into the gravel yard of the farm, the peace of this place, for a brief moment returned to me. The old dog barked a deep bark from somewhere in the house whilst screaming from across the yard in alarm, stood a large excited sow, tail straight up in the air, nursing five piglets. Escape had been achieved by this particular animal and if this one had got out so probably must others. Émile leapt out of the cart and, grabbing some half rotten windfall apples, thrust the sweet smelling handful before its snout, which was now twitching and sniffing for all it was worth. Licking its lips, chomping and foaming at the mouth, the big, old pig waddled after Émile, followed by its wagging tail and five

244

piglets, chasing their next feed. The excitement was not yet over: I followed after Émile and as I rounded the end of the house, snorting loudly were two stout beasts, rooting in amongst some vegetables. Drawing towards them, the largest ceased its hunt, lifted its massive head and looking me in the eyes – belched. The shock of this resounding noise seemed to surprise it and the other pig as much as it did me! Then, squeaking with one accord, the two pigs headed off to join Émile's band, undoubtedly to resume their rooting, snorting, squealing and belching elsewhere.

The kitchen stove was now low and after our glorious journey back the room seemed dark and cold. Brigitte fetched some sticks and, stoking the fire, soon had its flames roaring up the chimney. Taking the large kettle which had been filled to the brim, she placed it on the stove, sending water slopping about, instantly turning to steam as hissing, it soaked the warming cooker. She stood at the window gazing aimlessly beyond the orchard and past the fields, above the charcoal grey woods, high, high into the sky. Brigitte asked in a dream like manner,

'What do you call that sky?"

"It's a mackerel sky," I shared.

"A mackerel sky," Brigitte softly repeated under her breath.

"What are you thinking?" I gently asked, realising her mind was on something else. "What is it?" After a brief moment she calmly explained,

"I knew a man once, he was not so unlike you!"

"What happened to him?"

"He just disappeared along with other young Frenchmen; he was taken by those wretched Nazis and I never saw him again. They not only stole the country I love!" She turned her face towards me, the sunlight glistening in her eyes as tears welled up.

"Why do you look at me like that?" she challenged. Trying to comfort her I whispered,

"It hurts me to see you like this." Summoning a new found boldness I pulled her warm body towards mine and wrapped my arms about her. There was no holding back as she clung close,

245

sobbing, trying to fight back tears. We held each other longingly, an embrace that meant so very much: an embrace that encouraged me to dream. I now knew Brigitte's feelings for me were as strong as those I felt for her. The next words she uttered cut me like a knife and left me speechless.

"And now I will lose you too . . . I hate this evil war."

One hundred and one thoughts were scrambling through my mind, yet I couldn't bring myself to answer her, feeling totally inadequate, words didn't come easily, not knowing what to say.

# Chapter 30

The slow, lazy summer was slipping away, its last few days heralding autumn: a time when the countryside was changing, beginning to mellow. The long, dry sun blessed days were long gone; once again the wind and rain clouds, a distant memory, would return. Twilight would now fall early on the meadow lands, woods and river; the stars, faintly sparkling at first over the treetops as the sky paled, soon would be shining brightly. Weary crows settled in their lofty roosts for the night, "kra-kra", their haunting cry echoing in the dusk. An owl swooped low along the twisting, white river as it started its night hunt for food. Little else was stirring at this hour, just the murmurings of the trees in the quickening breeze and the feathers rustling on the resting owl, its eyes never still and its ears always alert.

I awoke after what could only be described as a restless night. I made my way cautiously downstairs: at such an early hour it seemed unlikely callers would be visiting but you could never be too careful! In the kitchen Henri was studying the morning from the window; he turned as I entered, smiled and, putting his steaming coffee to one side, beckoned me to follow him across the yard, to the cart hut. There one of the horses was already tethered; this old working mare carried an air of great pride and nobility, and she was beautiful. The cow pulled the plough, but she drew the cart. As Henri tipped some cereal in her feed bucket, on top of a dry root or two, he exclaimed,
"Only enough for the work she does . . ." Then nodding to the net of hay said, "grass makes horses fat and soft; there is nothing better for them than good hay." Henri handed me an empty pail and pointing to the trough indicated that I fill it. She drank long and well between her feeds, her great hooves thumping on the dry, earthen floor, dust rising and settling as she fidgeted.
"She's a fine old horse." I put to Henri.
He looked proudly on, then in a melancholic way uttered,

"Many hundreds of horses as fine as her will give up their lives in this war of ours, . . . thousands have died at Dunkirk and on the Russian front." For the next few minutes I helped him by steadying the mare's head, reassuring her whilst he set about harnessing up ready for their journey later that morning. The old mare's bright eyes seemed to smile at me. Henri explained they would ride four kilometers to a neighbouring village, taking an indirect route where they could, to avoid checks and encounters with officials. There he would meet again with the local, armed, underground group, the 'Maquis', and learn of the latest news from the BBC: and de Gaulle, the King of France with no French subjects. At that he laughed. There was word that an agent travelling down from Paris had joined them, a radio operator, a woman who was willing to lay down her life for France. They would need to be careful because he had heard of a good, old friend who had been caught helping Maquisards, all of whom had been shot by the French police gun squad. An elderly, malicious woman had sold him to the Gestapo for 'thirty pieces of silver.' Some French it would seem were no better than the Nazis. I had never before heard him speak in this way. The increased activity of the Resistance had made the Germans and Vichy police more determined: he had to be ever more vigilant. The local people had not as yet been subjected to the curfew, unlike many parts of France, but he was certain it would soon come. Pétain's 'New Order' would end. We strolled back to the house: outside Brigitte stood quite still, barefoot on the cool, dewy grass, smiling as she caught sight of us. Henri looked to me, indicating I should go over to her as he continued into the kitchen.

With a whinny the mare, strapped between the shafts and led by Henri, pulled the cart across the yard. Once Émile's chores had all been completed, he and Henri mounted the cart, making ready to head off to the next village. The old lady, wrapped in her thick, black dress and shawl, climbed up and perched beside her grandson: she would use the outing to stock up on produce from the village. They all nodded to Brigitte and me, Émile smiling brightly, and with a 'clak-clak' from Henri, the mare strained at first with the load, then trotted determinedly down the lane. Without a word or a glance, Brigitte took hold of my hand and led me through the orchard to the river's edge. Beside the bank, in the shadow of the over arching trees she sat, removed her shoes and started to wade in the frothing white waters. As I joined her, the flow of the water chilled my feet as we waded upstream, the water foaming and bubbling about our feet. A slither of silver streaked through the waters and disappeared under the muddy bank. Brigitte tried to steady herself by grasping an overhanging branch; she shrieked in pain, her feet pressing on sharp stones. In an instant she had lost her balance and splashed into the shallow water. Soaked and cold, outstretched on the river bed, Brigitte's roars of laughter had now reduced her to tears. The peacefulness of our paddle had given way to the chaos of her fall which Brigitte seemed to find hilarious. For a precious moment she lay, flapping her arms up and down in the water, still giggling with laughter. Successfully rescued, we walked back to the house; although she had only lain but a few moments in the water, her whole body was cold, her clothes soaked through. Long, wet tails of auburn hair framed her pale but beautiful face. She grimaced, picking her path carefully over the sharp gravel yard, half laughing, half crying; I put my arm about her waist, offering support. In the kitchen, before the smouldering stove, her body shivered. Brigitte rocked with laughter as she looked at me; I gazed on, helpless, not knowing what to do next. This youthful, country girl radiated a sweetness so tender, a joy so full of life. Simple, baggy clothes, now wet, clung to her, hardly disguising her shapely body. Tumbling locks, tangled by the wind, lay on her sleek neck and slender shoulders. Large hazel eyes sparkled, hiding beneath long, graceful lashes; her perfectly shaped face, pronounced by high cheek bones, enhanced her fine complexion and pale, tan freckles. A plain, gold crucifix and chain rested on her dress proudly glinting in the light. Brigitte's mellow voice seemed to dance with every word she spoke, gracious and kind, alive and pure. She was far fairer than anyone I had ever known, a mysterious vitality seemed to fill her very being.

Moment by moment, from the very first time I saw her I was falling in love; we hadn't created love, it had been given to us as a gift. My head said this would be impossible; my heart said I must tell her, and tell her before it is too late. Just thinking this way caused me much heartache, realising that soon I would never see Brigitte again; I didn't want to let her go, I wanted to go on feeling her tender touch, holding her forever, never ever to be apart. If I tell her I loved her more than I have loved anybody ever before, then my heartache will be hers also, and that I couldn't bear. For a brief moment in time our two lives had become entwined as one, in such a way that we should never part. Maybe it was all just a dream, for I am a believer in dreams: I had dreamt that our love would never die.

There was a low attic which ran the length of the main house, separate from my hiding place: here Brigitte slept. The bedhead was pushed up against a stout timber purlin carrying the narrow rafters which stretched up to the ridge, supporting the boarded roof. About the attic floor, pails stood, positioned to catch any rain that found a path around the tiles during a heavy downpour. At night bats would claw up between the tiles and boards and in the morning she would wake to the sound of birds on the roof, singing. A roof window cast a shaft of daylight, highlighting a brilliant-yellow sunflower bloom in a narrow china vase which sat beside a white candle, set on a crude wooden bedside table. Two large plump pillows, covered with a pink floral design, sat between her bed and the rich, golden roofing timbers; and a rose coloured bedspread rested above the sheets, dipped in the middle where Brigitte would lie.

She stood beside the bed and began to remove her dripping clothes, giggling to hide any embarrassment as she slowly

undressed. The sodden, burgundy cardigan which had hung on her body was discarded into the washbowl and the excess water rung out. Her slender body turned and swayed as, easing off the soaked flimsy cotton dress, she allowed it to fall about her feet. Only a pearl white slip covered her, clinging, translucent and wet. Brigitte, in a playful way, teased me, lifting the slip away from her body then allowing it to settle against her again, embracing her sublime form. Bathed in a beam of sunlight, Brigitte's fragile beauty shone. Revealed before me her graceful figure, the curve of her firm rounded breasts, her sleek legs, her body, almost naked, almost mine. An appealing and irresistible charm radiated from her smiling face, her eyes sparkling with life and love. Without fully realising what I was doing, I gently drew her towards me, warmly hugging her chilled body. Brigitte squeezed me in acceptance as I caressed her, kissing her forehead, her eyes of wonder and her warm, sweet lips. We held each other tightly, sensing that this thing couldn't last. She whispered tenderly,
"You English have no feelings, you hide them, it's stupid."
Feeling my heart quickening, I replied,
"You don't know how much it means to me: your touch, your love. You'll never know how much you mean to me." I moved my hands gradually along her slender shoulders and eased off the narrow straps of her slip and slid it down her body to the floor. She held me close, responding to my every kiss, not letting go. We stood, hugging one another, frozen in time. Brigitte gradually edged away from me, and whilst still holding onto my hand, slid between the cool bedsheets. I unbuckled my belt, stepped out of my trousers and as I knelt on the bed beside her she slowly unbuttoned my shirt: carefully, undoing each button in turn. Putting her hands under the shirt, she lifted it off me, sliding it down my arms. Her smooth hands glided like warm velvet over my body, inviting me to hold her, caress her, embrace her. Under the sheet we lay, our bodies wrapped together as one, delighting in the experience.
"Do you have the heart to love me?" she asked in a penetrating and hopeful voice.

"Love, what do you exactly mean, tell me Brigitte, it's hard for me to understand, things are so different now?" Her gaze rested on mine; she hardly paused,

"With you I shared what it was like to be a child, to believe in the loveliness of things and people. I see the image of love about me, the joyful song of the birds, their tireless flight upon the air, the intoxicating colours and perfume of the wild flowers, the glorious butterflies lightly dancing from flower to flower. It is love that offers a glimpse of something exceptional, something exquisite. Amazingly it's as if the way I feel for them is the way I feel for you. Love is all this and more. I ask why it is you stay with us; you ask how it is we will risk hiding you. To trust someone completely, to trust them with your life and to be prepared to give your life for them: love is the secret. If I am love, then all about me is love."

Tenderly she pleaded with me,

"Do what is in your heart."

The magic of the moment totally captivated me, my every thought, my every desire,

"I can't bear to be apart from you," I could hear myself saying as I pulled her towards me. "I don't want to lose you, I don't want to leave you . . . I love you. You fill my every waking moment; I fall asleep, my head full of thoughts about you."


Her breathing was gentle, reassuring and relaxed, her body warm and tender, outstretched beside me.

"What is it?" she asked, repeating my name.

"I've never known a woman this way before! I have never touched a naked woman before . . . "

Any awkwardness I felt was eased as she pulled herself nearer to me. Her way was seductive, few words were needed; with every move I longed to be close to her, I yearned for her body. Moving back the sheet I kissed her as I ran my hand up and down her legs, gently stroking her, arousing her. My nose lightly traced her face, down her neck to her breasts: I kissed each in turn. Brigitte brushed her fingers through my hair and down my bare back, her breathing now much deeper and faster. I stroked her breasts with my hands as I kissed her firm stomach and her navel. Our bodies were enlivened, relishing these joyous moments of passion together. True passion needs to be shared, it can not be kept to oneself, it's impossible. Just as light brings life to everything it touches, so it is with passion. It inspires, invigorates, energises, enriches, celebrating and glorifying the very moment. Such was the passion we shared. We lay together for some time. Brigitte turned, her leg drawn up and cuddled tightly into me, contented; we both dreamt and hoped this would never end, wishing it were simpler, wishing it could be easier. I softly whispered,

"You are everything to me. To be away from you Brigitte will be unbearable, yet that is what must be. We live in two very different worlds." My hand gripped hers tightly in reassurance. "I must return to defend my country and to keep the fight going for France; you must be ready when the moment comes, and freedom returns, to rebuild your beloved motherland. We must do this for ourselves and for those who come after us. Yet for the briefest of times, for one enchanted summer, our worlds have been as one. To be apart will be impossible, but it is how it must be."

"I don't want to lose you," Brigitte murmured. We embraced.

"I will come back for you after the war and find you, and we will be together again!" My eyes swelled with tears as I continued to promise, "You will be with me in my heart every single day until we are bound together again, forever." Tears rolled down her cheeks, her crying now inconsolable, her whole body whimpering in my arms as I struggled with my emotions, choking on my every word, uncertain of how that could be.

It seems that sometimes it takes a war for everybody to truly understand the real meaning of love, and what a world would be like without it.

No lamp was needed that moonlit night as Brigitte lay under her bedcovers. She smiled a knowing smile, one of pleasure and delight, fulfillment and joy. I had long since crept back to my little attic on hearing the others return, and there I dreamt of what it could so easily be like if I hadn't been an airman and this wasn't a war.

The old woman was down on her knees beside her cold bed, hands clenched tightly, praying to Mary for the family, the harvest, for peace and as always, Brigitte's happiness.

# Chapter 31

Henri lay in his room planning the harvesting as he had done every night for the past week. Bad luck had hounded him and his family for many years. First it was his wife's death and then the boy's handicap; there had been many a poor harvest in the past and then of course losing some of his plump pigs to the Germans; and now there was me, an Englishman that if found would bring an end to all that he had worked for, all that he loved. He thought again of the harvest and of games they had each year with the rabbits. Sometimes his sharp scythe would catch a bewildered animal, slicing off its leg; and for that poor creature there would be no more cool, juicy blades of grass, just a hot steaming pot. Whilst Émile slept soundly in his little room, a wise old owl sat listening on the barn roof. Everything was now quiet, everything dark, as I lay trying to collect my thoughts. In the distance I could hear the faint howl of a dog, a sleepless owl hooted; I slowly drifted into a contented sleep.

Morning came, chilled and fresh; the early mist that lingered had now lifted, a gentle rain fell softly, blessing the fields and charging the hungry river. Making my way down from the attic hideaway, Brigitte's voice sang out a melody that was familiar, but one I couldn't quite place.

Later that day a man called: a member of the Resistance. He looked just like someone out of a Maigret story: dirty, black, leather shoes, coarse, brown cord trousers, a grey, collarless shirt over which he wore a shabby, blue, serge jacket. A shadow was cast over his face by a large-brimmed, green cloth cap; only his pipe, long since cold, and his gold-rimmed glasses were clearly distinctive. Upon his shoulder a canvas bag hung: from it he took out clothes which had been prepared for my departure. The trousers I wore had been dyed black; he had a thick, black coat and dark blue beret for me: all to make me as inconspicuous as possible, according to Henri. That day we shared a rare delicacy:

congealed chicken's blood, fried in a pan with garlic and parsley … and coffee. I asked him how the war was going,

"Bad," he replied, "it's always bad."

Before he left I gave him one of the photographs of myself which I carried hidden in my uniform. This would be used to produce my forged papers and an identity card.

Over the last few days on the farm I spent more and more time with Brigitte, catching precious moments when we could be alone. My last night with the family was marked by a thunderstorm: Henri warned a storm was expected, and soon green lightning lit up the valley and woods whilst the thunder rolled through. Émile enjoyed every minute of it as he edged closer to me and Brigitte,

"It's God talking to us and He's got something He wants to get off His chest," Henri pronounced, with a mischievous glint in his eye. Sheets of rain poured from the roof and fell from the trees, swelling the puddles in the yard. As the storm passed over and the low rumbling grew more distant, the dark,grey clouds gave way to the glow of the moon. It seemed funny to think that the same moon that was shining on us here was shining down on Mum and Dad back in England.

I was not aware that by now they had got a letter from the RAF records' office in Gloucester, advising my parents that they had received information that my aircraft had crashed somewhere in France, and nothing further had been heard. It concluded with a renewed 'expression of sympathy with them in their great anxiety.'

Climbing the stairs to retire to our separate attics for one last time, Brigitte looked towards me and, flinging her arms about my neck, said to me in a hushed tone,

"Let's see if you can dance."

"Dance!" I exclaimed, "this is no time to dance."

"It's the only time," she said as she put her arms around me.

"But there's no music."

Smiling, she started to hum that same melody I had heard days before.  I wobbled on the staircase, resting on her to keep my balance and by the glow of an oil lamp, we danced.  She laughed, exclaiming that I was extraordinary?!

That night I prayed – I used to pray when I was a child with Mother, but I had long forgotten the way.  I prayed for home, for France and Émile, Henri and the old woman, but above all I prayed for Brigitte.

The next morning heralded the start of a most glorious day: Henri was busying himself in the kitchen and, in an unemotional manner, shared,
"I have given you shelter here in my house with my family," I didn't know exactly where this conversation was going, "but you belong here no more than Brigitte belongs in your country, and yet she has fallen in love with you and you are falling in love with her, if I am not mistaken?"  With a sense of gratitude and honesty I confessed,
"During my time here I have found true love, she means everything to me.  You cannot choose who to love, only whose love to accept"

Nothing Brigitte and I had said could prepare us for this moment. I touched her, holding her hand; she moved it away and cried,
"Why must you go?"
"Brigitte," I replied, "you are the most wonderful thing about this war," she interrupted me,
"I am not afraid you know, but I don't know how it will end."  I drew her towards me, cradling her in my arms.  Enfolding her in my coat I murmured,
"When I look into your eyes, I gaze into your loveliness, a loveliness I shall never forget."  Brigitte sobbed, speechless, holding me even tighter.  I'd never seen her look so lovely as she did that time.

257

The truck engine growled once, then again as the patience of its driver wore thin.

"You must go," Henri's words cut like a knife, "I am sorry but you must go now." He hugged us both, "We will miss you – you have brought new life to our family, but that is how it must be," he muttered softly.

As I pulled from her grasp she looked lost. Émile ran to me, throwing his arms about my waist; I could feel his whole body shaking. The old woman stepped out, took Émile's hand from my side and encouraged him to let go. She looked to me and smiled, a loving smile as she stumbled over her words,

"You come back". For the first time I saw a beauty in her I had never seen before. Brigitte stretched out her hand and, opening it, revealed her gold crucifix,

"I want you to have this," she said, her voice trembling. My whole body seemed frozen with emotion. From my pocket I took the crumpled, folded paper: upon the cream sheet my words to her began,

'My dearest Brigitte, my beloved . . .'

The truck crept down the gravel drive; I turned and waved for one last time. The vehicle rattled onto the road and out of sight. Brigitte wept as she started to read my love letter to her:

*'My dearest Brigitte, my beloved,*

*I have been longing to tell you, but afraid, of just how much I am in love with you. You are the most wonderful thing that could have happened in my life: that is how I think of you. You'll never know just how much you mean to me: your smile brightens the darkest day; your touch, I wish I never had to let go! I can't imagine leaving you and living a life without you.*

*I will think and dream of you every day we are apart – you will always be in my heart, believe me; we will be bound together forever until I am close to you again. Every word you share is known before it is said, every action seen before it happens; we are becoming as one, sharing the same dream. It is too late for that which we have not said and that which we have not shared. Thank*

258

*you for the special days, those endless summer days: I will not forget a single one you gave me. You gave me love, we laughed and cried, we had only just begun to live, with so much of our lives ahead.*

*You are the dearest one I have ever known. All that I want in this world is you, darling Brigitte. I give to you my heart, my love: a love that will last forever.'*

Slipped inside the letter was a small black and white photograph - the other photograph of myself which I had hidden in my uniform.

Over the past months I had grown to love this land: it was hard to find words that adequately expressed my enthusiasm for its simple beauty; a land like mine that was being torn apart by the ravages of war. Those last few moments, before day gives way to night, brings with it a sense of peace and gratitude that one has survived and stayed safe in this foreign country.

After an hour's tedious driving along narrow lanes and bumpy tracks, we finally arrived at our destination. The daylight was beginning now to fail, the dusk having provided ideal cover for our arrival. The wind was freshening and it felt as though rain was in the air: hopefully not the weather for any self respecting German or policeman to be on the prowl. The driver led me into the farmhouse: it had the same familiar dank and dusty feel and there to greet me was the portly old Maigret man! He invited me to sit and slid a steaming mug of coffee in front of me.

"Thanks, who are you?" I asked rather nervously out of habit.

"I don't think you should worry about my name," he insisted in a kind but firm manner. Several people joined us at the table, including a young woman who seemed in some way different to the others. A couple of old women served us a feast of pork and vegetables and one old chap asked my host how he managed to slaughter the pig without the Krauts knowing. He replied that he had told the Germans in a very confident way, that the pig must have fallen in the river during the recent flood and been washed away; which he said they swallowed! Everyone laughed. The mood during the meal was tense and business like. Several discussions went on around the table simultaneously, some I thought I understood, others I had no idea what was being said. Turning to one fellow across the table, the old man told him to let the dogs out for the night and to chain them well to the barn but to make sure they were hungry: he didn't want any unannounced visitors. He then looked at me and explained;

"The Germans see us as terrorists and bandits and the Maquis as guerilla fighters, they tolerate no dissidents in Germany killing them without a second thought; but we are soldiers fighting for liberty: Catholic and Communist side by side, striving to keep the identity of France. Many don't know exactly what to fight for: peace, yes of course, but we are fighting for freedom, a free France. Schemers, foreigners, buffoons and fools have brought France to its knees; for your Churchill, France means crossing the Channel: for Hitler it means crossing a bridge! Many say Britain is a spent force, but young men like you fight on, such is the optimism of youth. Germany needs fighting soldiers on the front and we must do all in our power to prevent them being deployed, to tie down as many of the enemy as possible."

This somewhat insignificant, little, grey haired Frenchman sounded increasingly like a military commander addressing his officers. The whole room was silent as everyone listened intently to his words, seeming to understand what was said even though he didn't speak in his native tongue!

"We carry out ambushes and attacks, hit and run raids, assassinations, acts of sabotage to create disruption and a spirit of defeatism; we operate clandestine printing presses that spread news from London and publicise German crimes, gathering intelligence to send to the Allies," and looking again towards me, "and we help shot down Allied airmen to return home." Of course, all of those about the table knew this and more; the explanation was for my benefit so I would be in no doubt of the risks they took and that they were fighting the same war as me. In a lighter, almost inconsequential manner, he added,

"Of course the Gestapo and security services fight back; the normal conduct and conventions of war are totally ignored." The gathering, realising the performance was over, began to resume their excited chatter, probably about the next operation. Over the talk of the others, the old man, catching my eye, beckoned me over to the chairs in the corner of the room; he nodded to the young madamoiselle who joined us,

"Your papers will not be ready for forty-eight hours," he elucidated, then glancing at the woman, stated, "It will be another day or so before we can take you down the line." I paid particular attention at this, imagining he was referring to my escape and return to England.

"You will travel south, disguised as a railwayman; this will mean you can more easily travel by train, then by the Comète Line across the border into Spain and to Gibraltar."[38] Not shifting his gaze from me, he set out the details of my journey and concluded, "Jac will take you!" There seemed little I could usefully say and, before I had a chance to come up with something, the talking abruptly ended as a voice announced it was nearly seven. An old, dark, wooden box was hurriedly revealed from beneath a pile of dirty sacks and what looked like a dead cat; with the movement the 'dead' cat squealed, grabbed a bit of bone and leapt off. The man stooped above the radio set, silence fell as he fiddled with the tuning knob and moved the aerial wire, endeavouring to get a clear signal over the static. After many squeaks and howls I heard for the first time for many a long while, a clearly pronounced, English voice: they had tuned in to the BBC. Coded messages, quotations and short sentences began to be recited, slowly and deliberately in French. Resistance and Maquis groups across the occupied lands would be secretly listening to their wireless sets. What seemed an endless list of jumbled words captivated the gathered crowd; they had received warnings of their operation earlier the previous day and now awaited the go ahead. 'For whom the bell tolls' was repeated twice . . . this was it, the room became alive again, as the man loudly declared,

"It is on." This was the secret phrase the group used to signal that whatever it was, was imminent.

"Some people want us to stop our attacks." Jac's words grabbed my attention, "To stop the Nazis taking innocent citizens hostage and killing them to avenge our actions." This pretty woman appeared to possess all the attributes of a soldier – confidence, discipline, bravery and sharp intellect. All this combined with good looks I considered made her a force to be reckoned with. In an authoritative tone she went on to outline our adventure. In a few days I would get my papers and we would be able to leave. They would prepare for me not only a good identity card but a ration card and coupon, tobacco vouchers, medical certificate, work and travel permits and passes, an exemption certificate from the labour programme and a railwayman's pass. She was quite explicit in pointing out that we must check that I had nothing with my name or initials on, as this would give away my new identity: I had become 'Pierre Marc Reine'. I had to melt into the shadows, moving unobserved, indistinguishable from the local people; anything I did which made me stand out would invite suspicion and scrutiny. I had to be on my guard at all times: a wrong word, a lapse in attention, the smallest detail overlooked would bring danger and risk of capture, interrogation and gruesome if not fatal torture. There is no such thing as 'Liberte, Egalite, Fraternite', now it is 'Treason, Hunger, Prison'. There will be Jerrybags she went on, German sympathisers and informers everywhere, for many believe that the German war machine is invincible. Today's friend can so easily become tomorrow's enemy! Finally she warned me to beware of the Bourgoise: they will not help, they have too much to lose. This was a woman who seemed to relish the demands that the Resistance made of her: a chance for adventure and excitement and to use her initiative and intelligence while facing all sorts of danger. Her fortitude impressed me; her attractiveness belied the depth of her convictions and outrage.

262

Above all she detested everything that Hitler and his Third Reich stood for and was doing to her kin and country.

"My country was stolen from me and I want it back."

Jac had flown to England to train in industrial sabotage: first at Station 17 near Hertford and then on to the Explosives School in Blandford, Dorset. She returned on one of those long, bomber flights, as she put it, with 138, jumping into the darkness of the countryside below now occupied by her enemy. She went on to tell me about the jump,

"Bandages were wrapped around my ankles so that when I landed they wouldn't break. Strapped to my legs was equipment which I would release on a line and pay out after I was in the air. The wireless operator had made contact with the reception committee on the ground through their 'S-phone' and was able to guide us into the Drop Zone.[39] With all the containers away we climbed to 600 feet; I sat on the edge of the hole in the aircraft floor, my legs hanging over. The red, warning light signal went out and the green light lit; as the dispatcher tapped my shoulder I jumped, the static line automatically opened my chute. Within a few seconds the equipment line went slack as the bundle hit the ground; I landed and went into a relaxed roll just as I had been trained. The group was there to greet me and soon I was being driven away as the canisters were loaded onto a dilapidated Citröen van drawn by a horse." Jac concluded her account there, conscious I suspect that I was shattered; the evening had been exhausting, so much to take in and now I found it impossible to fight back my tiredness. Having bid goodnight to my hosts I settled down for the night on a mattress laid upon the floor of their cellar. As I removed my coat to cast over the blankets, I discovered to my amazement Brigitte's gold crucifix and chain, lying in the bottom of one of my pockets: a memento I assumed, a gift of love, something that would always remind me of her and our precious time together. Soon another day will dawn and the world will wake to yet another day of war.

The group had been given the go ahead from London to hit one of the main railway lines supplying the German front: it would not be easy as the line was patrolled 24 hours a day by troops, whose number for some unknown reason had recently been doubled.[40] It may have been in response to other Resistance groups blowing up sections of line and rolling stock, jamming points, cutting signal cables and generally playing havoc with the network. Early in 1942, London was reluctant to allow overt sabotage operations in the Zone Libre - Free Zone, but times now were different, and their 'Green Plan' to destroy railway lines all over the country was being implemented. The French railwaymen were past masters in creating trouble, changing the labelling on the field rail trucks and re-routing them to the wrong destinations. For every shovel of coal that went into the train's fire another flew out into the fields under cover of darkness in the night. Even youngsters would innocently visit rail yards and smear the engine and truck wheel bearings and parts with specially formulated, abrasive grease which would cause them to wear, cease or fall apart. The Germans would regularly force French hostages onto trains in order to dissuade the Resistance from blowing them up; however, this hit was going to be on a military train on a daylight run eighteen kilometers north east.

Jac said that they had been watching the line, observing the patrols and recording their regular times. Surprise was vital. Knowing the countryside well, they had ensured all knew the route of retreat so that they could make their escape and disappear completely without a trace. Loaded with an arsenal of out- dated weapons retrieved from the woods on the farm, tools and equipment, we crept in a single file avoiding prying eyes, sheltering behind a hedge line as we made our way down the embankment to the line. All the equipment had to be simple to use and cheap to manufacture: I had been handed a British 9mm Sten machine gun, probably because they assumed I knew how to use it; I'm not sure I wouldn't have been more at home with a pistol. The spot chosen for the ambush was a deep cutting immediately after a bridge-crossing overhead. Thick undergrowth screened the trackside providing ideal cover for us as we lay in wait. The idea was to wreck the train in a spot where it would be difficult for the Germans to quickly clear the line, and also take the bridge with it. A single, hefty charge of 50 lbs of high explosives was buried three feet between the rails directly beyond the bridge, the detonator firmly implanted within. Care was taken to disguise where they had dug, washing off the earth from the stone ballast with a tin of water they had brought; it was completely unnoticeable. The hidden wire was run about fifty yards up the bank to a group of trees from where the exact moment to fire the charge could be easily determined. I shared my surprise with Jac about how much explosive was used. She admitted to me that in the past when they had just wrecked the track or derailed an engine, the Germans had got the line operating within hours. We positioned our three teams, one to provide cover for the firer near the engine and the other two groups, mid and tail end of the anticipated train. I settled into the bushes with Jac and the others sixty yards before the bridge.

Some two kilometers back down the line, the massive steaming beast was approaching us, groaning along the track. We couldn't see the engineer working tirelessly to drive the train onward, nor the train's fireman frantically stoking the boiler, but we could see clouds of soot-laden smoke billowing back down the line.

We could hear the train in the distance now trundling towards us with two columns of soldiers marching ahead, each side of the track, looking for anything suspicious. My heart was thumping madly, my hands clammy and throat dry: just a few more minutes to wait. One of the forward guards stopped, turned and raised his rifle to his shoulder;
 we thought he'd seen us, but just at that moment a bird rose out of the undergrowth and flew off. He relaxed his gun and continued cautiously tracing the railway line. The train rounded the curve, whistling as it trundled relentlessly towards the bridge and our cutting. The monstrous machine rolled purposefully on towards its destination; at its head was a platform car, there to protect the

loco from mines on the track. Behind the coal tender was coupled a truck with tools and machinery for repairs, then an armed, fortress car followed by wagons packed with soldiers. Anti-aircraft guns were mounted on a flatbed covered by camouflage netting, and the whole convoy was rounded off with another armoured carriage. The soldiers who hadn't quite reached the bridge stopped. As I glanced back, one of their number signalled for them to call off their patrol and mount the train as it picked up speed. Meanwhile, five kilometers down the line two of the Resistance were cutting the telegraph lines. The loco roared, smoke belched about it as it emerged from under the bridge, the engineer leaned out of his cab, straining to see along the track. Soon, very soon, we would know if all the planning and preparation had paid off. The engine was now in the open, dragging its soldiers and armaments ever closer to our ambush. The detonator battery was connected and just as the loco's front wheels reached the explosive, the detonator fired the charge. A tremendous blast echoed all around me as the enormous locomotive erupted ten feet into the air, lifting with it the carriages. The bridge spar directly above it rose briefly, hung in mid air for a second or two with the train, then crashed spectacularly to the ground below. I jerked back as bullets sprayed in all directions: this was very different from being stuck up high in the sky with the odd flack bursting about you. Having machine guns fired directly at you seemed much more personal! That day I would kill men I didn't know, who, just like me were fighting a war. I loosed my machine gun in blasts of two or three rounds sighting it from my shoulder. Part way through my thirty-two rounds the Sten jammed: I cocked it and pushed the magazine fully home. The ejection opening was blocked with an empty round, so I turned the gun on its side and, while shaking it vigourously, the case fell out. I went on firing at the Germans who were in complete disarray - those who had not already been killed in the crash. There was complete mayhem. It was carnage: bodies were blown apart in the explosion and crushed in the smoking wreckage; wagons and carriages over turned, rubble

266

piled upon bent and twisted machinery. The few men who were still alive were being slaughtered as they fled to escape by the crossfire of the Resistance fighters, who were well dug in and hidden. It was horrendous. A small band of Partisans had seized a loco from the station back down the line and this was now steaming relentlessly on a collision course with the wreckage.

Hundreds of German soldiers met their end on that day and a few dozen fled wounded or broken; the bridge and the locomotives were no more, and it would take weeks and weeks for this mess to be cleared. Above all, the much needed men and guns would never reach Hitler's front, and it would prove yet another bitter blow for German morale. Eight Resistance fighters were lost in the action, men who would be sadly missed.

A tired, yet elated band of 'terrorists' made their way home after what they described as a "useful day's work".

# Chapter 32

The following day, in true Baden-Powell spirit, we packed what seemed like everything and I dressed in a thick black railwayman's jacket and trousers, completing my disguise with an oily scarf and scruffy looking beret. I washed my hands which, whilst wet, I rubbed on an old, rusty water heater pipe so that I could wipe the resulting colour over my face and neck, taking care to cover my nostrils, ears and eyelids, as well as working up into my hair line. When it was dry the large splodges and specks were brushed off; and for the final touch, I chewed some garlic – old Richard would have been impressed: all the French smell of garlic! The men crowded into the kitchen, nodding their heads as they wished "Good Luck" to me and "Safe Trip". Several of the elderly gents had tears in their eyes as they bade me farewell. And so it was, on a grey November morning, we started our journey 'down the line'. A farm lorry took us south to the nearby country station where we were pushed and shoved into a long train: wooden seats and freezing cold compartments greeted us. French police strolled through the train, checking passengers, but before they had a chance to get to us, a shrill whistle sounded and a guard ran past the window waving a flag: with a jolt the train began its snail like journey west to Angouleme. The platform at Angouleme was packed; guards came through the train checking our papers. This was it: I was quite convinced they would see my Carte d'Identité and documents for the forgeries that they were. The process was long and nerve- racking. It is strange how the game can be lost before almost the first move. He acknowledged me, then passed them back before moving on! In a moment the train pulled away, its steady rhythm slowly building; we resumed what was to prove a long and arduous journey. Opposite me an oldish lady sat chattering away to herself under her breath. One young man had his head in a paper, whilst the German soldier beside me had captured the attention of Jac across the compartment from me. He smiled at her; she forced a smile in return, not wishing to annoy him: after all there were few eligible young Frenchmen for women such as her now. I settled back into my seat letting 'nature' take its course as we headed south to Marmande, Mont-de-Marsan and Bayonne, keeping clear of Bordeaux: Jac said it was too dangerous and should be avoided. We crossed the demarcation line, leaving the 'Free Zone' and on arriving at the station it was late, cold and dark as well as swarming with German police. The soldier who had flirted with Jac was only too willing to carry her small case for her, and readily escorted her across the platform. The police took an interest until, with an intolerant air, the soldier gestured them away. Realising their mistake on not recognising her companion, they sharply stood to attention, extended their arms in the Nazi salute and repeated 'Heil Hitler'. The soldier weakly returned the salute and both he and Jac strode through the check point unhindered. I bundled through with the other passengers and workers, relieved to be free of the interminable train. Jac caught my eye outside, her soldier now long since gone, probably reporting for duty. She led me away to meet our contact who would help us on the next stage of my journey along The Comète Line.

I lit a Gauloises and inhaled deeply, not that this was something I was used to but I needed to relax after the perils of the journey. The bitter evening air was fresh to my face, the rain shower now almost stopped. We sheltered in one of the high archways to the front of the railroad depot; the dark shadows offered a sense of security and certainly obscured our contact as he approached us from their gloom. The mysterious gentleman was in a long raincoat and wide brimmed hat which just rested on the stiff, upturned collar of his coat. He approached Jac and they mumbled a greeting to one another; we followed him to a black saloon parked across the square where a mangy dog was sniffing at the car's front wheels. No words passed between me and our contact, but I could tell by the way he conducted himself, he was a man of some social standing. The station clock struck the hour and, looking back, I noticed a large swastika drooped on the tower below it. To one side of the flag was a V sign daubed in white paint, a symbol of victory; Jac had said they were everywhere. I concluded there must be hundreds of French who listen to de Gaulle's shortwave pleas for action. Splashing through puddles, the car picked its way through the town's frantic traffic, avoiding the Gestapo and military which seemed to be everywhere and on the move. Crossing the river, our route traced the coast southwest towards the Spanish border. We drove on into the night for the best part of half an hour, then turned off the main road and, some distance further, pulled into a hamlet of small houses and cottages where we parked and were led into one of the dwellings. Jac introduced me to the doctor and his wife and, as we settled around their table, were handed a bowl of thick, beef soup and a generous glass of red wine: his wife having judged well the time of our arrival. Jac explained that they had for many months offered a safehouse to fleeing resistance fighters and airmen. It was too dangerous to stay near the town; Germans used the hotels and lodged with French families in many of the local houses.

"These are black years for France," the doctor commented in a pessimistic tone, pulling a seat to the table.

The following morning over breakfast he explained, in excellent English, the seriousness of his concern,

"After the fall of Paris, events took a disastrous turn: remnants of our army, wretched officers and soldiers, fled to the country, hoping they could make their last stand there, maybe even just trying to escape the war. Pétain became nothing more than a figurehead, the Vichy Government sank deeper into collaboration with the German occupiers whose grip was tightening; no part of France was free; the bodies of French men and women hang on ligatures about our town." He paused to gather his thoughts and emotions. "We strive to keep our identity and hold fast to the desire for liberation, but it is not easy, our spirit is being broken." His despair was self evident, but here was a man and a woman who were prepared to risk their lives to save France. I thanked him for his help and the risk they took.

"It is the only honourable thing we can do!" he said dismissively. A look of understanding appeared across his wife's face as she spoke in French; the doctor smiled and nodded in agreement as he translated for my benefit,
"It is not the manner of our deaths that is important but the manner of our lives. Enough blood has already been spilt." Jac told me that some nights the woman could not sleep for screams coming from the woods as collaborators were tortured by the Resistance.

We prepared ourselves for the next part of our journey, conscious we had to be wary of flushing the toilet too much in case the adjoining house was made aware of visitors staying. When we were ready the doctor did not hesitate to bid us farewell, his wife thrusting a parcel of food and drink into our bag.

Hidden in their shed were two ancient bicycles for our use. Our ride was not without difficulties: first my chain kept coming off when I changed gear, so I stuck to one and had to struggle up the hills. The heavy rain and strong winds during the previous night had left the roads covered in branches fallen from overhanging trees, and the paths muddy and almost impassable in places. Not only did the French folk use cycles but so also did the Germans. A patrol of two cycling soldiers merrily headed towards us on the narrow path that followed the canal. It was too late for us to divert: they had seen us and clearly intended to stop. One of the men spoke to Jac at length; he seemed courteous enough and after checking our papers and ignoring me, smiled and allowed us on our way. When they were out of earshot Jac shared that he was an Austrian who had been forced to join the Reich and fight for Hitler. She thought he was aware of who I was but he had reassured her with a knowing look that all was in order. We rode on until we found a secluded and quiet spot, thick with undergrowth and trees, to stop for our lunch - and here I learnt more of the ways of the Resistance. Young children and men exchange the soldiers' bicycle pumps for identical looking pumps air-dropped from England. They let down their tyres so when the

Germans had a go at pumping them up, the pump exploded, blowing off their hands.

"What of the doctor?" I asked. "Does he look after the Germans?" Often his waiting room was full of men who didn't want to work for the Germans. He would help young French men summoned to work in German factories by substituting the x-rays of sick people, making them medically unfit for service. Many would end up fighting for the cause. The German soldiers often sat unknowingly beside their enemy in the doctor's clinic.

We pedalled on until early evening, Jac having led us to a farmhouse in the foothills of the Pyrenees, close to the border. Here we were greeted by an athletic Basque man, thin as a stick and in his late sixties; he was to be our guide over the mountains and across the border into Spain.[41] Having gathered more supplies we struck out at a demanding pace along paths that I could hardly make out. The night was sharp and clear, the moon nearly full, set against a star studded sky. A man of few words, he strode on full of energy whilst my stamina was already waning. For two hours we climbed. On reaching the top, Jac pointed out to me the lights of the town of Irun and - Spain. We descended through the woods and finally reached the boundary between France and Spain: the River Bidasoa. Our guide picked our spot carefully, avoiding any German guards that might be patrolling, and joining hands we waded cautiously the thirty or so yards across the swift flowing river. Once across, ensuring we were not spotted by Spanish border guards - as they shot any escapees - we left the river bank, crossed a railway line and road, then climbed steeply until we reached a plateau, the mountains and valleys stretching before us, the sea laying some distance off. Daybreak found us approaching a rustic farmhouse, whereupon an old wizened farmer greeted us and took us in for shelter and a plate of cheese and hard-boiled eggs. Here we rested in safety until early afternoon. We awoke to the smell of a hearty meal of potato omelette, green peas and fried eels with wine and coffee which his plump, jovial wife had prepared for us. Before we were fully ready to leave for the next stage of our journey, (to walk to Irun and then on to San Sebastian), the old lady heaved out a large makeshift bed on a couch in their living room, and to my surprise disappeared behind it. There, tucked away, was a hefty looking sideboard, inside which, hidden from the most inquisitive eyes, was a suitcase within which was a radio transmitter-receiver. Should any officials call, she would take to her bed pleading sickness, refusing to reveal their secret. As the old lady set up the radio, I recognised it as a Type 3 unit on which I knew she would be able to relay messages back to England. She signed in with her Playfair code so her message could be decoded, and began to transmit. Little did I know that as we set out, having bid farewell to our French guide, news of my arrival was reaching England, and subsequently, Mum and Dad.

A 'CONFIDENTIAL' letter was delivered to them at their London masionette from the Director of Personal Services Air Ministry (Casualty Branch), 73-77, Oxford Street, W1. It explained, 'that information had been received from a confidential and reliable source stating that your son, previously reported missing, has now arrived in a neutral country'.

We reached Irun after a walk that reminded me more of the intense 'route-marches' of Initial Training, and from there we travelled by street railcar to San Sebastian. The tram ride, memorable for its half hour of swaying and lurching, finally brought us to our destination, a safe house just back from the beach. Our Spanish hosts were delightful and made us truly welcome throughout our stay: playing cards, talking and feeding us rather well. Meanwhile Jac was busy arranging with the British Consul to take us to Madrid. The overnight car journey took us south through the centre of the country and, as the dawn sun rose, the beautiful heartland of Spain unfolded before us: a countryside that appeared so different to what I had experienced in France. The official driver took us straight to the embassy in the centre of Madrid where we were interviewed to determine we weren't

273

German spies trying to infiltrate the escape line, and eventually we were told arrangements were in hand for our departure to Gibraltar in the next few days. Hanging about was a tiresome and boring affair, knowing I was on my way home, but not yet. The frustration of having spent days evading capture, secretly travelling through occupied France under the nose of the Germans, risking ours and others' lives, and now just sitting in the embassy garden, day in day out, not being able to go outside, was almost too much to bear. My attempts to relax and sleep were often hindered as I continued to fall prey to terrible headaches and nightmares, many of which I made no sense. It seemed strange to think I used to doze with four gigantic engines roaring next to me, but now I struggled. At last the final stage of our journey home was to begin: a train journey of many hours, seemingly stopping at every station along the way. The carriages were packed, the noise of idle chatter and children's screams assaulted my ears whilst the thick clouds of dust filled my nostrils, causing me to sneeze loudly. At every stop more women and children squeezed onto the train, trying to sell pastries, fruit or water; the journey seemed endless. Eventually we arrived near the coast and the border post of La Linea and cleared Spanish customs. For Jac it was the end of the line; I was indebted to her for getting me home. I shared my concern for her continued safety but she assured me the worst of the journey was behind her. We hugged one another as true friends and as I kissed her, grateful for all that she had done, I realised that for Jac to remain successful in outwitting the Germans she could never allow her emotions to show. She kissed me again and, turning away, disappeared into the crowd. I entered the British fortress of Gibraltar, home, and downed a stiff drink in celebration![42] I was soon billeted into basic accommodation, a barrack block away from the main camp for security reasons. I learnt that a small boat had docked on the Rock that same day, bringing with it seven passengers: an SOE agent, POW escapees and RAF airmen evading capture like myself.

During the next few days of waiting we shared with each other our stories and adventures, interspersed with lengthy de-briefing by RAF personnel - headed up by Donald Darling. He had once been a MI6 agent but was transferred to the British Military Intelligence Station in Gibraltar, reporting directly to Room 900 – the executive branch of MI9 in London. He was a likeable fellow and easy to talk to and during my meetings with him it was obvious he had a good knowledge of both France and Spain, as well as their languages. Familiar with Jac, respecting her and their escape line, he said he was always amazed at how many people were willing to be involved and was adamant that I would never again be able to fly into France for fear of being captured and, during interrogation, compromise the escape route.

The boat the boys had sailed in was a 346 ton trawler called the Tarana which operated a sort of ferry service between the south of France and Gibraltar, known as the Coast Watching Flotilla.[43] To their surprise they were picked up by what looked like a small Portuguese fishing boat and transferred to the Tarana; then, as they sailed south approaching Gibraltar, they had to help the crew re-paint the hull and super structure, alter the shape of its funnel and exchange the foreign ropes and gear about the deck for British gear. The men's dress was changed and finally the foreign flag was replaced with a White Ensign. To all intents and purposes this now was a ship-shape British naval vessel that slipped into Gibraltar harbour.

It felt weird, for during those days on the Rock we saw no signs of Jerry.

Meanwhile, a short, curt message in the form of a Post Office telegram brought great relief and excitement at home:

From AIR MINISTRY
6/11/42 YOUR SON HAS ARRIVED
AT GIBRALTAR STOP

Our flight home had been delayed because the aircraft had to take evasive action to avoid enemy fire as it had departed Africa. There was no better sight as we stood on the dock and watched the massive Sunderland flying-boat splash down and taxi towards us. With a labouring drone from its four engines, the Sunderland lifted over the water, turning on its course for Biscay and England. I could see the huge Rock rising from below, guarding the Mediterranean, and just make out a Union Jack flapping, defiantly.[44]

# Chapter 33

Our flight back to England was uneventful and on arrival at Bristol I sent a telegram: 'SAFE AND WELL HOME SOON'. We travelled by train to London where, upon our arrival, it sounded as if the whole city was celebrating: Churchill had ordered that the nation's church bells could ring out again following the 8th Army's success at Alamein. Our stay was just a few days, long enough to be issued with a uniform, travel warrant, leave passes and to be subjected to a searching de-brief and medical check-up. During my last day I learnt the most disturbing news.

On the 11th November, in response to our successful Allied Operation in north Africa, the Germans and Italians immediately invaded the unoccupied Free Zone of France: Hitler's elite bodyguard of SS Troops stormed Vichy, overwhelming its army. I knew that for the French the war was now on a knife edge: they would be seriously doubting if anyone would be able to stop the spread of Nazism and end the brutality. This must be their darkest hour, as the great cloud of war descended across the whole country. My interrogator in London had told me that during a radio broadcast Pétain had declared that the French people were to lay down their arms, contrary to the Allies wishes.[45] With a smirk he added, 'It seems as if Hitler now needs a whole army to fight against the Resistance.' It was clear to me this war was not going to be over soon, and I became increasingly anxious for Brigitte's future safety.

My trip home was brief, necessitated by an enforced hospital stay as directed by the military doctor, who insisted I undergo a prolonged period of observation. For Mum and Dad it was an emotional time: firstly the relief of having me home alive, after months of fearing I had been killed or become a prisoner of war. Then the realisation I was a different person, battling with the anguish of what I had witnessed in France and the problems this

277

experience had left me with. Even now I was still troubled with the most disturbing headaches at times, not as many, but enough to take their toll. The doctor said they needed to 'assess my medical condition', whatever that meant. So, after only a few days catching up at home, I made my way to an ancient stately home deep in the Oxfordshire countryside. This, requisitioned by the military, was used as a convalescent hospital and provided a sanctuary for service personnel such as myself.

In the miserable drizzling rain, my car turned off the road and took me up a dark winding driveway overshadowed by tall, gaunt trees whose heavy branches, now bare, bowed low across our path. Beside the track, rotting leaves lay in piles, fallen or swept to their final place of decay. Every so often the vehicle would shake as we discovered another pothole. The soaked tarmacadam surface glistened black and reflected the soft beam of our headlights as we travelled deeper into the unknown. On a bend where the camber shed the fallen rain to a gully on one side of the road, an ornate pair of black, wrought iron gates, almost fully open, foretold of the grandeur that awaited me; the carved stone sign embedded on one of the pillars displayed 'Beryl Manor'. It was possible to see even in half light, this impressive two storey mansion which boasted of a time and affluence long past, of a peace and tranquility long forgotten. Turning into the courtyard we stopped outside the main door, either side of which an imposing, stone lion lay reposed on a low column, looking as if they were on guard and ready to pounce. This gothic styled house loomed far above me, fashioned in a rich, mellow stonework which glowed warmly in the moonlight of early evening. Tall, candy twist chimney pots stood in pairs over the centre of the gable ends, and lattice stonework topped the generous, bay windows. The rain had now eased a little and, water collected on the roof, spouted forth from the mouths of gargoyles positioned in the gutter work. From behind the pair of large, oak stained glass doors, an orange light half illuminated what looked like a middle aged woman, dressed in nurses' garb. She opened the inside porch doors and beckoned us in.  By the time I had got out of the car and looked for my case, my WVS driver had retrieved it from the boot and was climbing the three, broad, stone steps to the door.  Even in the briefest of moments my hair, in the absence of a hat, got wet, and rain had started to drip off my jacket.  We opened one of the outside doors and stepped into the entrance hall from which several other doors led, as well as a magnificent carved, oak staircase, curving upwards.  All about were trappings of wealth and privilege: portraits hung either side of a large landscape depicting what I could only assume was of the house.  In the centre of the ornately tiled hall a hexagonal, mahogany table displayed a large, brightly glazed bowl and bouquet of flowers, equally as brilliantly coloured – probably false I remembered thinking to myself.  An impressive, long-case clock tucked away in a corner caught my eye and its slow, deep sounding movement seemed reassuring.  Propped against its case, a collection of odd walking sticks took rest, one sporting a horn handle; whilst in a rack near the front door a couple of umbrellas were drying, as evident from the small puddle beneath.  A high counter arrangement had been fitted to one side and looked completely out of character with the rest of the décor; behind stood the woman who had beckoned to us, clearly ready with pen in hand, to complete her administrative duty.

"So who do we have the pleasure of welcoming on this dreadful evening?" she enquired with an air of indifference.  Before I'd uttered a single word, my WAAF driver had supplied her with all the relevant details she needed.  The woman looked at me and murmured,

"Mmm."  It would seem I had little part to play in this because almost without delay the WAAF driver turned to me, saying,

"You will be fine here, they are expecting you and you are just in time for supper!" and turning to the administrator, then to me with a smile of acknowledgement and slight awkwardness explained, "I'll be off now then sir, back into that dirty night."  Without a thought I replied,

"Take care, it's not nice out there." No response was expected or offered, the door swinging tightly closed behind her. The faint red glow of her car's tail lights seemed to dance as they disappeared out of sight.

"Well it's good to have you with us," the nurse's monotonous voice broke the silence, "If you'd like to follow me I'll take you to your room; don't forget your case will you?" I estimated her to be in her forties, probably early, with strong features, upright figure and competent manner. She wore a flop hat tied under her chin, a white-collared, dark blue dress pulled in tight about her waist with a black leather belt, secured with a large, chrome buckle.

Pushing open one of the doors to reveal a long, dark, arched corridor, she beckoned me to follow, her black laced shoes clicking on the stone floor,

"This way, mind the small step," I tripped. "That's it, you'll probably remember and not do that again!" Very much doubting that, I tagged along behind her. The initial, warm atmosphere quickly gave way to a much gloomier feeling, tinged with a lingering, musty smell and the distinct, occasional aroma of disinfectant. Having past several doors either side of the corridor, she paused by one and turning the handle entered, fully expectant that I was following.

"This is you, your bed is over there at the end." A single, iron bed frame was positioned in the corner, with an overhead curtain hoop suspended on long, steel cables from the high ceiling. "Your room mates are having supper with the other men. I'll take you there if you like, you can leave your unpacking 'til later, I expect you're hungry after the long journey!" She led me in the direction of voices and just before we entered the dining hall she turned and said,

"I am Sister Rachel," and with hardly a pause called out, "a new inmate gentlemen."

A short, stocky woman with a mysterious smile, going by the name of Briony, assured me as she served up my meal that she would make sure I was well fed and didn't go short. The rest of the evening I spent chatting tirelessly to the other fellows, getting a bit of a picture on the place. Looking around the forty or so chaps it was evident that for many, not all was well.

The following morning, on the stroke of nine, the doctor and his assembled entourage did their round. This was a revelation to me; I'd never been in hospital before. Sister Rachel was at his side whilst a gaggle of staff trotted along behind; when it was my turn they walked on by, only 'tail-end Nurse Charlie', or whatever she was called, approached, and, in a whisper, told me that the doctor would see me that afternoon. Eddie, an alert looking man in the bed next to mine was, or I should say, had been a Spit pilot, but it was obvious something traumatic had happened to him, resulting in a lad whose nerves were in tatters: I couldn't see him flying again. We got on well and I steered clear of asking him exactly what had occurred, so we passed the time talking about home and cars.

My session with the doc was fairly informal and conducted in his office; it seemed more like a friendly chat to me!
"I believe when you bailed out of your aircraft, the injury to your head on landing may have resulted in bruising to your brain. Your probable cracked ribs and injury to your lower back are testament to the severity of impact. I want to explore the extent of your problem, the bearing it may have on your persistent headaches and what, if anything, we can do about it!" To that end he proposed they monitor me for the next few weeks before deciding the way forward. That night I lay awake for a long time wondering what Brigitte and the family were going through, turning over and over in my head what I could have done differently and what the consequences might have been. The rest of the chaps in the room seemed to be sleeping well, but poor old Eddie was going through it again. His frantic radio exchanges with other pilots in his squadron were repeated over and over in his sleep, his voice sounding more agitated and louder with every telling. No-one else stirred; Eddie's madness continued to disturb my night.

During the next morning I took the opportunity to ask him what had happened in the night: did he remember? A soulful looking Eddie asked,

"Was I talking?"

"I should say, I'm surprised you didn't wake all the chaps and the staff." It hadn't escaped my notice that before the nurses disappeared for the night they did their pill round and many of the chaps seemed to become strangely subdued.

"They're used to it now, they seem to know without being told," he replied with an honesty that was disturbing.

"Well I wasn't. It came as quite a shock; what was going on?" He sat staring vacantly into space, no expression or emotion, almost in a daze for a while, not a word passing between us; then he let it all pour out,

"I see and hear planes flying around, in my head: German aircraft diving through the clouds towards me, weaving all about me, firing, they're everywhere and I am on my own. I scream over the radio but no one ever responds. The noise of the aircraft is horrendous, I can feel myself shaking wildly, my Spitfire plummeting to the ground, completely out of control; I can't do anything about it, I am helpless. My heart is thumping hard and loud, my hands feel clammy and my whole body feels as though I'm burning up. The vision before me of all that's happening becomes blurred, the sound of the engines and guns, more distant; then suddenly from that chaotic moment, peace descends."

He sat on the edge of his bed looking drained, absolutely exhausted, his fists clenched tight, shaking and sweating as the battle had unfolded again, this time in the depth of his mind. Dreadful things were going on in his head.

"Why do you remember these things?" I pressed him. His reply came seemingly without a moment's thought,

"How do you expect me to forget?"

I couldn't help but feel for him, this horror that he would probably have to live with for the rest of his life. My own experiences had offered me just a glimpse of this world, one which I was only too keen to be rid of. Eddie turned towards me now, fixing my eyes and in a pathetic voice admitted,

"I don't like to be alone these days you see, no one should die alone." I gave him a reassuring smile and nod. It was hard to appreciate that this one time fighter pilot had been reduced to this; he probably believed that as a young man behind the flight controls of a legendary Spitfire, he was invincible and could do anything. He sat almost sobbing, his human frailty exposed before me.

"He often gets turns like this, he'll be fine again in a minute." A slim fair haired nurse whom he didn't seem to recognise, smiled as she helped settle him in his bedside chair,

"There you go, you'll be better sat there," and turning to me in a soft voice added, "he's been through a lot you know . . . it's heartbreaking what we see in here."

This was Nurse Poll, her name badge announced as much, a finer, young lady you would struggle to meet, although her baggy uniform hardly did her justice.

"Have you worked here long?" I enquired, trying to make conversation and explaining, "I've only just come, I arrived a couple of days ago . . . I think."

"Yes, it's easy to lose track of time, the days fade one into another; I've been here sixteen months now, I am hoping I'll be off soon to join Queen Alexandra's Nursing Service on the frontline, but I must press on or I'll be in trouble with Sister."

She slipped away as silently as she had arrived and, as I turned back to Eddie, I realised that far from listening in, he was fast asleep, probably shattered.


For me the time passed slowly, disturbed by the daily institutionalised routines, odd bouts of depression – missing Brigitte - and occasional headaches. The high spots of hospital life included my first proper bath for months; more food than I was used to; opportunities to tease the nurses mercilessly and a chance to feel safe again, free from the endless shadow of war. The newspapers reported on the continuing German offensive against the Soviets in Stalingrad: 'Huns fleeing in Disorder' as Rommel's Afrika Korps withdrew to Tunis and the first official Allied statement about the Nazi mass extermination of Jews made by Anthony Eden in the House of Commons. Many refused to believe this wholesale genocide.

Had it not been for the manor's well stocked library, complete with a comfortable armchair, I may never have enjoyed the lighter writings of Thomas Hardy and discovered his independent young beauty, Bathsheba, as well as those magic moments of sleep when I wasn't being disturbed by my memories or those of Eddie's. Us fitter lads would often pass an hour burning off our energy in the grounds, zooming across the lawns, in formation with arms outstretched, pretending to be fighter planes, making the noise of over revving engines or chattering machine guns, as we weaved between bushes and flower beds. A more leisurely activity would be a thrilling game of ping pong, or if the porter got the snooker table out we'd challenge the nurses to a game. We thought that this would be a walkover, but months of practice on their part meant they were far more skillful than we gave them credit for. Nurse Langhorn proved to be the undefeated champ: a quiet lass from the home counties yet masterly with a cue in her hand. She always wanted to be a nurse, driven she said by the example of Edith Cavell and her exploits in the Great War. Having spent a number of her earlier years in the St. John Ambulance Brigade, she said it did little to prepare her for the horrors of nursing during the war years in a 'Casualty Clearing Station.' It sounded dreadful, men lying everywhere with their limbs stuck out at queer angles, others groaning in pain whilst doctors worked to save them; and if that wasn't enough, more wounded were coming in all the time.

November had given way to December and the fierce autumn winds had succumbed to the freezing days of winter, and their starkness. A light dusting of snow settled, softening the roofs, rounding the hedgerows and hiding the paths. Silently and almost invisibly a myriad of light snowflakes danced through the air, gusts lifting then swirling them about. Branches were stiff with frost. Dead leaves frozen in icy crystals lay upon earth as hard as iron. Nothing was stirring. Winter had closed in. As the month progressed towards Christmas the snow got heavier. It covered the distant hills of the Cotswolds and cut off our local village, filling the roads to the hedge tops.

A mid morning doze of mine was disturbed by a general hub-bub in the ward; all the mobile chaps were gathered by the windows, laughing and joking. On the lawn directly outside were two opposing teams of nurses, totally absorbed in a game of football. Their black stockinged legs were kicking in all directions and clearly not always connecting with the leather ball. They cut an amazing spectacle as they dashed through the snow, pure white aprons flapping about, and their scarlet lined capes trailing behind. The highlights of the match were when a nurse lost her footing or was on the receiving end of an aggressive tackle and ended up tumbling through the snow. It was hailing now and pellets of frozen ice had settled in their hair and on their red scarves. On their way back inside, Nurses Poll and Langhorn, exhausted and exhilarated, their icy hair and eyelashes sparkling in the light, looked in on us; all agreed it had been the best match they'd seen in years!

For us 'patients', Christmas had a special poignancy, thinking about faraway homes and loved ones and the seemingly lost spirit of peace and goodwill on earth. We celebrated with just a few simple luxuries that were available, and the nurses had done their very best to decorate the rooms; and there was Bing Crosby's 'White Christmas' on the player, played over and over again. Life was not easy and I shuddered to think of what it would be like now for Brigitte and her family in the hands of those Germans. Although we sang our carols, no church bells rang out - to avoid them being confused with the air raid signals. In their dorm, the nurses sat about, smoking, playing cards and chattering about what they would do during their time off. Others were writing home or doing their hair ready for a night out, whilst a couple were dancing together to the music of Chesney Allen on the BBC.

A letter from home also brought with it a letter of greetings and news from Cara and Oswald, who had been taken ill; I retired to the Library to read this latest news from Shetland –

December 1942
Dear Lilian and Ronald,

Christmas Greetings from Reawick
We were overjoyed to hear from you that 'The Boy' is back safely, thank God for that my dears, you'll be altogether for Christmas. This year our Christmas time will be weird to say the least. My Oswald's been working at the phantom airstrip at Scatness Point, next to the RAF Airport at Sumburgh. Runways have been marked out, and lights erected on poles to mislead the Germans. Oswald 's been doing work on the air raid shelters for the houses and the ack-ack gun emplacements. The weather's been absolutely Baltic, and he's been laid up these past weeks with a bad bout of flu. I had to get the doctor out, he's still poorly but on the mend now. It's not going to be easy this Christmas, he's had no money coming in for several weeks now. Moore's want him back, as they have more work building the new slipway and on the boats in the Rae, now that the whole 'Bus' operation has moved there from east of the Island. I've never seen him like this before though my dears. "The Bus' has been a real boost to folk here in Shetland as well as to

those in Norway: I never knew that we were once part of Norway.

I am still getting to Lerwick on occasions working with the Norwegians over there. One of the Williamson's boys boat me and others across from the bay here to the sheltered harbour of Scalloway. When the weather's wild it's a reakin journey, the sea breaks over the bow and without waterproofs, my goodness I'd soon be soaked through. All of us go like mad keeping the craft bailed out. Other times we can go day after day when it's like a pea soup of a mist, the water's as flat as flat can be; that's a lot easier. Then I travel south overland by bus on the road into Lerwick. There I go, blethering on about me again.

Stefan's been billeted down on the front at Scalloway in Nicholson's old net loft, now called Norway House, it's a cold draughty old tin shack of a place, not where anyone would want to spend Christmas, so this year he's stopping with us. He's been grand since my Oswald's been poorly, getting supplies and peat in  The storms have been hellish this winter so far and the Germans more active than ever in tracking the 'Bus' boats; their losses are getting worse. Stefan doesn't think they can carry on much longer; he says they really need faster and bigger boats that are armed. David Howarth being no longer based at 'Lunna', operates out of the Headquarters of 'Dinapore'; a large imposing house requisitioned on the seafront near the new slip. He told the men in the yard that the Yanks, the US Navy, may stomp-up some sub-chasers for the runs. Our Oswald just barked from his sick bed, 'that'll show Jerry'.

On one of the runs a boat brought back Christmas trees all the way from Norway, and Stefan was able to sneak one out from 'Kergord', the agent's safe house. The girls said it was the best gift they could have, they were over the moon: you won't realize just how unusual a tree is here. Around the coast at Skeld there's a concert, Christine is performing some Highland dancing with others and Kathy's busy practicing a song on her recorder, but we can't be sure she'll play it on the night!

I'll sign off now Lilian and Ronald, and look forward to hearing your news. One holy storm is falling across to the south, a real ree, and it looks as if we're in for snow. Oswald hopes Ron you're still able to crack a joke, even though he can't. Take care of yourselves darlings.

Hugs to you all and a big kiss to 'The Boy' and as Oswald would say, 'a few drams at Christmas never did anyone harm!'

All our love,

Cara, Oswald and girls.

Amongst the cards, Eddie got a Christmas card from Wolverhampton, a black and white picture of a Spitfire in flight was opposite the greeting from Royal Air Force Station, Cosford: 'A Plane Man's Wish: That you will be happy at Christmas . . . and always!' It completely cracked him up, causing him to cry aloud. This was a pilot who'd never again climb high into the clouds.

For me the Doc's visit the next day landed a hefty blow. I had been far from prepared for his conclusion,

"Our opinion, after having monitored you carefully for several weeks, is that your parachute landing in France is likely to have caused bruising and compression to the brain. The periods of unconsciousness that you described don't seem to have persisted for long. The recurrent headaches you suffer, along with some nausea and short term visual disturbances would seem to support this. It is possible you have had some minor bleeding around the brain, a subdural haematoma, which is healing, but there may be a weakness here in the future. At the time you did not appear to experience any loss of memory or change of behavior. According to your account, which is good news in itself, although you said you wanted to sleep a lot and felt more emotional than you had previously; you need to give your brain a chance to heal, avoiding the pressures of action to you and the risk of your unpredictable condition to others who might rely on you. So that is why I am recommending you are transferred to ground duties."

He sat in silence awaiting my reaction, resisting any temptation to justify his decision further.

"What no more flying? I've got to become one of those desk wallahs?"

He didn't answer me and I could see there was no point in pursuing this line; he'd made his decision and that was it.

That night I had the most disturbed night of my stay. As I lay in my bed I could sense the whole room closing in on me. I knew things weren't right, not because of any pain, for I didn't feel ill as such; I was troubled by a sense of deep concern and fear, for what, I am still unsure. I didn't feel myself, yet I wasn't anyone else. At times my head was like a whirlpool with so many things and words churning around, and images one after another, unrelated, unrelenting, all so fast, faster than I could endure. I seemed to be flying through clouds, thick and turbulent, then plunging agonizingly downward, aware of great danger. A sense of hopelessness was all consuming; anxiety gripped as I saw flames licking about a plane, men were shouting, screaming and fighting to escape. A voice from within the aircraft was calling my name. Blood was spread across the grass of a muddy field, across a sheet over my stretcher; double doors with polished, brass handles were flung open and my stretcher, like a sledge, was dragged along the black linoleum of the corridor into a room, a room which had no ceiling nor roof, just sky above me, with planes weaving in and out of the clouds. Then I saw faces bent over me and strangers talking, not to me but to each other: about me? But I couldn't hear anything. One of them was Brigitte; she lent over me and I felt her warm voice caress me, "Good night my dearest, God bless you" And now I was all alone, nowhere and no-one to turn to: at that very moment words came into my head, words I was familiar with, comforting words – 'Though I walk through the valley of the shadow of death, I will fear no evil: for Thou art with me; Thy rod and Thy staff they comfort me'.

Waking was a moment of gratitude to me. The round, wood rimmed clock hung on the wall above the night nurses' station declaring the hour of 2am; underneath, a dim, shaded lamp cast a glow over her table, highlighting the nurse's relaxed figure, fast asleep in her chair.

I had made it through my war and survived, but now I was struggling.

# Chapter 34

A new chapter in my anything but straightforward life was about to begin. The RAF didn't want me to fly again, Mum and Dad wanted the old me home, and I yearned to be back in France, but not fighting in the war. As the doctor had said, rarely was there anything simple in life. It's a funny thing about coming home: everything looks the same, smells the same, and feels the same - even my slippers were waiting in the same place! Suddenly you realise you're the one who has changed.

My time at home was not easy: an endless round of questions and what seemed like cross examinations, especially from Mother. She couldn't understand why I was so annoyed about getting 'a nice and safe desk job', particularly as so many of her friends' sons weren't going to be coming home. Father was pragmatic and took the view that if I applied myself, an opportunity for a more proactive involvement would arise: he was clearly more positive than me! The two of us spent a bit of time together during the few days I was home. Having been busy on the allotment, he was now paying particular attention to his brassicas that he'd transplanted in October having religiously dusted them with soot all through the summer to stop some fly or other. All being well and if Jerry didn't target his plot, he expected a grand crop in the spring. His real news was that of changing his job. The Post Office had transferred him from Enfield to Dollis Hill, where he was involved in something called the 'Paddock'. The establishment, located in north west London, was some sort of underground bunker: Dad said it was meant to serve as a standby for the War Cabinet. The word was that Churchill preferred 'The War Rooms' at Whitehall, so much so that the upper floor above ground of the Paddock had been relegated to the Post Office Social Club and canteen. He didn't know what went on in the citadel below, it was secret! One of the chaps in his Home Guard unit called Edwin had left and joined something he referred to as an Auxiliary Unit of the Home Guard Battalion 203. Dad was really unclear what it was and said it all sounded rather cloak and dagger. Edwin had told him that he was one of six men in his squad, all of whom had been on special training courses, equipping them to go into hiding. They were ready to attack any invading forces behind their own lines. In a strange way Father seemed to hold a lot of respect for him, although he clearly doubted that a handful of old men with pickaxes in dug-outs could fend off the entire German invasion, even if they were trained.

In the meantime it seemed that 'Bomber' Harris's plan to destroy German industry was but a partial success and only marginally dented German morale; many had reservations about this strategy as the raids continued on Berlin and other cities. Already the US 8th Air Force had moved its bomber force into airfields in eastern Britain and the German aircraft were no match for the B-17 Flying Fortresses and B-24 Liberators. Hitler's forces in Stalingrad surrendered with the capture of 46,000 men: his army was beaten by the 'Soviet Steamroller'; however, the Siege of Leningrad, already in its second year would last a full 872 days with a frightening human cost to both sides.[46] Stalin proclaimed 'Death to the German Invaders', cutting their supply lines, as Hitler's troops launched their Scorched Earth Policy, destroying everything in their wake. Hitler time and again refused his generals requests to retreat.

As I scanned the papers for news of France, my thoughts turned once again to Brigitte and how much I longed to be with her. I began to write a letter to her; I could not be certain she would ever get it but that didn't deter me.

*My Darling Brigitte,*

*Although I am miles away from you, I want you to understand just how happy I am; all of a sudden my life has meaning. My love for you is stronger than ever. Whilst I have been home in England I*

292

*discovered these words which describe how I feel
about you my dearest...
'You are my love, like the finest apple tree in the orchard,
the fairest of all women.
I delight in your shade, and taste your delicious fruit.
You refresh me, for I am weak with love for you.
Your left arm you lay under my resting head,
   your right arm gently embraces me.
You rise up and beckon me to come away with you,
my fair one.'*

*You are the most beautiful thing that's happened to
me; you are the most precious person in my life.*

I carefully addressed the envelope, but I don't know if Brigitte ever got it; I wrote to her time and again but in spite of patiently waiting, I never received a reply.

The RAF administration job I had landed proved to be about the most unexciting thing that had happened in my life for a long while. My office was located deep within the corridors of a dusty Ministry building in central London. Half a dozen of us toiled in what seemed little more than a cupboard, which on account of its three, resident smokers provided an experience similar to working in a cloud. A prerequisite was for the windows to be open, even in the midst of winter. Our section head was a tall, upright pencil thin chap, bespectacled and sporting a distinguished handlebar moustache, who went by the name of Charles Hadley-Heath. He was a proper gentleman, with a very peculiar mind, a particular manner and astoundingly over sized feet.

The work held little interest for me and was boringly routine demanding minimum concentration and absolutely no initiative. Meanwhile the real war was progressing without me. Any imagination, flare or enthusiasm I had was squeezed from me within a matter of days. The sole saving grace was the other characters in the office, who somehow, contrary to human nature, endured the daily ordeal, undoubtedly in the knowledge that they were doing their bit for the war effort. The days dragged by, so slowly, month monotonously following month, with little to break the routine. One high spot we all celebrated was when the Government, being so sure that the threat of German invasion had passed, ordered that all church bells would ring out again but, unbeknown to us at the time, sixty thousand Jews were being massacred in the Warsaw Ghetto: Göebelles publicly reported that Berlin was now 'Free of Jews'.

# Chapter 35

By now I had learnt from a chap in the Naval Office that the German U-boats had withdrawn from the North Atlantic. His sailing experience had been cut short in '42 when on board HMS Curacao: whilst escorting the Queen Mary into Greenock, his cruiser was sliced in two by the liner. The policy was not to stop and pick up survivors because of the U-boat threat, so the Queen with her 20,000 American troops on board to join the Allied Force in Europe, steamed on. He was one of the few survivors rescued. He said all in all it was a very strange affair

So here I was, serving no real purpose, doing no good, without any ambition and with no wife, lover, or true friend. I was soon to become just another man living in a world and a time I did not want to be part of, and in a place I had no desire to be. Without me the war still battled on: people were still being killed, slaughtered, sacrificed and massacred: loved ones lost ... forever.

By late spring 1944, southern England and its Channel coast had become, with the establishment of some 1,108 Allied camps, a huge depot for tanks, trucks and aeroplanes,. Lanes were littered with ammunition and weapon dumps hidden from enemy eyes, and village pubs full of English speaking soldiers from across occupied Europe. Office life was becoming hectic! All in all more than six million people were involved in the landings. Wags at work said the only thing that kept Britain from sinking were the tethered barrage balloons! An invasion site less well hidden had been established on the coast near Dover, within sight of the Germans in Calais, only twenty miles away. It was so well known that even the King and Queen paid a royal visit to its dummy dock which covered three square miles off the Kent shoreline and the false airfields, with dummy aircraft and military equipment. It was hoped that the Germans would believe this would be from where any invasion would come: crossing the Channel at the shortest possible point, the Straits of Dover, many hundreds of miles from the Normandy beaches where the invasion was actually to take place.

This was not to be my world, but as I was to discover, importantly it would be the world of some whom I knew.

On a small island off the west coast of Scotland, 518 Squadron was based: this was the squadron to which my old colleague, Tony, from navigation school, had found himself assigned. His crew were briefed for their latest mission: the date, June 5$^{th}$; their task, to fly a special patrol out into the Atlantic, south of Iceland, cruising at 18,000 feet, sending back coded weather reports but far more than normal for such a patrol. Once fed and kitted up they headed for dispersal and their faithful Halifax, shimmering in the light rain that had just started to fall. There appeared to be more than the usual attention being paid by the ground crew and engineers to their craft and its equipment. At 05.50 on the 6$^{th}$, after a bumpy take off, they circled the airfield, carrying out final checks on radios and equipment before Tony set course on their first leg of the Bismuth patrol. After two hundred nautical miles, they settled down to a steady fifty feet above sea level to take the first set of meteorological readings. The weather had deteriorated and flying conditions at this height were becoming hazardous: handling was an on-going problem for the pilots. The wind had now strengthened and the rain had turned to hail. In response to their transmitted met reports and forecasts showing increasingly severe conditions, Group commented that they could not possibly be correct. All on board were struggling, including Tony, as he concentrated to determine their exact position. The weather had yet more in store for them: hail turned to sleet and snow, icing up their airframe, and lightning forked through the dense clouds into the angry seas below. During the final climb the Hercules outer port engine misfired, then failed completely, and if that wasn't enough, the plane became alive with St. Elmo's fire, electric blue light dancing about the aircraft, causing the navigational and radio equipment to malfunction.

In selecting the date of D-Day, both the moon and tide were known, but the weather remained the unknown. The initial date chosen by Allied Commanders was the 5th of June, but the weather forecast was dire. The unusual weather pattern had encouraged Rommel to leave the front and head home to Germany: invasion was not imminent, well at least for a while. It was decided that, although there were high winds, cloud and some fog over the beaches the weather however was to briefly improve, still far from perfect, yet a further postponement would create immense problems. Tony and crews of 518 Squadron Coastal Command provided vital information that had a direct impact on selecting the 6th June for 'Operation Overlord' ... 'D-Day'. The long wait was soon to be over: the long day was soon to begin.

At 21.00 on that same night of June 5th my old mate from basic training, Richard, was flight engineer on a Halifax, flying off the coast of France in the Bay of Biscay. The purpose of the mission was to drop double avenues of white sea candles, twelve in each lane as markers out to sea, in La Gironde estuary and the Basin d'Arcachon, misleading the Germans to believe the sea landings would be near Bordeaux. They then dropped parachute flares, which burnt for twenty-four hours, along a ten mile stretch of the coast, hoping to further convince the Germans that this would be the location of the invasion.

Richard's role was part of a much bigger plan: Jael, the overall strategic deception plan in Europe during the build up to the invasion of Normandy.[47] It was apparent from intercepting Germany's top secret messages just how seriously they were taking these non-existent threats. A few days earlier, on May 26th, a General Montgomery double made a public departure for Algiers but by then the real Monty had already arrived at D-Day Advance Headquarters at Southwick House, near Portsmouth.[48] Some forty-seven double agents meanwhile were transmitting messages to confuse and mislead the enemy. The Germans gave the Pas de Calais section of the two thousand five hundred mile long Atlantic Wall their highest priority, placing their strongest force there: seventeen divisions of the Fifteenth Army.[49] On June 2nd, the US 8th Air Force sent almost eight hundred Flying Fortreses and Liberators to targets in the Calais area to reinforce the deception, and Bomber Command flew circuits over the Channel, dropping windows to persuade German radar operators the invasion fleet was on its way.

Meanwhile at 22.56 on that night of the 5th, Nige was strapped into the pilot's seat of his Halifax: checks complete, engines running, crew checked in and ready, awaiting clearance to take off. Hundreds of men of the British 6th Airborne Division had assembled, along with tons of heavy stores, equipment, jeeps, field guns and light tanks, ready to be air lifted in the main wave of gliders, destined for Normandy.[50] Tarrant Rushdon Aerodrome had already played host to a number of secret missions and now it was the turn of six Horsa gliders, daubed with black and white Invasion Day stripes, each towed by a Halifax bomber, to thunder down the runway, heading for France and the battlefields near Caen. Nige concentrated, conscious that the glider was an eight ton monoplane, with an eighty-eight foot wing span, yet only made of plywood.

Thirty or so men of the Oxfordshire and Buckinghamshire Light Infantry, faces blackened, had clambered aboard for a trip to remember! The glider pilots had had to sit for days watching endless screenings of training films, simulating the run up landing to the target. They were special men, a new breed of airmen, not only trained as pilots but also as combat soldiers - and now it was for real. With a perfect rhythm, the bombers lifted off and the frail gliders followed closely behind, like 'Airborne Coffins'. The cable tightened as the glider zig zagged about the bomber's tail as they circled above the ancient hill fort of Bradbury Rings. It was important that the glider hovered above the slip-stream of the Halifax to lessen the huge strain on the engines: too high and the Halifax wanted to dive, too low and it would cause it to stall. Having crossed the Channel, at 00.11 hours and flying at about 5,000 feet, they approached their cut-off over Cabourg, where the gliders were released.

Nige saw below him his glider with its enormous wing flaps now down and its nose pointing earthward, diving steeply at over 120mph. Within minutes it would level off before attempting to land. The pilots had memorised the landing route – 'Crossroads … field with round clump of trees … village with pond … landing zone coming up now … go in between the houses'. Their objective was to seize the bridges over the parallel waterways of the Caen Canal and Orne River, at the eastern boundary of the British beachhead, and destroy the enemy's batteries at Merville. This is the route that any German attack on the Normandy beachhead would have to come along, between Bénouville and Ranville, three miles from the coast. As Nige over flew the landing zone, he thought that it was meant to be marked with flares, but it looked as though the 3rd and 5th Para boys who were to do the job, had only just arrived. To make matters worse, visibility on the ground was not good with patchy mist hanging over the river and canal. As it turned out, one of the gliders ploughed into a poplar tree, which cut through the fuselage, shattering the Perspex canopy, literally passing between the pilot and his co. The lead glider struck the bridge head on, its super structure bringing it to a shuddering halt. The task force major yelled a rallying call to his men as they then set about the capture of Pegasus Bridge.

The day was a very special day: the biggest secret ever ... D-Day. Excitement swept through Paris; although the news was sporadic, people rushed about claiming it would soon be over ... the winds of war were changing.

The build up to D-Day stretched from Fareham down through Gosport and into Portsmouth. Amphibious craft . . . ships of all shapes and sizes, over 7,000 in total: one day they were all there, the next, they'd gone.[51] Two massive floating Mulberry Harbours, each consisting of two million tons of steel and concrete, the size of Dover Harbour, were about to be towed across the Channel in sections, to be assembled off Normandy.[52] 'Operation Overlord', the invasion of France, was underway. As dawn broke, the invasion force, stretching as far as the eye could see, came out of the mist that hung over the sea, to the total disbelief of the Germans. They could amass no more than 170 serviceable aircraft, whilst the Allies committed over 5,000, flying some 13,000 sorties on that day alone. The Kriegsmarine readied its submarine flotillas at Brest and Lorient, but the bulk of their force had already been withdrawn to Norway.[53]

On one day in June 156,000 Allied troops landed on the Normandy beaches, supported by nearly 200,000 naval and Merchant Navy personnel: a culmination of three years planning and the largest seaborne invasion force ever assembled in military history. And on this day, tens of thousands would lose their lives in the sea and sand, the grass and fields of France, all in the name of peace.

For Nurse Poll, active service held little attraction: she hadn't been on the front line before, yet soon after the invasion she sailed into Normandy. The hospitals back home had for days expected wave upon wave of British casualties from across the Channel: their time would soon come now. She had seen more than she wanted of the human mutilation and broken lives that this war had created, even before she embarked on her journey. She always found the inevitable physical injuries disturbing and the emotional trauma she faced devastating. As the ship came into the harbour she could hardly hold down a sensation of nausea welling up from deep within her stomach. Bodies floated in the water about the boat, mutilated and bloated. Amongst the debris and destruction upon the shore, piles of dead men lay on the sand red with blood; there, upon the beaches where they had landed, they had fought and, unable to escape, had died. It seemed totally unreal, as still bullets ripped at the water around her. Everywhere she faced carnage and suffering on a scale she had never seen before and was completely unprepared for. For weeks the pressure of work in the field hospital never let up; her resilience and courage helped her face an endless stream of wounded and dying soldiers: daily Poll faced the most horrendous sights. No soldierly training could have prepared her for this. As a member of the British General Hospital team based near our 2nd Army beachheads, each day she tirelessly fought to save the bodies and lives of young men, broken and damaged. Landing ship tanks and hospital carriers would evacuate the wounded and injured from the battlefields and beaches to the hospital ship HS Llandovery Castle waiting off-shore. Each landing ship tank would disembark one hundred and sixty walking wounded and thee hundred and fifty injured soldiers on stretchers to the hospital ships, which would evacuate them, within hours, back to England which was prepared to receive the massive casualties from 'Operation Overlord'. The boats would bring back much needed quantities of blood, plasma and the new antibiotic, penicillin, to help in her battle in this war.

School chum Franklin clearly didn't find his father's enterprise of aircraft precision instrument making exciting enough. I am unsure whether or not my joining the RAF influenced him in any way, but just a few weeks after D-Day he was flying over the enemy lines in northern France. Having successfully passed out as a first class army gunnery officer, he moved to Old Sarum Airfield just outside Salisbury. This was the principle base for the training of Air Observation Post units and used for the formation of the new Auster Squadrons, working closely with British Army units in artillery spotting and reconnaissance. In 1944 he completed his Army Pilot's training at the RAF School of Army Co-operation, and Captain F. Levine took to the air in his unarmed, flimsy Taylorcraft Mark 5 Auster of 'B' Flight, 661 A.O.P., assuredly sitting above the three inch thick armour plate fixed under his seat. This fabric covered, wood and steel light aircraft boasted all round visibility with its Perspex blister canopy, and when Franklin banked the craft he could even look out through the roof and spot a target that he had already flown past. For hours on end Franklin was to fly at the lowest level from which he could observe clearly, often down to just fifty feet, over the Normandy countryside between Caen and Falaise, towards the enemy lines. He would radio back clear instructions for the advancing ground infantry and artillery guns on the Auster's 22 set. Only twenty-two and a half feet long, with a wing span of thirty-six feet the Auster was small and slow moving, often cruising at around 80 – 90 mph. It was also highly maneuverable at low altitudes as being camouflaged it proved difficult prey for enemy fighters, but not, unfortunately, for armed infantry staring skyward. Although Franklin believed his little Auster was invincible, that didn't stop him taking evasive action. The enemy's machine gun fire resembled a line of red dashes zig zagging up towards him in a vicious and deadly pattern. They would only fire on the Auster if they felt certain they would hit it, but if they missed him they may not get a second chance, for Franklin would direct artillery fire down onto their guns.

Franklin, at the fore front of the action, helped seek out enemy positions, improving the accuracy of our guns, directing them onto new targets within minutes and immediately radioing back their devastating impact. His dad's old workshop could never begin to compare to his new found career.

On the eve of D-Day, General Dwight D. Eisenhower had asked the BBC to send the coded Action Messages to the Resistance groups across the Channel, alerting them to the forthcoming invasion and asking them to carry out acts of sabotage during the landings in order to disrupt communications and to stop the Germans from moving troops to the fighting front.[54]

Jac and the group had been seated in the farmhouse kitchen, attentive to their radios, listening to the broadcast, already planning the destruction of telephone exchanges, bridges and roads and blowing up more railway lines, fuel and ammunition dumps. Jac's comrade, 'Maigret', had already travelled to Paris to fight with the Free French, leaving her to head up the group. Over the following weeks, SOE's, 138 Squadron Lysander Lads and Bomber

Boys were busy airdropping some of the 103 uniformed Jedburgh Teams into the heart of enemy occupied territory. The role of the three man Jeds was to help organise, equip and train the local Resistance, and relay messages from Allied High Command – in short, to mobilise local forces. Captain Charles E Brown (US), known as 'Pice', along with two Frenchmen, 'Sous' and 'Reis', having completed their training and briefings, waited in the large country house known as Station 61. They were the men of the 'Lee Team' to operate under the control of SOE Agent 'Hamlet' of the Salesman circuit in France. From radio contact with Baker Street and Tempsford, it was evident Jac was organising the reception in France for this new Haute-Vienne Team. Set for early August, the DZ was Châteauneuf-la-forêt, south east of Limoges. On the night of the 9th August, Lee dropped from a pair of Stirlings, almost two miles from Jac's landing beacons.[55] Fortunately they landed safely and, on 22nd August, with Jac and the other Resistance members' help, they set up base in the city of Limoges, where they successfully diverted Germany's military forces away from the Allied invasion.

# Chapter 36

Exactly a week after the D-Day landings, the war struck home again: our 'Island Fortress' was under attack!

We had had few visitors to our office, and even fewer uninvited, but in that June one such arrived. On that fateful day, the Luftwaffe launched one of its evil flying bombs.[56] Our usual office chatter ceased, just long enough for us to clearly hear the distinctive whistling sound of an approaching 'doodlebug'. It grew louder and nearer, then the drone stopped, and fifteen seconds later we would know who was for it. As we sat frozen in our chairs, Charles strolled to the open window and gave a cursory glance heavenward. Instantly, an alarm rang, signalling our evacuation, and along with other staff in the building we joined the throng, bustling and barging our way down the crammed corridors. The alarm echoing about the offices had become somewhat irrelevant as panic had now taken over. The whole structure shook with the deafening blast. On one of the stairways an army fellow stumbled towards me, confused and injured. His hair was partially burnt off, as were his eyebrows and lids; his eyes stared penetratingly at me. Part of his nose had gone and his lips were bleeding. I reached out to grab him as he fell towards me and found myself clasping bloody stubs of hands. I felt sick. Engulfed with fear and screaming, he fell into my outstretched arms. He was in a terrible state and found it hard struggling to get outside, to where nurses swiftly whisked him away. I wasn't at all sure whether or not he would survive and it struck me again how lucky I was to be alive. Our lives are shaped by our experiences, even more so those horrifying experiences. As we forged our way down and out of the building I glimpsed, pinned down by the debris, part buried by the rubble, a young man shocked and splattered with blood. It was evident as wardens moved the masonry, that his leg lay in front of him, across the other side of the corridor. Unaware of his pain and that he'd lost his leg, he sat there dazed, just shaking his head.

I recall thinking this was a nightmare from which I would never wake.

Even Mum and Dad didn't get away totally unscathed. Dad's mate from work lived just around the corner from them but fortunately both he and his wife were out when his house off Avenue Road was struck by a V-Bomb. Dad was heading back from the tube when he saw the V-Bomb streaking across the sky, then dive silently earthward.[57] As he got near home Mum said he'd become petrified that Albert and his missus had copped it. Father sobbed with relief when Albert called around later that night, asking if they could stay over until things were sorted out.

For the men and women of London, the sinister outline in the sky, glowing red at night, and the throbbing roar of the V-Bomb's engine brought only fear. Neither cloud nor daylight disrupted these indiscriminant attacks. The 'doodlebugs' were frightening, the V-2s were horrific, the explosions coming before the sound of their rocket engines.[58] If the attacks continued, London would suffer greater devastation than that which it had already endured. A tired and dispirited people needed to fight on bravely as terror rained from the skies. That night, as I walked the city streets, the worst of human nature was in evidence amid the surrounding rubble and chaos: unscrupulous looters, after robbing the dead, cut off fingers to steal their rings. Down one back alley in a shady doorway, slouched a plump, middle-aged woman whose words stopped me in my tracks,
"Have you got someone luv?"
My reply came without hesitation,
"Yes, she's in France".
The woman stifled a snigger and, before I could begin to see where such a conversation would lead, two frumpy looking ladies in the uniform of the 'Sally Army' approached her and began their battle.

Hitler's new breed of weapon, his pilotless jet bomb, had long been known by Allied Intelligence, and bombing of the launch sites was well underway; however, that didn't stop Hitler ordering a massive strike against England soon after D-Day which resulted in confusion; thank God only four reached our shores.

As the Allies advanced into northern France, liberating towns as they went, slowly but surely the city of Paris came within their grasp. Hitler still hoped to hold Paris, instructing his military commander of the city, Lieutenant General Dietrich von Choltitz, 'Paris must not be allowed to fall into the hands of the enemy except as a field of ruins'. Speaking of Hitler as mad, Choltitz had no appetite for such destruction. With the growing success of the invasion force, the Resistance combatants were re-formed as the 'French Forces of the Interior', attempting to fuse the Resistance into a single French Army, their number swelling with every day that passed.[59]

Early in the morning of 19th August, several hundred police marched into Police Headquarters, the Préfecture, opposite Notre-Dame, singing the banned Marseillaise and took possession in the name of the Republic and Charles de Gaulle. With the agreement of Von Choltitz, further uprisings of the people in Paris did not take place and he did not order the destruction of the city.

On the night of 24th August, the 2nd Free French Armoured Division, under the command of Major General Philippe Leclerc sent an advance party of three Shermans and six half-tracks into the city.[60] The following morning, to a tumultuous reception, its main force swept from the southwest into the city, whilst the US 4th Infantry entered from the east.[61] Paris had been liberated. Choltitz signed the surrender and by midday, the French Tricolore flew from the Eiffel Tower.[62] On the 26th August, General Charles de Gaulle entered the city: the day of triumph had arrived and more than two million people were there to greet him.[63] The Allied forces pressed on through Europe, the men believing Berlin would soon be within their reach and they would be home for Christmas; but even now we were still only at the beginning of the end in Europe.

In the office the word was that the end of the Third Reich was in sight. The Nazi offensives were now only temporary interruptions to our continued advance on Germany. The opinion was that the Germans could not gather enough strength for a major operation, but that didn't seem to stop Hitler's obstinate optimism.[64] We knew well of the differences between Allied generals, and often discussed them over lunch: Eisenhower's goal was not German cities but dead German soldiers. Yet these differences were insignificant compared to the split amongst the Germans.[65] The unsuccessful attempt on Hitler's life earlier in the year had divided the German hierarchy: some had been presented with complimentary doses of poison for their involvement or awareness of the assassination attempt; for others found complicit in the plot, Hitler meted out barbaric deaths.

All in all, the New Year was turning out to be a very unusual one. Cinema newsreels showed that our troops had advanced across the Rhine and on into Germany, while the Soviets were surging through Poland and the now devastated Warsaw on their way towards Berlin from the east and south; Stalin's march of communism pressed on into eastern Europe, looking for revenge.

I clearly recall Richard Dimbleby's radio broadcast as he entered the German concentration camp of Belsen with advancing Allied Troops – before him lay ten thousand unburied bodies, *'The World of a Nightmare. The living lay with heads against corpses and around them moved the ghostly procession of emancipated aimless people, nothing to do and no hope of life ... this is what the Germans did, make no doubt about it'.*

On 26th April, around half a million troops swarmed into Berlin's streets, desperate; fierce fighting broke out as the Russian offensive struck the city. The shambolic Third Reich, a spent force in its death throes, was fighting to protect their Fatherland and families. Throughout the bombardment of his beloved city, Hitler remained in his bunker beneath Berlin's Chancellery. The elegant Eva Braun, thirteen years his mistress, was at his side, as were his commanders, who now urged him to flee the city. But there he remained as he rehearsed his suicide and the deaths of his faithful, including his new wife Eva. Within a few hours news broke that Mussolini had been captured by Italian partisans and shot with his mistress Clara Petacci, then hung in the centre of Milan by the ankles along with seventeen of his fascist henchmen. The following day, May 2$^{nd}$, the papers were to report, Hitler bid his final farewells, retired to the sitting room of the bunker and shot himself; Eva, his wife of only a few hours, chose poisoning for her end. The German people were told that he had fallen in battle. That same day the Red Army reached the German Reichstag and raised the Red Flag above this symbol of Nazi power.

On May 7$^{th}$ 1945, the unconditional surrender was signed and the German troops marched into captivity; the following day 'Victory in Europe' was declared.

It didn't escape me that in just a few years Hitler had managed to raise Germany from weakness to being an unparalleled power and then finally left her in utter chaos, having exterminated millions of Jews and laid much of Europe to ruins. This was a legacy that the people of his country would never forget, and many I imagined, never forgive.

On the office wall above Charles's desk were the words of Churchill, taken from his speech of January 1940. Somehow they had a particular poignancy this day in May 1945:

*The day will come when the joybells will ring again throughout Europe, and when victorious nations, masters not only of their foes but of themselves, will plan and build in justice, in tradition, and freedom ...'*

On the morning of VE-Day, a violent thunderstorm broke over London. Bunting that had been strung up across the roads had sagged with the weight of rain. At first there seemed little appetite for celebration. At three in the afternoon the BBC broadcast Churchill's announcement - hostilities would end at one minute past midnight that night, the 8th May, although the ceasefire had already taken place. He ended his message with, 'Advance Britannia, long live the cause of freedom! Long live the King.'

The reality was striking home. Tens of thousands of people took to the streets to celebrate war coming to an end: many had thought this day would never come. As I strolled down the Mall, the chanting crowds were already building in front of the palace. Spectators pressed against the railings, expectant to see the royals, pretty young girls were perched on the shoulders of soldiers, others climbed the Victoria Memorial or clung to trees, waving handkerchiefs and Union flags, calling for the king. Everyone was beaming, some dancing arm-in-arm; red, white and blue scarves, hats and bows coloured the crowd. The cheering raised to a crescendo as the king, in naval uniform, and queen stepped out onto the palace balcony, closely followed by the Princesses Margaret Rose and Elizabeth who was wearing her ATS uniform. Along the packed Mall, which was now just a sea of people, weaved a black open topped car with Churchill seated in the rear, en route to meet the king. As he joined the royal family, the revellers went wild, waving, shouting, hugging anyone and generally having a ball. I barged through the crowds with servicemen and women and as I picked my way through Green Park their chorus of 'Roll out the Barrel' fading into the distance, overjoyed youngsters raced about, smashing dustbin lids together and firing off squids. On reaching Piccadilly Circus, I was amazed to see folk everywhere, hundreds of them, even clambering up the boarding around Eros. Their celebrations had now developed into a riot of spontaneous madness. Groups of young women danced about The Circus, weaving through the crowds and, just as I felt totally remote from all that was going on, a spirited Land Army lass dragged me over to join her and a band of liberated uniformed WRENS; we conga-ed up and down the pavement, laughing and kissing for what seemed like hours. From this wild party a few of us made our way from pub to pub, drinking and singing well into the warm, balmy evening. Only the unfaltering king's broadcast brought a sense of seriousness to the celebrations – as well as the dwindling supply of beer! On reaching Leicester Square, a large blazing bonfire greeted us: on top was an effigy of the now dead Hitler, brightly illuminating the faces of onlookers as they gazed up at the fireworks exploding in crimson showers. This was a day when it seemed you could do everything and anything in the name of 'Victory'. The 'gallant' GIs set the tone with loud behaviour and the London 'Bobbies' joined in; I couldn't help but wonder if 'Lasting Peace' would go hand in hand with Victory?

As night fell, lights went on all over the city; for the first time in years London was ablaze, but this time with lights.

The most strongly fortified position in western Europe and the only British territory occupied by the Germans was also about to be liberated. If Vice-Admiral Hüffmeier didn't follow the orders of the German High Command, then he would be completely isolated, and the last permanent outpost of the Third Reich, the Channel Islands, would be in a state of siege. On 9th May, at 7.14am, the Germans signed the unconditional surrender. Following Churchill's declaration, scenes of jubilation upon the arrival of the British liberating forces were broadcast announcing the freeing of 'Our dear Channel Islands'. The next day, as patriotic celebrations broke out, the one time bored and lonely Germans, now prisoners of war, started work dismantling hundreds of miles of barbed wire and digging up nearly two hundred thousand mines on the islands.

For many in Britain VE was not a time to celebrate, for they had lost loved ones, others would be lost too as the World War was not yet over. Japan fought on in the Pacific.

# Chapter 37

My recollections of the evening of VE-Day are somewhat vague: Father alleged that my alcoholic binge could well have had something to do with that. I undoubtedly enjoyed the atmosphere that night and from what I can recall, the pretty young women made it even more enjoyable. The celebration lunch Mother dished up on Wednesday looked pretty amazing, although I myself could only manage a few mouthfuls; Dad said I didn't know what I was missing, as casting restraint to one side, he tucked in. Mum, as a special treat, opened a tin of delicious pear halves in their syrup juice. After lunch we set to with the others in The Close to prepare for our street party. There were tables arranged down the middle of the road, streamers draped around the down-pipes of the houses and along the garden walls, and Mrs Taylor was still busy gluing together more paper chains. Although her three boys weren't at home she told me they would be back very soon now. Vera from next door, along with the other women, was helping Mother lay up the tables that had been covered with white bed sheets. Mrs. Harris seemed to me to be a different woman to whom I remembered and whispered in my ear that she would miss those old times down the shelter. Colourful paper hats were produced and the rule was that we all had to wear them, regardless of age, although I couldn't help noticing that some of the women with head scarves didn't tow the line. Despite food rationing, a real spread was laid and soon was devoured by one and all.

It was a real relief to know that no longer need we look up into the sky to check if any bombers or V- bombs were overhead. All in all the day turned out to be a very happy occasion, yet it was hard to forget that millions had suffered to make this day a reality.

Within three months the Americans had perfected a weapon a million times more deadly than Hitler's V-bombs.[66] Japan had created the savage young Kamikaze suicide pilots but they had unleashed the first atom bomb on Hiroshima. Scientists pronounced on the radio that the effect would be, 'like that of a severe earthquake'. Nearly a hundred thousand people were instantly killed, some vapourised and a similar number were injured, many of them to die later. My copy of the Daily Express for once accurately declared in its headline, 'THE BOMB THAT HAS CHANGED THE WORLD'. A second bomb dropped on Nagasaki resulted in the Japanese surrender: they did not want to see the same things happen to Tokyo. The following day we all celebrated VJ-Day.

We had truly seen the world change but few of us realised just how much and how far reaching the change would be: World War Two had ended and it seemed to me that a deadly new Atomic Age had begun.

In spite of this horror, life at home went on in much the same way. Surprisingly the people of Great Britain decided that Churchill was not the man to lead us in peace time and in the first election for ten years I found myself unable to vote, as the Polling Station officially pronounced I was off the record, probably because they thought I was dead. The Labour philosophy, 'Let us Face the Future' helped ensure a landslide victory for Clement Attlee, whoever he was!

Many of us wanted to put the evils of the war behind us and move on but it was far from easy. Towns and cities stood in ruins and whilst new homes, hospitals, schools and roads were being built, it was evident it was going to be a slow process. The war had left the country nigh on broke and everywhere I looked I was reminded of that. And then there were the Trials. There was no shortage of newspaper coverage, continually reminding us all of what had happened. I suppose it was human nature to focus the blame on a few, but I couldn't help but think that to a lesser extent we all had played a part. For nearly a year, twenty-two leading members of the Nazi Party waited to hear their fate as the

Nuremberg War Trials and the world considered their crimes: war crimes and crimes against humanity that reportedly killed eleven million human beings.[67]

A reality that hit me hard was 'demobilisation'. In many ways the last thing I wanted to do was leave the RAF. Although it had been my life for only a few years, it had affected me more than anything else. Between the fighting there had been some grand times and I had made some good mates, with many of whom I was still in touch. Of course, had it not been for the RAF, Brigitte would have escaped me. We all have a place within us where we guard our precious memories: mine were few, but none the less important to me. The moment had come for me, along with thousands of others, to hand in our uniforms and rifles, ready for a new life on civvy street, and I certainly didn't relish the idea. My 'Royal Airforce Service and Release Book' spelt out that they were not discharging me from the Service and I could still be recalled: probably if there was another war! My five years of service was summed up by the following few words –
RAF Character – *VG;* Proficiency – *Satisfactory;* Brief statement of special aptitudes or qualities or any special types of employment for which recommended – *Has shown a high standard in his trade and should prove very capable in any employment of a technical nature* ...and that was it! I carefully placed the small and insignificant looking Service and Release Book, along with my Log Book, an assortment of French and German propaganda leaflets, some old franc notes, plus a dozen or so photographs of the lads and me, into a sweet tin. On top I laid my RAF Caterpillar Club badge, for surviving a parachute jump, along with my two medals for surviving the war. I shut the lid on that part of my life and placed the tin in the oak sideboard in the lounge, next to the cardboard box containing Dad's medals, and closed the drawer.

Encouraging us to believe we all had a real future, the Government's posters read, 'Industry and Commerce want to get going. You will find you will be welcome.' It didn't sound hugely convincing to me. Finding a job was going to be a real problem: for years women had filled men's jobs, and successfully, and now we were back many were understandably reluctant to give up their new lives. My venture into 'the real world' came after several months determined hunting, and a reluctance to be demoralised by early failure and rejection. I took up my post on the running platform of a London double-decker bus: equipped with my cap, uniform and a shiny new ticket puncher. I never thought I would become a bus conductor. My Opo for the routes was one time army tank driver Wynny, who seemed to bring all the same aggressive driving skills to steering us through the busy streets of London as he had adopted on the Western Front. We got on like a house on fire and had it not been for the irritating passengers, would have had a whale of a time. With the seats on the bus removed we could squeeze more in and, of all passengers, the returning GIs were the noisiest on their way back from jitterbugging or boogie woogie-ing at some dance hall or other. Wynny said that apart from them being, 'over loud, over paid, over sexed, over our women and over here … many of them for good, they were fine'. I think what led us both to this opinion was that they had a social life and we most certainly didn't!

Rationing was biting harder than during war-time; Mum commented that the queues were even longer, and bread was becoming a luxury. Pre-fabricated homes started to spring up, twenty or so, on the edge of the allotments. Dad was most put out: he understood returning soldiers had to have somewhere to live, but he also needed somewhere to grow his vegetables.

Meanwhile it seemed a fight was going on between the Russians and the West over a united Germany. The Russians kept up a blockade on relief supplies into Berlin and, for what was nearly a year, France, the USA and the Brits organised air lifts of food and fuel to the German people. It seemed weird that here we were coping with rationing whilst flying thousands of tons of supplies in each day.

The ensuing years of the fifties slipped by not uneventfully, but leaving me more and more frustrated and yearning to get back to my family in France and Brigitte. As I tuned my radio to the high flying Biggles, the Goon Show and Dick Barton, Mum and Dad were enjoying a growing classical record collection which they played on their new Stereophonic Dansette record player; they even talked of a holiday at Butlin's. The spirits of the whole nation were truly lifted by the celebration of the royal wedding of Princess Elizabeth and the Duke of Edinburgh at Westminster Abbey. Mum loved all the splendour of the occasion broadcast live on BBC Television, and I've got to admit she looked really quite stunning compared to my last glimpse of her in her unflattering ATS uniform on VE-Day. However, for Dad and me the Olympic Games held in London were far more gripping; but the real joy for Mum and the nation came with the crowning of Queen Elizabeth in the Abbey. Mum just loved the pomp and ceremony of the coronation and couldn't stop talking about how beautiful she looked and how obviously in love she was with Philip. There was no end of headlines for the newspapers: Edmund Hillary and Sherpa Tensing climbed Everest, the highest place on earth; the Hungarians had a revolution and the Soviets had started a new battle: this time to control space, launching their satellite Sputnik 1. Throughout all this excitement ... I just sold bus tickets.

Life at home had become more and more difficult to handle, I found the oppressive atmosphere of our small maisonette stifling. Mum and Dad went out of their way to try and make it work, but I was becoming more and more restless and they couldn't understand why. Everyday I ached to tell my secret of those magical months in France, but I daren't risk shattering my dreams. My job offered no prospects or hope for a real future, and opportunities to find work that was more challenging and better paid continued to evade me. The only vague comfort came from colleagues who told me I was lucky to have a job, and there were many ex-servicemen worse off than me: but I found none of this encouraging. I had tried to put Brigitte and France out of my mind, but increasingly she occupied more of my thoughts and clearly was distracting me from my work. One morning I was called in to the depot manager's office and told that unless I sorted myself out I'd be looking for another job - there were plenty of others keen to work. Wynny had gone, moved to the West Country to start a business in farming, but not until he'd confronted me,

"I don't know what it is with you, but you're not yourself. Whoever stole your heart mate, go and get it back."

I desperately needed a change. With little to keep me in England, the appeal of France had grown even stronger as the years had passed. I believed my memories would dull, but they hadn't: quite the contrary. I thought about Brigitte more than ever. I still dreamt constantly of returning to the tranquility of that haven I had found deep within the heart of war, and of my love for that woman.

A new year was beginning. Winter had stripped the trees of their autumn glory and had arrived with real vengeance: it would forever be known as 'The Big Freeze of '63'. It was a bitterly cold time with drifts over twenty feet deep and the sub-zero temperatures and freezing fog brought travel to a standstill. Little appeased the city folk as they waited in the February gales to board my bus and begin their perilous journey to work. With the coming of the March thaw and the lengthening days, the season had truly turned.

The long, dark, cold days of winter passed and my thoughts once again turned to France. The coming of spring filled me with new life and hope, reminding me of those enchanted days. April had all but gone and as May arrived I planned for my journey ... a cycling holiday.

And so it was after many years I found myself back in France, in the village, excited, but ill prepared for what I would find.

# Chapter 38

I awoke early, disturbed by the workmen's voices in the village square below. Al Jolson's words from the evening before were still resounding in my head as I lay turning over my many thoughts, and I wondered about the young woman, who she was and why I felt I knew her. Today I would start my journey back, to find the whitewashed farmhouse, the sweet scented orchard, the babbling river where we played, and dear Brigitte. The idea excited me, even more so knowing that for Brigitte it would be a complete and utter surprise. I opened the shutters to reveal a flawless, blue sky and the sun shining brightly above the roof tops. In a lazy fashion the men were dismantling the stalls and clearing the square of all the paraphernalia of the fête the day before. There was clearly no rush, and no reason not to stop and jaw, take a pipe or an early morning vino. Slumping back into bed I picked at the bread and cheese that had been left the previous night: the bread had dried, the crust quite hard and the cheese had a certain waxiness to its texture. For someone who was hungry however, they were gratefully devoured, although I still couldn't face the wine.

Downstairs, the strong smell of coffee drew me into the bar where my hosts were busy. A stout, jovial looking woman occupied herself washing the glasses left from the night before, raising to the light as she gave them their final polish before arranging them on the shelf behind the bar. Her husband dithered about the three vacant breakfast tables, collecting the used crockery, cutlery and dirty ashtrays, and, noticing me enter, asked if he could serve me coffee. Within a few minutes a delicious cup of aromatic coffee, dark and beautifully rich, was placed on the table before me, along with a jug of piping hot milk, crystallised sugar, the freshest of bread and pure yellow butter. In a hoarse voice the woman called across to me, enquiring if my sleep was good. I confirmed it had been long and sound and, when she asked about my bicycle injury, I told her the accident had appeared to give me no lasting problems. Having thanked them both for their hospitality, I made a start on my breakfast whilst continuing to chat to her about all manner of things. She wanted to know how long I wished to stay and what I was doing in this out of the way place. She was friendly, interested but not prying; I took to her kindly ways and we talked together for some while during which time my coffee got cold, her glasses got shinier and her husband, becoming bored, disappeared. During our conversation I made a point of asking about Henri, Grandmamma, Émile and Brigitte as well as the farm, but she knew nothing of them, explaining that they were newcomers. They had worked in the business for only two years and knew nothing of the outlying farmsteads. Neither of them had found it easy to fit in: village people were kind but very private and after all, unlike them, her husband and herself were free from the weight of the past. I assumed from this she was meaning the war and occupation. Having finished my lukewarm coffee, I thanked her; bidding me farewell, she wished me a good day and said she would see me that evening.

I stepped out into this new day, apprehensive, yet looking forward to the gifts it would bring; I felt truly hopeful. Avoiding the square with all its activity, I made my way down a shady lane that ran beside the hotel and was immediately struck by the buildings, either side, grey rendered, austere and modern. Although when here before I hadn't explored the whole village, I never recalled seeing anything like this. At the end of the lane where it crossed a road I was faced with the choice of three routes: the busier and wider option appealed and continued to puzzle me with its contemporary ugliness. I hadn't been conscious of this in the square but then maybe the bustling fête and failing light of the day before had distracted me. Picking my way along an alley, cosily nestled between two houses, I was brought to a sudden stop by what lay before me: a panorama of ruined buildings, a village of destruction. Everywhere I looked lay desolation. As if signalling the existence of some higher force, the sky darkened and, looking up, I could see the presence of a massive black rain cloud swamping the blue sky, obliterating the sun. Wandering aimlessly through the remains, a deep sense of sadness and death filled me. Row upon row, street after street of homes reduced now to rubble: death had not just come to the people but to the whole village. It became increasingly clear to me that this was no natural disaster: this had been delivered by the hand of man. There were no bomb craters, no shelling, the buildings had not been bulldozed by tanks, I could see no signs of defences; it may have once been like any other village, that is except for the fact that this was the village I had known those twenty years earlier. In a clearing the village well stood, the menacing usage to which it had been put marked with a simple wooden cross erected alongside. A gas pump still stood at the curb side, between the row of concrete pylons and the decaying garage premises. Wrecks of old saloon cars were heaped in its yard and the cars that had once filled their tanks with fuel here rested about the village – rusting, rotting. Blackened by smoke and the passage of time, the moss covered ruins stood as monuments to the once glorious village; avenues of trees lining the road were the only remaining life. Joyful birdsong filled the air and for a precious moment reminded me of the peace and tranquility of the farmstead. I continued to follow the twisted steel tramline strolling towards the village green, the smell of newly cut grass and wet soil lingering, then past the fairground edged by a picket fence. Further on, the old church stood as an empty shell, its roof, steeple and bell tower destroyed. Standing inside this large building I was surprised to observe that the altar was still substantially in tact, its white, stone table glaring, starkly reflecting the sun as it appeared from behind the cloud. To one side lay the rusty remains of a pram, in front of which, between the communion rails, was a hole, perhaps a yard wide, in the stone floor. The bronze bells, melted from some intense heat, rested on the church floor below the arches which once supported the tower. As I stepped out from the coolness of the church, the midday humidity struck me. A tall, metal, mission cross of Christ stood rusting. Two children were seated on steps below the church, throwing stones at a wall, probably completely unaware of what had happened here.

Looking down the hill out of the village, nestling between the rolling verdant fields and the mature chestnut wooded vale, I could see the bridge across the sparkling River Cherane which meandered its way east. Here the men had played their lines all those years earlier. Today it appeared deserted. I was amazed beyond belief at all that I had seen as I made my way back towards the centre and my hotel. I struggled to make sense of it and felt heavy hearted, not understanding the reason for the destruction as I returned from the hideous past to the future.

Across the square individual tables were arranged outside one of the hotels where a handful of customers sat reading newspapers or taking their morning coffee. I slid out a seat from under one of the tables and, relaxing, took in the scene before me. A petite girl in her teens attended my table and took my order; on realising I was from England her pretty faced beamed as she answered me in her schoolgirl English. At the next table an elegant woman, I judged in her sixties, was busying herself jotting in a small, brown, leather notebook. She looked up and politely acknowledged my presence with a smile, just as the bells of a church rang out its peal. She caught my eye again and I returned her smile, nodding in recognition of the church's call. When peace returned she leant across and with warmth in her voice questioned,
"Is it right you are from England?"
My reply was cut short, interrupted by the waitress bringing my coffee.
"I was in England many years ago before the war, working as a language tutor for a family in Kent." She looked towards the church, "I do not expect you have heard our church bells before?"
Her reaction clearly demonstrated her surprise at my response.
"Yes, but not this church. I have been here before, many years ago in the war, but everything is so, so different. I only just

recognised the old village; it is devastating to see it in such ruins, what on earth happened?"

"Were you not here when the Germans came?"

"No," I told her, "I left just a few weeks before and travelled through Spain and Gibraltar, returning to England."

She sipped her coffee, gathered her thoughts and, casting a knowing glance, began to share with me her story.

"I did not live here then but travelled in to teach in the school. In the November of '42, the Germans invaded our Free France, maybe many of us never truly understood what this would mean, but we soon learnt. They swept across our land, a triumphant and ruthless enemy. Within days they had occupied the village. Ignorant of all formalities, the Nazis seized our town hall, the last symbol of French authority, and established it as the Third Reich's headquarters for the locality, demonstrating to all that their authority was above question. Never again would the building echo to our poetic French tongue but instead shake to German commands. They claimed they would seek out and eliminate all terrorists that opposed the progressive march of Nazism. At the other end of the village from their headquarters stood the church of Our Lady of Notre Dame, the sole remaining sanctuary for the people in this time of turmoil. For nearly half a year the soldiers left the village to worship in this holy place. Then on 30th May 1943, when villagers gathered in great numbers, many not having entered its doors since the funeral of Pierre Mâchél, they met to remember Joan of Arc on her feast day, and that's when the Germans struck." The woman looked again towards the church, an expression of melancholy filled her face as she recalled those times for me. "We were as one on that Sunday, celebrating the life of Saint Joan who had led our forefathers to freedom, when forty or more soldiers burst into the church, their Commandant at their head, and as a frozen force stood listening, waiting, ready to strike. With great dignity Father Bernard, gathering his robes about him, knelt in front of the altar and began praying aloud.

Every last soul in the church knelt in chilled silence, broken only by the Priest's utterances. Elderly couples clasped tightly each other's hands, children edged nearer to mothers and grandmammas; men, fearing the worse, glanced to one another seeking reassurance. The priest's voice washed through every part of that place, almost as if in a whisper. As he prayed, the tension in his voice was unmistakable: his voice trembled as he called upon God to mercifully grant His salvation to save this community, these people, each of them and the dear children in their time of suffering and strife.

His litany was broken only by the occasional sobs of the old women and the crying of children who knew not why they were crying. Suddenly, a lone female voice rose up from the choir, as sweet and as pure as you could imagine, lifting melodiously high into the gods. Her song of joy brought life, light and hope; soaring ever higher, like a bird it danced amongst the sunbeams and shadows way above us. All were now listening intently as her voice seemed to be calling to each and every one of us. In a brief interlude, cares and concerns were put to one side as the moments of magic raised us all to another place. As dramatically as they had entered, the troops left; the only sound they made was the clicking of their boots striking the stone floor; yet no-one turned, not one looked back. From that day until the German surrender, no more services were allowed in the church, no-one entered that hallowed place." She paused, her mind full of memories, her eyes full of tears. The pain on her face seemed insuppressible, growing with each moment.

"How long does a soul have to wait to heal?" Her words haunted me; I didn't know what to say. "I told you no-one ever entered that place again whilst the Germans were here, but that is not entirely true. On one fateful day in June 1944, I was in Limoges with my husband when the Nazis swarmed through the village, herding captives into the church and barns, leaving a trail of destruction in their wake, and showing no mercy, they killed them."

Between us no word was shared. Silence descended for a brief moment. She re-living again the memories of that time, whilst I was just so grateful Brigitte and her family lived outside the village, well away from it all.

"I know grief: my son had come here that day and was murdered with the other men." This was a woman I had only known for a few minutes but in that time I had learnt so very much and was allowed to glimpse at her most tender self. Her honesty had created a bond between us. A grey car pulled up close to where we were sitting; the elderly driver stayed behind the wheel, his engine still running. He cast a glance in her direction, rising from her seat she turned to me one last time and uttered under her breath, perhaps half hoping someone would hear,

"If only I had stopped him that day: he would still be alive."

They drove away, weaving across the square, narrowly avoiding an emerald green motorbike and sidecar which careered wildly in a frenzied manner towards the hotel. The pretty, young waitress came across to my table asking if I wanted another coffee; she explained about the woman,

"Madame comes here each Sunday, orders coffee and just sits listening to the idle gossip and the church bells. The patron says she has come here every week since the war ended all those years ago."

"The Madame spoke of a killing: what exactly happened?" The waitress looked at me in somber fashion, hesitant in her reply: clearly she knew something of this but was uncomfortable to discuss it.

"I will get you the patron; his aunt lived here then; I think he will be able to tell you about it." Sipping my coffee, the boiling drink bit my lips and scalded my tongue; I cooled it quickly with a gulp from my glass of water. She was soon back, apologizing that the patron was unloading vegetables in the back yard but would join me shortly.

The afternoon was mellowing, a golden light warmed the square, its rich glow washing the façades of the adjacent buildings. Few folk were around at this time of day: a young couple wandered hand in hand between the flowerbeds whilst three or four young boys chased each other, arms outstretched, pretending to be aeroplanes. A mysterious mood seemed to descend as I watched; I felt increasingly like a spectator watching a silent movie as I looked on in a daydream.

"Monsieur," the man's gruff voice broke my train of thought, "you ask about our village … yes?"

# Chapter 39

"Marianne tells me you have been speaking with Madame Laroche and you want to know what happened on that day in June."

He sat beside me at the table and calling Marianne he asked for two more coffees. Cautious not to offend I explained the reason for my inquisitiveness and what I had been told.

"Ah, Madame," he murmured knowingly; with the arrival of the coffees he settled back into the chair and began retelling the story. His aunt had lived in the village during the war years and as a young lad he'd stayed at holiday times with her. Visitors would travel on one of the trams that ran each day from Limoges on to St. Junien, stopping on their way at Cousion. Here they would spend the morning shopping and in the afternoon relax, picnicking on the green or by the river, where he would join the men fishing. The otherwise peaceful village would come alive on those days. Many men of the village were away, working for the Germans, or as prisoners of war. French and Belgium refugees, along with Spanish loyalists fleeing the Civil War, had settled here taking sanctuary, working in the village and on the land. Cousion was never prosperous: the smart cars here were owned by the *bourgeois* in Limoges and kept in the village away from German eyes. Aunt would say it didn't really feel as if they were at war: nothing really happened, to the outside world we were insignificant ... that was until the massacre.

In the villages round and about there had been extreme retaliation by the Germans for increased Resistance attacks.[68] There was looting, rape, mutilation and execution of wounded fighters at the hands of the Nazis; they struck out in revenge. After the invasion of Normandy it got worse with the Nazis becoming frustrated and enraged: maybe they knew all was now lost. The countryside was swarming with Das Reich, the Maquis being able to do little to stop them: Sten guns and Gammon grenade bombs were no match for tanks, but they could slow the movement of German troops to the front.

To this day no one really knows exactly what caused the 2$^{nd}$ Waffen SS-Panzer Division, Hitler's Guardians and Himmler's crack troops to descend on Cousion, but descend they did. Some say it was in reprisal for the blowing of a railway bridge in Saint Junien and the burning of a German soldier chained in their ambulance; some claimed there was a stronghold of Resistance in the village. There was talk of the abduction and intended execution of a high ranking Nazi officer and of the Maquis being responsible. Whatever it was, the Nazis were following orders to crush the forces of resistance. Such unimaginable brutality was common place on the Eastern Front where many of these troops had just been fighting, having now returned, humiliated, by their defeat.

After a prolonged silence, out of respect as much as anything, he carefully placed on the table a tired looking notebook which he had brought with him. It proved to be a child's school exercise book, a book that had once belonged to his Aunt Michelle.

"Sometimes I feel I am guardian of her words, left to me as the only record. My aunt was one of the very few who survived the massacre, and afterwards she wrote all that she could remember. In the years that followed she never truly got over her overwhelming grief as entire families, relatives and friends were lost on that day, and the life she loved had gone forever."

We looked at each other, hesitant to speak.

"Shall I read to you the account in her own words?" he asked.

"Yes, if it would not be too upsetting for you."

He began to translate :

*'Here I record how the people of Cousion-sur-Cherane on June 10$^{th}$ 1944, as Victims of History, lost their lives.*

*We had just finished our lunch when large army lorries loaded with soldiers, half-track trucks and a staff car full of officers escorted by motorbikes roared through our village. A hundred or* more armed troops in green and yellow camouflage jackets leapt out of the lorries and lined up in front of our town hall. In the fields behind were more soldiers with guns, moving through the grass and trees, searching for something. Some soldiers, led by a major, marched down our main street to the sound of our crier banging his drum, calling everyone out of the buildings. Dressed in my old work clothes, with my family, I went out and gathered with the others in the Champ de Foire – the fairground. The major, standing before a large picture of the Führer spoke through a French Vichy officer who said they wanted an identity check of all of us, and they would search all buildings looking for guns and ammunition. None of us were too worried, it had happened before and we expected they were looking for Maquisards. I was surprised at how many of us were there, perhaps four or five hundred; all the villagers, the refugees and the folk from nearby who were visiting to shop and collect their meagre rations; more than I had ever seen. We stood in the hot afternoon sun, babes and children in their mothers' arms; none were excused. People continued to come from all directions swelling the crowd, army trucks were unloading still more people, some I knew were from nearby hamlets. By now I was becoming more anxious, it had never been like this before. Children who were in the village for medical checks that afternoon were led out by teachers and soldiers, their mothers gathering them up as they came onto the field. The majority of us were calm, having seen little in the way of persecution or reprisal over the years, after all we were not the guerrillas they were seeking. Soldiers separated the women and children from the men, and it still didn't occur to us what they were doing. An order was given and soldiers with guns corralled us women and children together. We implored the soldiers not to separate our families and, fearing the worst, many started to wail in despair. No one knew what to do. Ignoring our pleas we were herded away: they said for our own safety. Along the roadside, soldiers sat by machine guns mounted on stands, looking menacing, others stood about, talking - laughing. I remember being struck by our echoing wooden clogs as we were

330

*marched down the street not knowing where they were taking us. An old woman with a fractured leg was being pushed in a wooden barrow. I saw a girl and some lads cycle into the village, I think just out for a ride, and soldiers rushed forward, seized them and took them away. As we were being led off I consoled a young mother who couldn't understand what was happening, but I was now becoming increasingly worried, sensing a Nazi storm was brewing.*

*As I arrived at the church, its doors were flung open and more than four hundred and fifty of us were crammed inside to the surprise of a few girls and boys who were busy preparing the church for their first communion the following day. As soldiers carried children inside in their arms, a mysterious looking box with cords attached was dragged into the nave by two soldiers and we were ordered not to touch it. I could hear outside in the distance explosions and gunshots, and many of the women started to panic. Suddenly there was a thundering blast, clouds of thick, acrid smoke belched through the church, choking us and making it hard to breathe. Women and children screamed, thrashing about in terror, stumbling over bodies that lay on the floor, piled one above the other. Many surged towards the doors, intent on forcing them open so they could breathe. Swinging them back, troops with machine guns fired, ripping at the masonry, raking the women and children with bullets, tearing them apart. The noise was unbearable. The smoke bomb had caused complete confusion, suffocating many; the bullets meant certain death for others and now the merciless beasts tossed in grenades through the windows. Bundles of straw, faggots and furniture were thrown onto the bodies and pews and set ablaze with incendiaries and flame guns. The church was soon like a furnace and I could feel the intense heat burning on my face; those that hadn't been killed instantly lay groaning in agony, babies screaming, children wailing and someone crying out, "They're killing us."*

*Masked from view by the dense smoke, I had crawled behind the altar and there I pretended to be dead, lying quite still, struggling to breath, stifled by flames, as the evil killers fired on anything that moved. I needed to escape this place and what might soon prove to be my fateful grave. A large, broken window behind the altar offered me the best hope. Standing on a stool I clambered up and, half supported by the back of the altar, I pulled myself through, ignoring the pain from my wounded shoulder and, fear spurring me on, I leapt to what I hoped would be freedom. Tumbling to the ground outside I landed in a dense bush which broke my fall and provided an ideal hiding place, at least for the moment. Waiting to hear if I had been spotted, I lay completely still, breathing deeply, the clear air stinging my eyes. A voice called to me and, looking up, I could see clearly a young woman holding something wrapped in a black shawl, trying to follow, grappling to climb through the window. I stretched up and tried to grasp her hand but it was no good, she was out of reach. A single shot rang out and, as her lifeless body slumped, then fell back, she let go and the bundle toppled into my arms.*

*For many minutes, I couldn't judge how long, I hid buried in the thick undergrowth, listening to the gunshots and shrieks over the sound of the roaring inferno inside the church; I felt sick deep inside. The young child, probably drowsy with fumes, wrapped in the shawl was now snug inside my coat, quiet, thank God. It knew nothing of this barbaric massacre, of the hideous carnage metered out that day, and the murder of its brave mother: we lay together just hoping to survive.*

*The fires were spreading and I could see black clouds of putrid smoke drifting in columns from many parts of the village. Terrified for our safety, and believing the soldiers had moved on, I cautiously scrambled out from under the bush and slid down the earthy bank praying that the babe would remain silent. I picked my way through the church garden shrubbery at the rear, watchful, alert to the all too real threat of being seen. The only soldier was some way off, busy vomiting in a hedge. At the far end of the plot where the priest grew his vegetables stood a dilapidated, wooden store hut. Crawling, cradling the child beneath me, I gradually edged along a trench with tall foliage over-hanging either side and finally, completely exhausted, we rolled into the hut; and there we lay.*

*The child was wide awake, its pale face staring at me through the gloom, her little hand holding tight a cloth doll which she was sucking, much in the way of a comforter. If only she would stay quiet, we might have a hope. For some long while all I could hear was the noise of falling rubble and tiles over the sound of the roaring fires - then to my alarm ... voices, close to. She started to grizzle and cry, softly at first; I threw myself on top of her to try and smother the sound, but it was no use. The small, window light smashed and a face peered in. The door was wrenched back wide on its half broken hinges to reveal a burly soldier looming above us. His appearance was menacing with his rifle slung at his side and one hand on its trigger; his goggles strapped to his helmet glinted in the light as cigarette smoke curled round his face. I instinctively pulled the child tightly into me as he called to the other soldier. An argument broke out between them: I was unsure what was being said but knew it must be about us. The soldier cocked his gun and pointed it towards us intent on our execution. It was unbearable and I couldn't help but sob, as much for the child as for myself. The second soldier barged in, pushing the gunman to one side who in turn swung the rifle towards his fellow, just as the other thrust a knife into the gunman's chest. As he went down a shot rang out: the second soldier who had saved our lives had been hit and collapsed onto the ground.*

*A shrill whistle pierced the distant air; the wounded soldier spoke softly in French, perfect French, telling me that now they would leave and we would be safe. The sudden noise had caused the child to stop crying; I laid her in one of the earthy vegetable boxes so I could drag the young soldier and prop him against a sack. Blood was seeping from his jacket and as he coughed, more blood*

333

*dripped from his mouth. Our young saviour could have been no more than eighteen. Blood spat from his lips as he spoke, "In the beginning I was fighting for my country much like any other soldier, not wanting to kill but glad not to be killed. But hatred has persuaded so many to do abominable things to each other that they would never normally consider. I am so very sorry. I have grown sick of death, I no longer believe in war, it's bullshit. If we don't lose the war Hitler will go on and on in his madness." He choked, then quietly drifted into an endless sleep: this brave young man who had given his life for us. The child and I lay with the dead in that place until morning.*

*Before they left, the Nazis slaughtered all the animals, plundered every building and killed any who fled and those in hiding, wanting no witnesses to survive, then ritualistically they torched the entire village. Smoke could be seen far away in neighbouring villages. Many peasants from outlying farmsteads came into Cousion over the following days on foot and bicycle to see what had happened and to search the burning ruins for relatives and friends, the sense of horror clearly visible on their faces. A small number of SS soldiers did return to try and bury the human remains in two huge pits they dug, but they gave up, burning bodies instead and dropping them down our wells.*

*I learnt much later that the men were separated into six groups and marched to outbuildings in different places around the village. There the men were gunned down in cold blood before they were set on fire. Five young men escaped with their lives from one of the barns and lived to tell; a sixth dear friend who escaped was later shot dead and soldiers laid his body against the wire fence to the cemetery, tethering a horse to his outstretched arm.*

*A stench of burnt flesh hung over our 'Village of Death' for some long while as for many weeks we grieved, praying over newly discovered bodies.*

*My village that had lived for one thousand years was dead.*

*On that One Day in June nearly six hundred and fifty people were killed - over two hundred of them our children.'*

"My aunt," the hotel's patron continued," who was the only woman to survive the massacre, said that when the authorities came to Cousion-sur-Cherane they did not have enough death certificates, so the officials resorted to using pages torn out of children's school exercise books to register the deaths. They said that they wouldn't be needed anymore now that all the children were dead."

# Chapter 40

That afternoon I had learnt so much that had disturbed me. In
following my dream back to France, I'd seen the intensity and the
inevitable consequences of war: the pointless destruction of this
beautiful land and its people, and it had shaken me. For just a
moment I had felt the pain of many and the heartache of those left
to carry on, living life to the full and sharing their experiences so
others might be free and learn to live in peace.

Leaving the hotel my wanderings took me beyond the square, past
a closed patisserie and down a back road which led me to a busy
café. I ventured inside, conscious that I hadn't eaten since
breakfast and the lingering smell of cooking told me my appetite
had hardly been satisfied with coffee alone. A bell rang as I
opened the glass door and, apart from a couple seated in the
window, no one else paid me any attention. A diamond, tiled
floor stretched the length of this narrow space, the blue and white
tiles reflecting the harsh, afternoon sun. Down one side ran a
long, dark, wooden counter upon which all manner of
paraphernalia sat, including an ornate till and a steaming coffee
machine, as well as a glass display cabinet filled with tempting
pastries and mouth-watering glazed fruit tarts. A sprightly woman
in her mid forties finished preparing a baguette before stepping out
and serving one of the half dozen or so occupied tables. I slid
back a bent, cane chair from under a vacant table and made myself
comfortable. On the cotton check cloth was a glass bowl of sugar
and matching cruet and a menu printed on a stiff, cream card with
hand written prices which I attempted to make sense of. Bustling
up to my table with a pile of dirty plates in her hand, balanced
against her apron, the woman took my order.

There was an incongruous feel to the place: in attempting to be
modern, it hadn't quite managed it. Bright, yellow paint covered
the walls as well as the ceiling, from which a line of spherical,
glass lights hung: I imagined them to be on most of the time as the

rear of the café appeared really quite dark. A leggy, rather sad looking plant trailed down the wall from a pot fixed above my table. To one side of the pot hung a black and white photograph of the old village tram terminus and, from the style of the women's dresses, I would think it was taken well before the outbreak of war. As the woman returned with my food and wine, another photograph caught my eye. It was mounted in a similar frame but this picture was of schoolgirls, four rows of them: it was exactly the same as the photograph that I'd seen in my hotel room the day before.

"Who are they?" I asked, in my broken French, interrupting her on her busy errands, my curiosity getting the better of me. She explained in poor English, helped by hand gestures that it was a photograph of one of the classes in the old girls' school here in the village, before the occupation. On starting back to the counter, a gentleman who was waiting to be served, helped her translate for me that the only one she knew in the photograph was the owner's mother!

It struck me that maybe a relative of one of the girls' probably had something to do with the hotel I was staying in … that must be it.

I whiled away the next half an hour or more, eating, whilst trying to make some sense of a French newspaper, and relaxing, watching the customers. I was surprised just how busy they were getting, but then it was approaching tea-time. For one passing moment I did wonder if I might recognize someone, but in spite of all the comings and goings, no-one looked familiar, Finished, I now considered it was time to pay, then head back to my hotel: I needed to get a bicycle organised for tomorrow so that I could try and find the farm. The idea excited me and I knew it wouldn't be easy as some of the countryside looked the same, but it was, after all, over twenty years ago that I was last here and, in that time, a lot had changed.

"I hope the food was good for you?"

The question came from a young woman who appeared from behind the counter cabinet. My heart missed a beat.

"Did you want another wine sir?"

"No," I stumbled as both she and I recognised each other. "Did I not see you last night outside the cinema?"

She beamed and that same dazzling smile lit her face as it had when we first met; a smile I had seen before.

"I'm sorry, you know me? Oh yes, now I remember, you smiled at me. I am Nicole."

As she was explaining, the waitress called to her from somewhere behind the coffee machine, I think to tell her that I had been asking about her mother's school picture.

"You know anyone in the picture monsieur?"

I am sure she knew I didn't but was kind enough to ask nevertheless. I shook my head.

"My mother here in the back row, on the left, her hair short," I looked on as she nodded towards the photograph. "It was many years ago, before the Germans, and war," I sensed that something more than answering my curiosity was spurring her to explain, "but this is a newer photograph of her. Here she was in her early twenties." She turned and pointed to a photograph hanging behind the counter, I hadn't seen it earlier because the waitress had been standing in front of it.

I was speechless: the face of such a sweet, rare beauty and once again totally captivated me as it had before. I could feel my heart pounding: I was sure all could hear it. This was surely more than I could believe, more than I could hope for.

"You are unwell?" Nicole asked.

"The man?" I stammered.

In the same frame as the photograph of Nicole's mother's, was another much smaller black and white photograph tucked in one corner, of a man. Nicole excitedly explained,

"My Grandmamma said it was my Father, he gave the photograph to my Mother when he left for England, but for all my life I have not known him, and she said he didn't know me, he never knew he had a daughter. She told me that they were very much in love

338

with each other, more than anyone else, and nothing would ever change that, and he would have loved me. Grandmamma also told me that theirs was a true love; war had forced them together then pulled them apart ... and I, Nicole, had been part of their love."

My whole body was tense and shivering, my mouth dry; I could no longer see clearly, my eyes full of tears as I tried to make sense of her jumbled words.

"You knew my mother Brigitte, didn't you monsieur - yes?"

She took me to a table away from the others, and there we sat, gazing at each other.

"As I started explaining, it was clear you knew her; seeing you with the photograph . . . you really have changed little."

In my wildest dreams I never, ever dreamt I was a father with a daughter as beautiful as Nicole and that fate would bring us face to face after all that had happened. It is hardly surprising that she didn't recognise me: she'd never seen me before and why would she expect her father to come to the village after all this time. Even if she did know who I was, why on earth should she trouble herself? I had never helped bring her up, I had never played with her, laughed or even cried with her – I didn't know her and certainly she knew nothing of me! I searched for something to say,

"Do you still all live on the farm? I had such a wonderful time there."

"I still live there yes, caring for the animals; dear Grandmamma would help me look after them until she died, five years now."

"And Brigitte, is she well, does she live with you?"

"No." Nicole placed her hand lovingly over mine then falteringly began to explain where Brigitte was.

"It had been a Saturday in early summer, four days after English soldiers landed in France. Grandpapa was going to the village to get a harness for the horse; my Uncle Émile went to keep him company and drive the cart, and for a medical check in the school. Mother went with them to shop and took me. I was only one then, all that I know is what I was told. The village was busy as it is often on a Saturday: several trams had already come in the morning with visitors. Suddenly it changed: without a warning German soldiers swarmed on our peaceful village, from then on no-one knew what was happening."

I was aware her voice was becoming increasingly emotional and my thoughts more unclear and muddled. I knew what I wanted desperately to ask but couldn't bring myself to. She went on to explain whilst holding back her emotions, that her grandpapa Henri and uncle Émile were dragged away with others and shut in a barn; mother and her were taken to the church along with the other women and children. For many minutes I had known what Nicole was about to tell me, but knowing this in no way lessened the devastating effect her words would have on me.

"Dear Grandpapa and Uncle Émile were murdered by those Germans, and Mother ..." she couldn't carry on, closing her eyes she sobbed, "... Mother died to save me."

"If I'd only known," I sobbed and held her hand between my hands and stared into her sad eyes. I realised now that the war had finally found my Brigitte.

"I didn't want it to be as this, I thought I could bear to tell you. Aunt Michelle rescued me from the church that day when Mother bravely tried to escape with me."

I took from my wallet the gold crucifix Brigitte had given me on the day I left her and pressed it into her palm. Instantly Nicole recognised it from the photograph showing her mother wearing it.

"But she gave this to you?"

"No, she entrusted it to me; she would have wanted you to have it!"

"I wish I could remember," she said mournfully, "Grandmamma, she told me what happened before she died; she said it was hard to understand things." Obviously the tragedy was very real and her pain deep, she struggled to make sense of it. Reverting to her native French she shared more of her story; how a wave of violence swept through the village and the people, devastating all in its path: all that is, except their humanity and love. Nor did it destroy the memories, for without these she said, we may be condemned to make the same mistakes. Some will never forgive: that doesn't make them any the worse - it just means they will always have to live in hate. I used to ask how it was that so many Germans could do these things, but then I must also ask that of us: it was not one man who did this, it was all of us following orders; we didn't understand what might happen, and believed that every German was evil. But one showed me that was not true, he wasn't like the rest, he gave his life to save Michelle and me. Before the Reich could squeeze every last bit of compassion from him, they killed him. She whispered very softly, "I will always remember him."

Nicole, to whom we had given life, had become a young woman in the image of her mother: a beautiful soul, full of life and love. The love that Brigitte and I had shared at a time when there was so much hate in the world. Fate had thrown two strangers together: for a moment two lives became entwined and one love grew ever stronger.

"From the first moment I met Brigitte we fell very much in love," I confessed to Nicole, "I have never forgotten her, we were inseparable, neither of us knowing how and when it would end, nor understand why it had to. When I left, your mother was a beautiful young woman and now you, her daughter, are as beautiful as she."

We sat silently, as I had so often sat with Brigitte, just feeling as one in each other's presence.

"Where is Brigitte? Would you take me to her?"

Nicole beamed and oh, for the briefest of moments I could see my sweetheart's face looking at me.

"Of course," she said, "she would want us to do that."

She went across to the counter and, after talking to the waitress, came back with her jacket and bag.

"We should go now, if that is good for you; we will see her grave before it is dark."

The cemetery was across on the far side of the village. We walked together: Nicole chatted about the things she had been told of her early life as we made our way through the ruined houses. Once there, I was taken aback to see so many graves: row upon row endlessly stretching into the distance towards the trees that bordered the graveyard. Name after name after name, in memory to the hundreds of men, women and children who had been murdered on that 'One Day in June' and who now lay here. There were names of those I did not know, lives I'd never touched, save the one, and souls that were no longer, except for that one who lived on in me. Some graves were anonymous looking slabs of grey-brown stone, plain with just a simple plaque; others with prominent crosses mounted on ornately scrolled columns stood as memorials to this tragedy. A few were decorated with mementos, symbols that must have been very special to the person buried therein. Flowers adorned many, their blossoms in stark contrast to the drab stones. An elderly couple having left a bouquet on one of the slabs, a candle glowing, just visible in a jar beside it, shuffled their way along the gravel path Every grave appeared different: this was not what I expected. There was no uniformity to them, no similarity, except for the date on which each died. As we strolled between the rows, Nicole leading, I felt a sense of peace sweep through me. This place seemed to echo to the sound of many voices: the chorus of the old and the young, their songs filling the air, the songs of those who had left here only memories.

A tablet erected on a wall declared :
'REST IN PEACE. THOSE WHO REST IN PEACE DO SO BECAUSE THEY ARE LIVING IN ETERNITY'.

I had been dreading the moment when faced with Brigitte's grave but now I searched in hope of discovering the place where she finally rested. Nicole stopped, stooped down, then turned to me and smiled. A simple stone with a cross carved above her name marked the grave: below the dates were the words, in French, 'Died for France'. A white porcelain vase had been placed in front of the headstone, in it sat a single, fresh poppy, its red flower head embracing the crimson sun which was now setting low in the sky. Resting each side of Brigitte were Henri and dear Émile: upon whose stone was a small, faded picture showing off his mischievous smile. Suddenly I could see Brigitte before me: joy welled up from within, a wave of emotion washed through me and tears spilled from my eyes. This was my moment, a special time again with dear Brigitte and with our love Nicole, who is for me now, my everything. She is my life, my all, my love and the life that comes after us both. Brigitte's own sweet voice had long been silent, but now her words and ways, her smile and laughter were living on in our beloved daughter. I had only known Nicole for a brief while, the life that lit her eyes, the love that shone from her face; in so many ways she had become a reflection of her mother and for that I was so grateful.

Turning to Nicole, who was standing praying, I heard her whisper the words, 'Mother of God pray for us, now and in the hour of our death, Amen.' Between her hands she held Brigitte's crucifix which she then kissed. Aware of my glance, she looked at me as I uttered,
"Everything about you, Nicole, reminds me of her."
She silently took from her bag a letter, and passing it to me looked expectant as I started to read – *'My dearest Brigitte, my beloved'* Reading on to myself, Nicole smiled a knowing smile; I shared with her the last few words of the letter – *'You are the dearest one I have ever known. All that I want in this world is you darling Brigitte. I give to you my heart, my love: a love that will last forever.'*
Giving back the letter to Nicole I confessed,
"If only my time with her could have lasted forever. It's when we lose the ones we love that we know how much we loved them. I never want to lose either of you again."
In a soft voice Nicole said,
"You don't have to."
The burden of all that had happened weighed heavily on my heart.

"When my time comes I would like you to bury me near to your mother, next to my love; will you do that one thing for me?"

Taking her hand, together we walked and talked, and in those precious moments we learnt and shared so much with each other.

"Your mother did not just live in France Nicole, she loved France. You are the future of France. Think of the France you want for your children, a France at peace, and believe in it just as Brigitte would have."

Unfolding before us, stretching as far as the eye could see, was an army of vibrant blood-red poppies, thousands upon thousands of them, rejoicing in the evening sunset as they danced from side to side, kissed by a gentle breeze. The blue sky darkened, and as we looked up, a flock of birds took to the air, circled above our heads, and then flew away into the distance towards the horizon where a lone star faintly sparkled.

It is said that angels look down and smile upon us: we both believed in one particular Angel.

"Now I am an old man I forget many things, particularly when it hurts; some things though I'll never forget … and I still have dreams!

*'Each generation imagines itself to be more intelligent than the one that went before it, and wiser than the one that comes after it:'*

George Orwell – Isle of Jura

*'not repeating the mistakes of either.'*

Colin Beazley – Isle of Gigha

# STATISTICS
All statistics represented are approximate: reference sources differ on exact numbers.


## FIGHTER COMMAND
### In the 114 days of the Battle of Britain

RAF pilots killed -            544
Luftwaffe aircrew killed –     2,500
RAF aircraft destroyed –       1,000
Luftwaffe aircraft destroyed – 2,000
It is estimated that only 3% of RAF bullets hit German aircraft.

### Between 1939 -45

RAF aircraft Fighter Command loses were:
3,690 killed; 1,215 wounded; 601 POWs;  4,790 aircraft.

## BOMBER COMMAND
### Between 1939 – 45

Survival chances in a Halifax bomber were 2.45 per crew of 7.
In total 55,573 aircrew were killed and over 12,000 aircraft were lost.
For every 100 aircrew who served:
60 would be killed
3 would be badly injured
12 would be POWs
1 would evade capture
24 would survive unscathed

Of over 955,000 tons of bombs were dropped during the war.
It is estimated that only 3% of bombs dropped fell within 100 yards of the target.

Halifax production totalled 6,178 with bomber versions flying a total of 75,532 sorties.

# SPECIAL OPERATIONS EXECUTIVE

No. 138 Squadron whilst based at Tempsford delivered 995 agents; 29,000 containers and 10,000 packages in 2,494 sorties and lost a total of 70 aircraft.

In all, over 33,000 clandestine flights were flown and over 43,800 tons of stores supplied to the Resistance. The SOE F-Section alone sent 39 women agents into the field. 91 men and 13 women gave their lives for France's freedom. It is said that the life expectancy of agents sent into German occupied territory in 1945 was 3 weeks.

## D – DAY

## Run up to D – Day

It is estimated 200,000 tons of bombs were dropped on occupied France and the Resistance cut the French railway lines no less than 950 times.

## The Invasion

The Allies: 36,976 dead and 209,672 wounded, another 16,714 aircrew and 4,101 aircraft were lost. There were 10,000 casualties on D–Day alone.

The Germans: 240,000 dead and wounded and 200,000 missing or captured. They lost over 3,600 aircraft, 1,500 tanks 3,500 guns and 20,000 vehicles.

Between 15,000 and 20,000 tons of bombs were dropped between the night of June 5th and June 6th.

# V – BOMBS

V-1 Flying Bomb: about 8,000 were launched against London; 2,400 reached their target and killed 6,184 and injured 17,981 people.

V – 2 Rocket: about 1,300 were launched against London; 517 reached their target and killed 2,754 and injured 6,523 people.

# HOME FRONT

20,000 Bevan Boys went down the mines - 1 in every 10 conscripts was chosen by ballot to go to the mines.

By 1944, 1,000,000 tons of vegetables were being grown on allotments and more than a quarter of all fresh eggs were laid by chickens kept in garden sheds.

More than 12,000 women joined up to nurse the sick and wounded.

By 1943, 90% of single women aged 20 to 30 were working in factories, on the land or in the services, of which about 640,000 worked in the armed forces.

1 in 10 women ATA – Ferry Command pilots were killed.

# THE WAR
## British and Allied Merchant Shipping

50,000 seamen perished.

5,150 merchant ships were lost 2,828 of them to U – boats.

## Submarines

76 British submarines were lost and 1 scuttled or surrendered of a fleet of 218, only 3 were sunk by U – boats.

52 US submarines were lost of a fleet of 288

782 U – boats lost and 380 scuttled or surrendered of a fleet of 1,219.

Of the 40,000 German submariners who set to sea, 27,491 crew and officers were killed and approximately 5,000 were taken prisoners of war.

## Royal Navy

90 Allied warships were sunk with the loss of 6,000 seamen.

## Coastal Command

Coastal Command lost 5,000 men and 700 aircraft.

## THE WAR WAS RESPONSIBLE FOR THE EVENTUAL LOSS OF APPROXIMATELY 50 MILLION MEN, WOMEN AND CHILDREN FROM ACROSS FIVE CONTINENTS.

1.8 million Frenchmen, 5% of the population were taken prisoner; 810,000 military and civilian fatalities and 230,000 wounded.

By the end of 1945, 60,595 British civilians had died, 86,182 were seriously injured and in total 326,000 military personnel lost their lives. Three and a quarter million properties had been destroyed by bombs, 92% private dwellings.
130,000 children had lost one or both parents.

7,060,000 Germans lost their lives and 25,568,000 Russians lost theirs.

11 million American men enlisted; 6 million women replaced them in armament factories and 295,000 men were killed.

300,000 Italians went to war, 10,000 returned home.

Over five and a half million Jews disappeared under the rule of the German Nazis. More than 400,000 died in the Warsaw area alone.

The Soviet troops discovered, when they entered Auschwitz, 348,820 men's suits, 38,000 men's shoes; 836,000 items of women's clothing, 5,525 women's shoes; an enormous quantity of toothbrushes, spectacles, toys and 7 tons of human hair.

*'One death is a tragedy; one million is a statistic.'*

**Joseph Stalin**

# Glossary

Abwehr – German Military Intelligence/ Secret State Police
AC2 - Aircraftman Second Class
AFU - Advance Flying Unit
AG - Air Gunner
ANS - Air Navigation School
AOP - Air Observation Post
AOS - Air Observation School
ARP - Air Raid Precautions
ASI - Air Speed Indicator
ATA - Air Transport Auxiliary – Ferry Command
ATS - Auxiliary Territorial Service
BBC - British Broadcasting Corporation
Bevan Boys- Young British men conscrip -ted to work in the coal mines
Bf - German Messerschmitt fighter prefix
Bismuth Patrol – Bomber on long range meteorological flight over the North Atlantic
Blue Police – Collaborationist Police in the German occupied area
CO - Commanding Officer
Coned - trapped in a cone of search – lights
Corkscrew - Flying manoeuvre to avoid fighter attack
CTO - Chief Technical Officer
CT6 - Clothing and Textiles 6 part of the Ministry of Supplies
D-Day - Code for landing of amphi – bious Allied Forces at Normandy on 6th June 1944
Do - Dornier Aircraft
DR - Dead Reckoning Navigation
DSA - Distinguished Services Award Medal
DZ - Drop Zone
ETA - Estimated Time of Arrival
FANY - First Aid Nursing Yeomanry
FFI - French Forces of the Interior
FIDO - Fog Investigation / Intense Dispersal Operation
Flak - Anti-aircraft fire

Flaps - Large surface at the trailing edge of wing, air brakes
Freya - German early warning radar
Gee - Meter showing location of radio transmission from 1942
Gen - Considered as reliable info
Gestapo - German State Police
GI - US Military Personnel (Gov Issue)
Gill - Engine ventilation flap
Glycol - Aircraft engine coolant
G'meter - Aircraft accelerometer
Gong - Decoration or medal
GTS - Glider Training School
Hali - Halifax aircraft
HCU - Heavy Conversion Unit
He - Heinkel aircraft
HMS - His Majesty's Ship
HQ - Headquarters
H2s - British radar navigation and blind-bombing aid, from 1943
IC - In charge/command
ID - Identity
ITMA - It's That Man Again (BBC radio programme)
ITS - Intermediate Training Squadron
ITW - Initial Training Wing
Joe - Slang for secret agent
Ju - Junkers aircraft
KGB - Komit Gosudarstvennoi Besopastnosti (Russian equivalent of SOE)
LAC - Leading Aircraftman
Lanc - Lancaster aircraft
Leg - Determined steady course Flown
LNER - London and North Eastern Railway
Matlow - sailor
Met Office - Meteorological Office
MI5 - Military Intelligence 5 – Security Services
MI6 - Military Intelligence 6 – Secret Intelligence Services

MI9 — Military Intelligence 9 - Escape & Evasion Directorate

Monica — British radar early warning device against fighters from 1943

MT — Motor Transport

NAAFI — Navy, Army and Air Forces Institute

Naxos — German night fighter radar homing on British H2s transmissions

NCO — Non Commissioned Officer

NKVD — Forerunner of KGB

Oboe — British blind-bombing device fitted to Pathfinder aircraft

OCU — Operation Conversion Unit

OHMS — On His Majesty's Service

Op — Operational Mission

Oppo — Pal, friend, mate (opposite number)

OTU — Operational Training Unit

Overlord — The Allied Invasion of France 6th June, 1944

Pitot Head — Instrument below wing, registers airspeed

P/O — Pilot Officer

POW — Prisoner of War

Prop — Propeller

P/T — Physical Training

QFE — Field Elevation

QM — Quartermaster

RAE — Royal Aircraft Establishment

RAF — Royal Air Force

RCAF — Royal Canadian Air Force

RFC — Royal Flying Corps

RPM — Revs, Revolutions per min.

RSM — Regimental Sergeant Major

R/T — Radio Telephony

SAC — Senior Aircraftman

SAS — Special Air Services

Sealion — German codename for the invasion of Britain in 1940

SIS — Secret Intelligence Services

S/L — Squadron Leader

SOE — Special Operations Executive

SOS — Morse Code distress signal

Sprog — New inexperienced person

SS — Schutzstaffel – originally Hitler's bodyguard

Torch — Allied Invasion of French North Africa in 1942

U-boat — Unterseeboot (undersea boat)

V-bombs — Vertgeltung (Retaliation) missiles

VE-Day — Victory in Europe Day 8th May 1945

VHF — Very High Frequency

VJ-Day — Victory in Japan Day 14th August 1945

Window — Tinfoil strips dropped by Allied bombers to distort German radar image

WAAF — Women's Auxiliary Air Force

Waffen SS — Fighting SS

Wehrmacht — German Armed Forces-Heer, Luftwaffe, Kriegsmarine

WOP — Wireless Operator

WRENS — Women's Royal Naval Service

W/T — Wireless Transmission – Morse rather than voice

WVA — Women's Voluntary Assoc.

WVS — Women's Voluntary Service

YMCA — Young Men's Christian Association